SUBSTANCE ABUSE TREATMENT

Sylvia I. Mignon, MSW, PhD, is professor of human services and criminal justice at the University of Massachusetts Boston. For Dr. Mignon, substance abuse is much more than an abstract concept. She has worked in all facets of substance abuse treatment, especially detoxification, inpatient rehabilitation, and outpatient services, including individual and group therapy. For many years at the University of Massachusetts Boston, Dr. Mignon served as a core teacher in the Substance Abuse Studies program.

In addition to her specialty in substance abuse, Dr. Mignon has completed research and published journal articles on family violence and the death penalty. Dr. Mignon is lead author of *Family Abuse: Consequences, Theories and Responses*. She is also the lead author of *Substance Use and Abuse: Exploring Alcohol and Drug Issues*. Dr. Mignon has done extensive research on the substance abuse problems of female court defendants and issues of women in prison, especially the challenges of incarcerated mothers. Dr. Mignon's latest research focuses on the substance abuse and mental health problems in Native American grandparenting families.

SUBSTANCE ABUSE TREATMENT

OPTIONS, CHALLENGES, AND EFFECTIVENESS

Sylvia I. Mignon, MSW, PhD

SPRINGER PUBLISHING COMPANY

Springer Publishing Company, LLC
11 West 42nd Street
New York, NY 10036
www.springerpub.com

Acquisitions Editor: Stephanie Drew
Production Editor: Shelby Peak
Composition: Graphic World Inc.

ISBN: 978-0-8261-9578-4
e-book ISBN: 978-0-8261-9579-1

14 15 16 17 / 5 4 3 2 1

The author and the publisher of this Work have made every effort to use sources believed to be reliable to provide information that is accurate and compatible with the standards generally accepted at the time of publication. The author and publisher shall not be liable for any special, consequential, or exemplary damages resulting, in whole or in part, from the readers' use of, or reliance on, the information contained in this book. The publisher has no responsibility for the persistence or accuracy of URLs for external or third-party Internet websites referred to in this publication and does not guarantee that any content on such websites is, or will remain, accurate or appropriate.

Library of Congress Cataloging-in-Publication Data

Mignon, Sylvia I., author.
  Substance abuse treatment : options, challenges, and effectiveness / Sylvia I. Mignon.
     p. ; cm.
  Includes bibliographical references.
  ISBN 978-0-8261-9578-4 — ISBN 978-0-8261-9579-1 (eBook)
  I. Title.
  [DNLM: 1. Substance-Related Disorders—therapy. WM 270]
  362.29
  616.86'06—dc23
                                       2014009888

Special discounts on bulk quantities of our books are available to corporations, professional associations, pharmaceutical companies, health care organizations, and other qualifying groups. If you are interested in a custom book, including chapters from more than one of our titles, we can provide that service as well.

For details, please contact:
Special Sales Department, Springer Publishing Company, LLC
11 West 42nd Street, 15th Floor, New York, NY 10036-8002
Phone: 877-687-7476 or 212-431-4370; Fax: 212-941-7842
E-mail: sales@springerpub.com

Printed in the United States of America by Courier.

In memory of Aunt Cissy

CONTENTS

PREFACE

Substance abuse treatment in the United States is not a smooth continuum of services available to all those who seek them, and no definitive agreement exists regarding which treatment approaches offer clients the best chances of recovery. *Substance Abuse Treatment: Options, Challenges, and Effectiveness* is an effort to move the field of substance abuse studies forward by summarizing developments in treatment and examining treatment outcomes. The goal of this book is to provide a clear and succinct review of different types of treatment. Although this work primarily reviews what is known about each treatment type and "best practices," it also sheds light on what is not yet known.

Substance Abuse Treatment: Options, Challenges, and Effectiveness synthesizes research in an effort to translate research findings into quality treatment approaches. This work emanates from my many years as a clinical practitioner working with substance abusers and addicts, as an instructor teaching college-level substance abuse courses, and as a member on the Advisory Board of the New England Addiction Technology Transfer Center (ATTC), a national effort to translate research findings into improved clinical practice.

Chapter 1, Introduction and Overview: What Is Treatment Effectiveness? looks at how we can determine whether treatment is effective. It sets the scene by defining *treatment effectiveness* and examining the overarching issues of what determines whether specific treatments are effective. This chapter also provides readers with an overall feel for the book, with an eye toward translating complex research findings into easily accessible material. It examines the benefits and perils of comparing and contrasting types of substance abuse treatment, including problems with research methodology. Chapter 2, Treatment Goals: Abstinence and Harm Reduction, examines how and by whom treatment goals are formulated. It compares and contrasts abstinence and harm-reduction approaches in treating substance abuse and discusses the ethical and political considerations in harm reduction.

Chapter 3, Motivation for Treatment, looks at individual motivation for treatment, known as intrinsic motivation, and the role treatment can play in motivating clients. It examines the age-old practices of how to get substance abusers and addicts to acknowledge they have a problem and commit to treatment. It examines extrinsic motivation, that is, motivation from outside sources, including coerced treatment required by courts. Chapter 4, The Substance Abuse Treatment Industry, examines the historical development of substance abuse treatment in the United States. It looks at the development of the National Institute on Alcohol Abuse and Alcoholism (NIAAA) in the early 1970s, the contributions of the Substance Abuse and Mental Health Services Administration (SAMHSA), and the National Institute of Drug Abuse (NIDA). It examines the cost-effectiveness of treatment and the extent to which the profit motive and availability of grant money determine the type of treatments that are available.

Chapters 5 and 6 offer in-depth reviews and analysis of the many varieties of contemporary individual and group treatments available to substance abusers. Chapter 5, Inpatient Substance Abuse Treatment, reviews the important changes that have taken place since the 1970s in inpatient treatment. Various types of inpatient treatment, including detoxification programs, rehabilitation programs, therapeutic communities, halfway-house programs, and sober houses, are examined, as is the reduction in lengths of stay in inpatient rehabilitation programs as a result of reduced insurance coverage. Chapter 6, Outpatient Substance Abuse Treatment, reflects the fact that the majority of research has been on the effectiveness of outpatient types of programs, including brief intervention, individual and group therapy, and family therapy. In recent years, much emphasis has been placed on the counseling styles of motivational interviewing, contingency management, the community reinforcement approach, and adjunct therapies. This chapter reviews medications to treat addiction, including methadone, as well as the newer medications, such as acamprosate and buprenorphine.

Chapter 7, Self-Help Groups, examines the types of self-help programs with a focus on Alcoholics Anonymous and Narcotics Anonymous and the efforts made to evaluate their effectiveness. The main lessons of self-help research regarding effectiveness are teased out of a complex and disparate literature. This chapter also explores the relationship between professional treatment and self-help groups. Chapter 8, Treatment of Diverse Populations, addresses groups that have received less professional attention for their substance abuse problems. It examines the role of culture, race, and ethnicity in substance-using behavior. In addition, it addresses the substance use problems of and effectiveness of treatment for adolescents; women; the lesbian, gay, bisexual, and transgender (LGBT) population; those with HIV/AIDS; and older adults.

Chapter 9, Treatment of Co-Occurring Disorders (Dual Diagnosis), examines the relationship between substance abuse and mental illness and the challenges inherent in treating clients with both substance abuse and mental health issues. It reviews the research that suggests that recovery is made more difficult and complex because the client has both problems. This chapter also focuses on the relationship between substance abuse and anxiety, as well as depression and personality disorders. Chapter 10, Substance Abuse and Criminal Justice Populations, examines what is known about the effectiveness of the various types of treatment provided to criminal justice clients in multiple settings. Substance abuse tends to be overlooked by the juvenile justice and criminal justice systems, yet promising approaches to treatment hold the potential for reduced recidivism and significant increases in cost savings. This chapter examines treatment for those on probation or parole, those in correctional therapeutic communities, and clients receiving treatment through drug courts.

Chapter 11, Substance Abuse Prevention, reviews what is known about the effectiveness of substance abuse prevention efforts aimed at children and adolescents. It examines specific prevention efforts, such as DARE (Drug Abuse Resistance Education) and other school-based programs. Chapter 12, The Future of Substance Abuse Treatment, examines current issues in providing substance abuse treatment. Although measures of effectiveness have become more complex, we are still learning about the importance of providing care quickly in a courteous and professional manner. Chapter 12 also discusses why the professionalization of substance abuse clinicians is of critical importance and the benefits of national and state standards for certification and licensure.

ACKNOWLEDGMENTS

*L*ike the village needed to raise children, a community is also needed to write a book. I am grateful for the support I received from my husband, John, and my children, Anna and Cameron.

I am especially grateful to Dr. Marjorie Marcoux Faiia and to John F. Kohler, both of whom read and commented on the entire manuscript. Dr. Faiia brought to the manuscript her many years of experience as a substance abuse professional and academic. She helped me cultivate clarity and comprehensiveness of content in each chapter. John F. Kohler brought more than 20 years of clinical experience in the substance abuse treatment field to the project. He offered the invaluable insights of one who has helped thousands walk the road of recovery. I am also grateful to my colleague William M. Holmes, who turned his keen research methodologist's eye on the first chapter.

INTRODUCTION AND OVERVIEW: WHAT IS TREATMENT EFFECTIVENESS?

What is effective treatment for substance abuse? The answer depends on whom you ask. There are very different answers from researchers, from substance abuse clinicians, from alcoholics and addicts themselves, and from their family members and employers. In some ways the success of substance abuse treatment can perhaps be more easily measured than that of other types of treatment for medical problems, because it is often directly related to abstinence from alcohol and drug dependence. However, things are not as simple as they appear. Today we know that simply "not drinking" or "not drugging" is not the same as recovery from substance abuse and may be only the first step toward recovery. Although most clinicians and researchers seem to agree that treatment is needed, many kinds of treatments exist, resulting in controversy regarding which treatments may be the most effective. These are the murky waters that we attempt to negotiate in the text.

In simplest terms, *treatment effectiveness* is measured by a reduction in substance abuse and a reduction of accompanying problems (McLellan, McKay, Forman, Cacciola, & Kemp, 2005). Treatment effectiveness is sometimes also measured by a reduction in attitudes favorable to substance use. Eliminating or reducing substance use is a critical initial goal. Beyond that, there are the long-term goals of improving health and social relationships, as well as reducing public safety risks. Today there is agreement that no single most effective treatment exists (Institute of Medicine, 1990; National Institute on Drug Abuse, 2009; Read, Kahler, & Stevenson, 2001). Rather, some treatments may be more effective for some people than for others, and the search for effective treatments continues. See Box 1.1 for general substance abuse treatment principles from the National Institute on Drug Abuse (NIDA).

BOX 1.1 NIDA Treatment Principles

- Addiction is a complex but treatable disease that affects brain function and behavior.
- No single treatment is appropriate for everyone.
- Treatment needs to be readily available.
- Effective treatment attends to multiple needs of the individual, not just his or her drug abuse.
- Remaining in treatment for an adequate period of time is critical.
- Counseling—individual and/or group—and other behavioral therapies are the most commonly used forms of drug abuse treatment.
- Medications are an important element of treatment for many patients, especially when combined with counseling and other behavioral therapies.
- An individual's treatment and services plan must be assessed continually and modified as necessary to ensure that it meets his or her changing needs.
- Many drug-addicted individuals also have other mental disorders.
- Medically assisted detoxification is only the first stage of addiction treatment and by itself does little to change long-term drug abuse.
- Treatment does not need to be voluntary to be effective.
- Drug use during treatment must be monitored continuously, as lapses during treatment do occur.
- Treatment programs should assess patients for the presence of HIV/AIDS, hepatitis B and C, tuberculosis, and other infectious diseases as well as provide targeted risk-reduction counseling to help patients modify or change behaviors that place them at risk of contracting or spreading infectious diseases.

Source: National Institute on Drug Abuse (2009).

This is not the first attempt to review what is known, but is a comprehensive effort to evaluate types of substance abuse treatment. The variety of reviews of substance abuse treatment include Bergland (2005); Hester (1994); Holder, Longabaugh, Miller, and Rubonis (1991); Miller, Walters, and Bennett (2001); Miller and Wilbourne (2002); and Read et al. (2001). Many reviews are meta-analyses found in scholarly journals that combine findings of a number of studies. Meta-analysis is a statistical technique that allows the results of independent studies to be combined to address related research hypotheses. Typically meta-analytic reviews are aimed at academics and researchers and therefore may not be readily accessible to students and lay readers. The intent of this book is to provide a clear and accessible review of what is known about treatment effectiveness, as well as to clarify what is not yet known.

This book also grows out of a concern that complex research designs make research findings inaccessible to clinicians. The quality of client records may be more highly valued by administrators than the quality of the treatment. Research can become the end in itself rather than the means to more success in recovery for those who have alcohol and drug problems. In reality, research cannot tell the whole story—individual alcoholics and addicts and their families have their own stories to tell. However, we do not want to lose sight of the purpose of research as informing practice. In this book we are searching for overall trends rather than the research outlier.

Many forces may impinge on addicts as they enter treatment—family pressures, legal pressures, and financial pressures. Ideally research methods inform treatment efforts as we keep our eye on the prize of seeking more successful treatments. Although high-quality research is needed, there is also much to be learned from the intuitive feelings and experiences of clients and clinicians.

As in most professional fields, trends come along and then fade according to politics and available funding. The treatment field developed and promoted the disease concept in the 1930s primarily through Alcoholics Anonymous (AA), which began in 1935. This then became "addiction as disease" and over time developed into addiction as "brain disease" in the 1980s. The *Treatment Works!* slogan of the 1990s, and the emphasis on managed care in substance abuse treatment and health care overall, has developed into evidence-based practices, to be discussed later in this chapter. (For a discussion of the roots of the disease concept, see Mignon, Faiia, Myers, & Rubington, 2009; White, 1998; and Yalisove, 1998.)

In this text we grapple with whether the field has made substantial improvements in treatment or whether we continue to recycle ideas while adding a more complex statistical bent. Humphreys's (2006a) views of psychotherapy may be claimed by the substance abuse treatment field as well: "The psychotherapy field succumbs repeatedly to the illusion that the latest therapy fad is a new, fantastically more powerful car engine rather than a new hood ornament for the same old car" (p. 1238).

PROBLEMS WITH DEFINITION

Substance abuse has always been a nebulous concept. Substance abuse is typically defined for each study; there is no universally accepted definition that guides research designs. The author was taught in graduate school in the 1970s that it was not the amount of alcohol and drugs ingested but the effects on the user that should guide diagnosis. These negative effects include problematic personal relationships, health problems, negative effects on job and career, and legal difficulties. The inability to go to work because of a hangover or other more serious medical consequences of intoxication affects the earnings of the alcoholic and has consequences for the entire family.

Then there are the problems associated with comparing alcoholics and addicts. Are they the same? From a clinician's point of view, in the early 1970s alcoholics and addicts were considered different from each other. At the Washingtonian Center for Addictions in Jamaica Plain, Massachusetts, where the author did her graduate social work training, alcoholics and addicts were segregated: The alcoholics were considerably older, with the average client age in the mid-40s, whereas the drug addicts were in their mid- to late 20s. Today these distinctions have lost their meaning. We talk about polysubstance abuse, and addicts and alcoholics are treated together because typically they are abusing a variety of substances. However, problems associated with alcohol use are greater than problems stemming from the use of all other illicit drugs combined (Tucker & Simpson, 2011).

The closest we have come to agreement on a definition of substance abuse is provided by the *Diagnostic and Statistical Manual of Mental Disorders (DSM)*. The *DSM*'s fourth edition, text revision (*DSM-IV-TR*), has been considered the standard for defining substance use and dependency problems. The *DSM-IV-TR* is both reliable and valid, but it does not adequately take into account cravings for drugs or alcohol. Some criticize the distinction made between substance addiction and other addictions, preferring an overall diagnosis of an underlying addiction problem that can manifest in different ways, such as drinking, gambling, and binge eating (de Bruin, van den Brink, de Graaf, & Vollebergh, 2005; Dodes, 2002).

The next version of the manual, the *DSM-5,* was published in May 2013 by the American Psychiatric Association and has stirred plenty of controversy—it is the first significant overhaul of the manual since 1994. Some of the dramatic changes include the removal of Asperger syndrome and incorporating it into the autism spectrum disorders. Regarding substance abuse, gone is the dichotomy between *substance abuse*, emphasizing social consequences, and *substance dependence*, emphasizing the physical addiction to alcohol and drugs. In the *DSM-IV-TR* substance abuse required that a patient fit only one criterion, such as failing to fulfill major work, school, or home obligations; recurrent use when in potentially dangerous situations, such as driving; substance-related legal problems; or persistent social and interpersonal problems. Substance dependence required three of a possible seven criteria emphasizing the physical addiction to the substance. Now we see the title of *substance use and addictive disorders.* The new typology is *substance use disorder*, with severity specifiers and physiological dependence decisions (American Psychiatric Association, 2013). The *DSM-5* uses a one-step process rather than the two-step process of the *DSM-IV-TR* (Schuckit, 2013). In response to the complaint that it was not included in the *DSM-IV-TR*, craving for drugs and alcohol has been added. See Box 1.2 for a description of the new substance use disorder diagnostic categories.

Gary Greenberg's *The Book of Woe: The DSM and the Unmaking of Psychiatry* (2013) is a revealing examination of the development of the *DSM-5,* as well

---

BOX 1.2 *New Diagnostic Categories Related to Substance Abuse or Addiction Within the DSM-5*

Alcohol-related disorders
Caffeine-related disorders
Cannabis-related disorders
Hallucinogen-related disorders
Inhalant-related disorders
Opioid-related disorders
Sedative- or hypnotic-related disorders
Stimulant-related disorders
Tobacco-related disorders
Unknown substance disorders
Gambling disorder

The severity specifiers are 2 to 3 of 11 criteria, which means the person is positive for *moderate substance use disorder*, and 4 or more criteria, which is indicative of *severe substance use disorder*. *Physiological* dependence is defined as showing evidence of physical tolerance to the substance or displaying symptoms of physical withdrawal (criteria 4 and 5). No evidence of physical tolerance or withdrawal is called *without physiological dependence*.

Source: American Psychiatric Association (2013).

---

as previous editions of the *DSM*. Greenberg (2013) documents the ties of the American Psychiatric Association, publisher of the *DSM*, to pharmaceutical companies, the disagreements of experts, and the lack of evidence for some diagnostic categories, as well as the politics at the highest levels of the field of psychiatry in the United States.

These changes in the *DSM-5* will have huge repercussions for the substance abuse treatment field. The dichotomy between abuse and dependence has been useful in determining the type of treatment the client needs. That is, substance abusers are likely to need less intensive treatment than those who are considered physically addicted to alcohol, drugs, or both. One rationale offered for why the distinction between abuse and dependency was removed comes from Dr. Marc Schuckit, arguably one of the foremost authorities on substance abuse treatment today and the editor of the prestigious *Journal of Studies on Alcohol and Drugs*: "Our goal was to try to make the criteria easier for the usual clinician to use, and so we're no longer asking them to remember one criteria set for abuse and a separate set for dependence" ("*DSM-5* to Include Controversial Changes," 2012, p. 1).

Problems with definitions of substance abuse and treatment are the beginning of a long list of issues awaiting resolution. McLellan and Meyers (2004) point out major problems with current treatment. The authors state that the field needs to distinguish more clearly *use* from *abuse* and *dependence*. However, with the changes in the *DSM-5*, this distinction may no longer be considered important. Another problem is that even though we have tools to screen for and assess substance abuse, we may not be willing to use them. Primary care settings do not typically use screening tools to uncover substance abuse problems. For adolescents in serious accidents, one study found only 12.5% were screened for a blood alcohol level, although the American College of Surgeons has defined this as an "essential diagnostic test" (Mader, Smithline, Nyquist, & Letourneau, 2001, p. 170). Of the 15% who screened positive for alcohol, only 59% received a referral to a social service agency. It is a clear reminder that even though we may have the ability to screen and accurately assess substance abuse problems, this does not mean that substance abuse will be discussed with the patient and a referral will be made for treatment. In cases of car accidents with serious injury or death, the blood alcohol content can become a factor in legal cases. Therefore, defendants and their attorneys may try to avoid having a blood alcohol level test or may seek to suppress the results. See Box 1.3 for a description of a person with severe alcohol dependence.

BOX 1.3 A Case of Severe Alcohol Dependence

Upton Sinclair, best known for his indictment of the meatpacking industry in *The Jungle* (1906), wrote about famous writers, actors, and celebrities and their alcoholism. Here, Sinclair shares his perceptions of his own alcoholic father:

> He was so considerate, so good, and so utterly pathetic. In all the years I argued and pleaded with him, I cannot recall that I ever heard an angry answer from him. But nothing could save him. He was a traveling salesman, a "drummer," and every deal began with one drink and ended with another and another. He would make all sorts of vows and resolutions; he would "drink only beer," he would "never drink until evening"—but always in the end he would disappear, and then I would have to go and find him. The time came when we could no longer handle him at home, and I had to take him to a Catholic hospital where the good nuns had strong men at call.
>
> It seems to me that my father could have been so happy, and we so happy with him, if only there had been no alcohol in the picture. Yet it was as if there were a doom upon him; he could not resist it. I would discuss his problem with him, and tears would come into his eyes and mine; he would make promises, but he could not keep them.

Source: Sinclair (1956), pp. 27–28. Reprinted with permission.

Today we have reached the point where physicians are likely to ask about drinking behavior; however, an acknowledgment of drinking two six-packs a day may not necessarily indicate to a doctor that there is a problem deserving of professional intervention. In one study of a harm-reduction program for those with mental illness and substance abuse problems, social workers refused to or were poorly prepared to screen clients for substance use disorders (Ackerson & Karoll, 2005). One difficulty with the research was locating a psychiatrist who had expertise in substance abuse.

Screening for substance abuse is now covered by Medicaid, Medicare, and other health insurances for primary care offices. Therefore, it is likely that more screening will take place. Screening, brief intervention, and referral to treatment (SBIRT) received expanded insurance coverage in September 2011 to assure that physicians and allied professionals in their offices can bill for substance abuse screening ("Emblem Health" 2012). It is unclear at this early point whether the compensation for this service will have a big effect on physician willingness to screen for substance abuse. Chapter 6 offers an in-depth discussion of the importance of brief interventions in medical settings.

MEASURING TREATMENT EFFECTIVENESS

The measurement of treatment effectiveness is no small task and today requires extensive knowledge of how to gather and analyze rather complicated data. Most evaluations from the 1970s and beyond look at contacts with patients once or twice after completion of treatment to see whether there are reductions in use of alcohol, drugs, or both. Indicators of recovery include improved health status, job stability, and whether there is reduced criminal activity after treatment. However, one problem with most reviews of treatment effectiveness is the basic assumption that a client receives only one type of treatment (Cunningham & Blomqvist, 2006). Although few with alcohol problems avail themselves of treatment, those who do tend to use different types of alcohol services within a year, including detoxification (detox), individual counseling, and self-help programs. AA is the most frequently used intervention.

Moos and Finney (1983) are credited with opening the door to the importance of determining how treatment works. Although there is consensus that different types of treatments work, "little research has actually investigated the active ingredients of these treatments" (Longabaugh et al., 2005, p. 235). That is, a lot of research on substance abuse treatment is not anchored in theory and does not reflect a good understanding of how effective treatments work, an area in which more research is needed (Morgenstern & McKay, 2007; Tucker & Roth, 2006). How theoretical or practical should this work be? Theory gives evaluation an anchor by tying the work to a base of knowledge and provides a foundation for the work that is to take place (Mulvey, Hayashi, Hubbard, Kopstien, & Huang, 2003). Theory also provides a framework from which to begin, encourages the identification of appropriate variables, targets the most appropriate areas for funding, and offers a structure for interpreting research findings.

As indicated, outcomes of substance abuse treatment can appear simple and straightforward, including completion of a treatment program, reduced substance abuse, reduced illegal activity, and improvement in employment or school status (Reisinger, Bush, Colom, Agar, & Battjes, 2003). Yet these traditional measures often do not tell the whole story. It is important to get the perspectives of the clients and the counselors as well (Reisinger et al., 2003). How the clients perceive their situation and the process of client change are not well understood. We have done little to find out what clients want from treatment. This can result in pressuring clients to accept services they are not interested in (Humphreys, 2006a). It can be difficult to study drug abuse because it often involves illicit substance use and behaviors that are illegal and therefore subject to arrest and processing in the criminal justice system (Gfroerer, Adams, & Moien, 1988). Although this may be less true today, the stigma and legal consequences for substance abusers and addicts remain.

What Makes It Hard to Evaluate Treatment Effectiveness?

There are significant problems with research methods used to measure treatment effectiveness. Estimates of U.S. drug and alcohol problems range between 10% and 15% of the country's population; therefore, the use of substance abuse treatment by the U.S. population is so low that it can be difficult to get a sufficiently large sample size in research studies (Cunningham, 2005). In the field we can compare any type of treatment with no treatment, and we compare different types of treatment to determine whether one is better than another. Some sample sizes can be small, or research designs can be inadequate or inappropriate (Finney, 2000; Kraemer et al., 1998; Moyer, Finney, & Swearingen, 2002). Comparisons among studies are appropriate only if they use the "same standard treatment condition or control condition" (Finney, 2000, p. 1493). This is hard to accomplish and may not account for the intensity of different types of treatment. Some people are pessimistic about the effectiveness of treatment because of the use of inappropriate methods of evaluation (Humphreys, 2006; McLellan et al., 2005). Research that includes studies with inadequate statistical power can bias the results of meta-analyses, which combine results of several studies (Drummond, 2002; Kraemer, Gardner, Brooks, & Yesavage, 1998; Moyer et al., 2002).

It is important to be able to locate clients for follow-up, and a critical part of research is to follow up with clients at specified points in time (Hartmann, Wolk, & Sullivan, 1995). It is a concern to rely on client self-report—clients' memories may not be good and may be impaired by drug and alcohol use (Hartmann et al., 1995; Reznicek, 2012).

There are also differences in characteristics within the patient sample. This can easily be seen with co-occurring disorder patients—the severity of the mental illness has bearing on the outcome of substance abuse treatment (Dennis, Scott, Funk, & Foss, 2005; Finney, 2000). There is a treatment difference when a group of clients who are determined by clinicians to have a poor prognosis is compared with a group of clients who have a good prognosis for their treatment outcomes (Finney, 2000; Heather, 2007).

Although much of the work on treatment effectiveness may point to some client changes during treatment, the conclusions drawn are typically based on client outcomes after treatment (McLellan et al., 2005). It therefore can be difficult to tease out the effects of treatment from other variables that affect behavior. In the words of Reznicek (2012): "For drug treatment to be successful, it must directly affect subsequent behavior" (p. 104).

Randomized controlled clinical trials have long been the "gold standard" for evaluating treatment efficacy in substance abuse, as well as all kinds of health care research (Tucker & Roth, 2006). Evidence is the most important thing, but the kinds of evidence and the breadth of evidence that are important can change over time. How to put research into practice has become its own research area. This is an acknowledgment of and attempt to rectify the little effort that has been made historically to tie research results to improved substance abuse treatment services.

Randomized controlled trials began in the 1940s when the U.S. Food and Drug Administration adopted them to examine new drug therapies and see whether they were working (Tucker & Roth, 2006). Randomized controlled trials were well accepted from the beginning and can be relatively simple, using a random process to determine one group that receives the treatment and one group that does not. The goal is to find the real or true effects of treatment by reducing other factors. These studies are best suited for studying specific types of treatment and technical interventions within homogeneous samples, that is, patients with similar characteristics and issues, such as age, race, gender, and the type and length of drug use. However, we are typically looking for results that are not exclusively related to a specific program but rather are generalized to a larger group. The focus is more on outcomes, such as how long the client stays sober or clean after treatment. However, treatment programs do not typically randomly assign patients and do not account for a mix of types of patients and issues; they treat the patients who seek their assistance and, most often, those who can pay for it (Tucker & Roth, 2006). By standardizing treatment, randomized controlled trials therefore do not consider individualized needs of patients and do not offer knowledge of changes in behavior over time.

Then there is the important issue of distinguishing treatment effectiveness from efficacy. This key distinction provides a framework for expanding models, and together effectiveness and efficacy can give more information than either approach alone (Tucker & Roth, 2006). *Effectiveness* has to do with how well things work in the "real" world. *Efficacy* has to do with something that works well in a controlled setting, such as a clinical trial. Randomized controlled trials are important for evaluating treatment efficacy. Yet research that assigns respondents randomly to treatment or control groups does not allow us to understand what makes substance abusers enter treatment and how motivation and social factors influence the process of recovery, clearly crucial in efforts to evaluate treatment.

Research that evaluates effectiveness examines the real setting in which patients are treated and is used to examine heterogeneous samples. The context in which treatment is delivered is important, and there are more individualized approaches to treatment used by staff members. The emphasis is not on the treatment outcome, as in efficacy studies, but on the treatment process (Tucker & Roth, 2006). Randomized controlled trials emphasize the effects of short-term treatment when it is increasingly recognized that substance abuse is a chronic disorder, perhaps requiring multiple interventions over time. See Box 1.4 for a comparison of *effectiveness* and *efficacy*.

Treatment effectiveness studies developed as an adjunct to randomized controlled trials to increase external validity. *External validity* relates to how well findings of a study can be generalized to a larger population. It addresses whether the same results can be found in other settings, with other groups, and with treatment variables. External validity focuses on whether the conclusions of a study are likely to be supported by other studies. In contrast, *internal validity* focuses on how well a specific piece of research is designed, how well the variables are measured, and whether there is confidence in the accuracy and quality of the specific study. It addresses the confidence

---

BOX 1.4 Effectiveness and Efficacy

Effectiveness refers to how well the treatment works in clinical practice. *Efficacy* refers to the evidence that treatment works in controlled randomized clinical studies. Efficacy research can be criticized for having limited generalizability to real-world problems (Carroll & Rounsaville, 2003). Effectiveness research can be criticized for designs that may not be able to answer basic questions regarding treatment effectiveness and to rule out alternative explanations of research findings.

The hybrid model developed by Carroll and Rounsaville (2003) seeks to bring effectiveness and efficacy together. It does this by combining the strengths of each. From efficacy research it includes random assignment and blind delivery of treatments, training of providers in delivering study treatments, objective outcome measures, blind assessment of outcomes, and evaluation of the integrity or fidelity of study treatments. From effectiveness research, the authors emphasize specialized training for clinicians, enhancing the diversity in client samples and treatment settings, assessment of client and clinician satisfaction with treatment services, and evaluation of the cost-effectiveness of treatments.

Source: Carroll and Rounsaville (2003).

we have in the cause-and-effect relationship. Thus, we can see the importance of both internal and external validity in substance abuse treatment research.

Today it is common and expected to have treatment program evaluations, although there can be anxiety on the part of program staff members to open themselves up to criticism that may result from the evaluation process. In the politics of substance abuse treatment, program reputation and funding are at stake. An evaluation plan is required to be considered for most kinds of grant funding. Hartmann et al. (1995) noted the following:

> It is also our experience that the evaluation of treatment outcomes remains a sensitive and highly political proposition for many. For example, while the authors would have enjoyed the opportunity to closely examine the effectiveness of specific program and treatment modalities, such efforts were seen as too threatening at that time. (p. 49)

Although some consider AA a fellowship, it can be seen as an important treatment modality (Mignon et al., 2009)—and even the most used treatment modality. Yet arguably one of the most important treatments does not easily lend itself to randomized controlled trials or evaluation research (Cunningham & Blomqvist, 2006; Kelly & Yeterian, 2011; McCrady & Miller, 1993). The evaluation of AA and other self-help programs is discussed in Chapter 7.

Treatment effectiveness has become such an important issue that there is even a literature that examines the quality of the studies that are done on treatment effectiveness (Tucker & Roth, 2006). One meta-analysis reviewed 339 research studies from 1980 through 1992 (Morley, Finney, Monahan, & Floyd, 1996). Morley et al. looked at sample descriptions, treatment delivery, follow-up or outcome assessment, and estimates of treatment effect. They found an overall quality score of 9.7 out of a maximum score of 28.5, which is hardly good news. The strengths were found in reporting the number of participants and in following up with clients after 12 months. One weakness was that clients might have been under the influence of alcohol when responding to questions. Another weakness was clinicians not using the training and treatment manuals to better assure standardization of treatment. Moyer et al. (2002), building on the work of Morley et al. (1996), used the same methodological quality index and the same coding procedures. They also expanded the range of studies to include 1970 through 1998. Although Moyer et al. (1996) reported the overall quality to be 9.7, Moyer et al. (2002) reported the wider date range to have about the same overall quality of 9.5. In comparing studies from the 1970s to studies in the 1990s, Moyer et al. (2002) concluded that methodological quality has improved "somewhat" between 1970 and 1998. This is hardly a ringing endorsement for successfully studying the efficacy and effectiveness of substance abuse treatment.

As indicated, many factors interlace when clients enter into treatment: client personality; socioeconomic status; culture; family history; gender; and forces impinging on the client, such as family pressure, legal pressure, and medical problems. According to Reznicek (2012), "Given the ability to control all or some of these variables, outcome studies may not be measuring the effects of treatment as much as surveying the lives of people who have attended treatment" (p. 96).

ACUTE AND CHRONIC SUBSTANCE TREATMENT

A number of researchers see addiction as a chronic disease—it can take years for abuse and dependence to manifest and can require treatment over time (Kelly & Yeterian, 2011; McKay, 2005; McLellan, 2002). Alcoholism and drug addiction as a chronic disease can be characterized as periods of drinking, drugging, or both followed by treatment, a period of abstinence, and then another relapse. For many people there is the long duration of addiction—in one study the median time from first to last use was 27 years (Dennis et al., 2005). It takes males longer to recover when they started to abuse substances before age 15, have had three or more treatments, or have co-occurring disorders. Treatment is hardly a one shot deal, and these findings make clear the difficulty of recovery. Dennis et al. (2005) remind us that we need to focus on long-term outcomes, not just short-term ones, even though it can be difficult to track client populations over many years. This does not mean that short-term interventions (known as *brief interventions*) are not helpful; they simply are not helpful for those whose substance use is chronic and for those in need of long-term recovery.

Although today addiction is typically viewed as a chronic problem, it is most often treated in its acute phase in detox programs (McLellan, 2002; Scott, Dennis, & White, 2004). Addiction professionals need to find ways to support continued recovery with the very short treatments offered (Scott et al., 2004). Multiple detoxes, "revolving doors," and treatment "tune-ups" can be part of the maintenance of substance abuse problems rather than a way to achieve recovery over the long term. See Box 1.5 for a description of an alcoholic patient who had numerous hospital emergency room visits.

There seems to be general agreement that emphasis on acute treatment such as detox needs to be expanded to include longer term treatment models (McKay & Hiller-Sturmhofel, 2011). The extended care continuum takes as its goal the stabilization of the client and fewer relapse episodes. Some barriers to this approach include insurance limits and lack of funding for extended treatment. There has been a dramatic decrease in inpatient treatment and expansion of outpatient treatment within the past 35 years, as well as far more use of medications to assist with recovery (McLellan et al., 2005). A high dropout rate early in treatment results in fewer clients being eligible for the continuing care approach. Lack of motivation to continue longer term treatment, as discussed in Chapter 3, is an important consideration. Disagreement over treatment goals, such as abstinence versus reduced intake, harm, or both, can be problematic, as discussed in Chapter 2. There can also be difficulties in scheduling treatment appointments when work obligations and child care are issues. Not surprisingly, higher treatment and

---

BOX 1.5 The Case of Richard

Richard was a chronic alcoholic in his early 50s. For many years he had come to the emergency room of the local hospital for treatment of medical problems associated with his alcoholism, including severe gastric and liver problems. Richard became known to staff members as one of the "regular customers" who came to the emergency room for a brief "tune-up" before returning to his uncontrolled drinking. He lived a very isolated life, and no relatives were involved with him. Over time medical staff members lost their interest in treating him and provided care with little to no empathy. Over the 6 years the social worker knew Richard, she tried to engage him and offered treatment options to him. Richard at no time indicated interest in seeking help. The last conversation the social worker had with Richard was about his worsening health and that the doctor had indicated he would not live long unless he stopped drinking immediately. Richard acknowledged to the social worker he understood that to be the truth. Within months, hospital staff members were notified of Richard's death.

Source: Case reported by Sylvia Mignon, former director of social service in a community hospital in Massachusetts.

---

retention rates are more likely when clients are highly motivated, receive help from a highly motivated staff, and are offered longer term treatment in convenient settings (McKay & Hiller-Sturmhofel, 2011).

For most people with alcohol and drug problems, there is no professional treatment. For others, treatment becomes a "career," with clients coming in and out of different treatment programs, known as the "revolving door." Most studies seek patients for follow-up about 6 to 12 months after treatment. As we have seen, it is problematic that most reviews of treatment effectiveness take as a basic assumption that a client receives only one type of treatment (Cunningham & Blomqvist, 2006). Although some people see alcohol or drug problems as chronic conditions, others see them as conditions requiring different treatment over time. Relapse does not diminish the importance of treatment but rather reminds us of the limits of existing treatment (Reuter & Pollack, 2006). No amount of treatment can solve the problem of substance abuse, especially considering that few substance abusers seek treatment.

Importantly, it remains unclear when an addiction is no longer a problem and whether that status is determined by the addict or others. Overall, there is a mismatch of treatment for substance abuse disorders—we primarily offer short-term treatment for a long-term problem (McKay, 2005). Longer term treatment promotes better outcomes, although more studies are needed. Examples of the few long-term treatments available today are AA and methadone maintenance. However, McKay (2005) considers "extended interventions" to be for a period of longer than 6 months. Treatment protocols for depression, diabetes, hypertension, and obesity are becoming longer to acknowledge the chronicity of these problems. Extended substance abuse treatment may be good for those who have not been able to reduce their intake on their own or with brief interventions (McKay, 2005). It is ironic that managed care within health systems has promoted treatments for addiction that are shorter and less expensive, as discussed in Chapter 4.

McLellan (2002) asks the important question about whether we are evaluating treatment correctly. He draws comparisons between addiction to alcohol, drugs, or both and chronic illness such as diabetes, asthma, and hypertension. He makes a convincing argument that emergency room or hospital treatment is defined as relapse for these illnesses; McLellan's review of the literature found that 40% to 60% of patients with these diseases relapse. He acknowledges that not all cases of alcohol and drug addiction are chronic and that some recover without treatment. However, the view of addiction as a chronic disorder translates into requiring continued vigilance over time and perhaps even for the entire life span, similar to the philosophy of AA. The question becomes whether treatments should focus on acute or chronic manifestations. Without a plan to address chronic issues, the risk of relapse can be high. Because of the immediate needs, we focus on the acute phase, and for the homeless, that is the necessary case. There cannot be longer treatment without the acute phase of treatment such as detox. Rather than putting resources into early treatment, resources need to be spread out over time.

Outcome measures 6 or 12 months after treatment are not necessarily measuring the treatment but rather are measuring the client's interaction with the community to which that person has returned. The conceptualization of addiction as a chronic problem means appropriate treatment is not being offered and that a "continuing care approach" is needed (McLellan, 2002, p. 251). Monitoring of clients over time is necessary but is not incorporated into the health care system. This requires greater integration of substance abuse treatment services within mainstream health care and the social service system. Overall, McLellan says that addiction treatment has been offered from the perspective that specific periods of treatment and intensity of treatment bring about such change that it lasts long after treatment has ended. Clearly, this is not always the case. AA has a basic understanding of this; it offers a long-term treatment opportunity through a one-day-at-a-time approach.

The need to care for chronic diseases over the life of the patient extends to substance use disorders. Because substance abuse is a chronic disorder, modest positive treatment outcomes should be expected (Morgenstern & McKay, 2007).

TREATMENT MATCHING AND EVIDENCE-BASED PRACTICES

Treatment matching became a big issue in the late 1980s into the 1990s. The idea was to find the specific treatment types that would best address specific client characteristics (Read et al., 2001). The national Project MATCH study initiated by the National Institute on Alcohol Abuse and Alcoholism (NIAAA) in the late 1980s was trying to determine whether there were improved treatment outcomes based on this matching effort (Project MATCH Research Group, 1998). It remains the largest and most expensive effort to examine treatment effectiveness (Cutler & Fishbain, 2005). No strong support for treatment matching was found, and only 10% of matching predictions received support, as discussed in Chapter 6.

The 1990s saw the rise of evidence-based practices that permeate the health care system. *Evidence-based practices* focus on interventions that are derived from scientific research findings and show that clients do better with these specific practices (Drake et al., 2001; Eliason, 2007). In the practice of medicine, for example, it means seeking the best evidence and research findings available to make decisions about the most appropriate treatment (Mullen, 2004). It includes the process by which decisions are made in individual cases using the "best" evidence and inherently judging this evidence as more important than clinician "intuition" (Mullen, 2004). Although emphasis is placed on scientific research results, well-trained and skillful clinicians are needed for evidence-based practices to be successful.

The adage *Treatment Works!* that was popularized by NIDA in the 1990s offers no insight into the interventions that work the best. For whom does treatment work? Under what conditions does it work? White (2005) pointed out that the popular slogan is an oversimplification of the process of recovery. *Treatment Works!* gives the impression that treatment is one uniform approach rather than a variety of approaches from outpatient to inpatient, with different philosophies and counseling techniques. It gives the impression that professional treatment is needed yet glosses over, and can even overlook, the role of others such as family in the recovery process. Moreover, it assumes that treatment is the only way to recover, ignoring that some alcoholics and addicts stop using on their own (Granfield & Cloud, 1999). In practice, some people receive treatment and it does not work for them (White, 2005). It assumes that professionals are responsible for whether individuals recover but also blames individuals for their failure to recover. It is interesting that *Treatment Works!* and evidence-based practices developed in the same decade. It is likely that the *Treatment Works!* refrain gave way to evidence-based practices because it is so inadequate.

Most evidence-based practices are not translated into improved or new approaches to treatment, an important concern for delivering treatment (McGovern, Fox, Xie, & Drake, 2004; Miller, Sorensen, Seltzer, & Brigham, 2006). This is the gap between theory and practice that occurs in many fields but may be especially the case in substance abuse treatment (Miller et al., 2006; Powell, 2005; Read et al., 2001). There is much information on substance abuse treatment, but we are still just beginning to develop research on evidence-based practices (Miller et al., 2006).

Klingemann and Bergmark (2006) claim that "the addiction treatment enterprise faces a crisis of legitimacy" (p. 1230). They find that addiction treatment between 1950 and 1975 moved from control policies toward policies that supported treatment, the time during which the welfare state grew. Evidence-based practices will have the greatest influence on treatment policies or at least give the impression that is the case. This orientation toward evidence-based practices extends to just about everything in society. Yet social movements and lobbying efforts have far more influence in responding to addiction, and health care issues overall, than do scientific research findings (Klingemann & Bergmark, 2006).

Little attention has been given to how clients in treatment influence the treatment process. Client choices have a big role here. It is not only professionals and policy makers who make treatment decisions; client attitudes and choices may be more significant (Klingemann & Bergmark, 2006). Although it is hard to argue against evidence-based approaches, in reality most clinicians do not offer evidence-based practices to clients (Drake et al., 2001). The buzz-phrase *evidence-based practices* seems to get more attention for services provided by agencies, yet there is little effort to study individual clinicians and how they use evidence-based practices (Mullen, 2004).

The Research and Clinical Gap

Bringing together research and clinical practice has been a big issue within the substance abuse treatment field (Carroll et al., 2002; Eliason, 2007; Wolfe & Meyers, 1999). The integration of science- or evidenced-based practices garnered attention in the field in the 1990s and early 2000s and continues today (Marinelli-Casey, Domier, & Rawson, 2002). This effort is attributed to a variety of factors such that research findings need to provide the support and underpinnings for developing effective treatments in all areas of medicine. This includes efforts to have substance abuse and mental health insurance coverage equal to the insurance coverage for those who have other medical problems. The Mental Health Parity and Addiction Equity Act became law in 2008. The Act does not require group insurance plans to provide mental health and substance abuse treatment coverage, but if these disorders are covered by insurance, they must be covered at the same level as other medical and surgical benefits. This law took many years to become reality and is considered a hard-won battle fought by substance abuse advocates.

The research-into-practice model was established by the federal addiction technology transfer centers (ATTCs) in the early 1990s. *Bridging the Gap Between Practice and Research: Forging Partnerships with Community-Based Drug and Alcohol Treatment* (Lamb, Greenlick, & McCarty, 1998), written for the Institute of Medicine (IOM), developed a number of strategies that focused on linking a variety of issues: research and clinical practice; development of knowledge, research findings, and policies and their implementation; dissemination and transfer of information; client or consumer participation in bringing together research and practice; and building partnerships between community-based agencies and researchers. The Clinical Trials Network was another effort by the NIDA in 1999 to build partnerships between community treatment programs and researchers by focusing on a range of behavioral and drug treatments for substance abusers. These efforts spurred opportunities to bring both research and practice together, yet more needs to be done. For example, physicians have not typically embraced substance abuse treatment, including the appropriate use of medications. Integration of research into practice, although the focus of the ATTCs, has been slow in developing (Snow & Delaney, 2006).

There is agreement that clinical practice does not keep pace with research findings (Wolfe & Meyers, 1999). It often takes years to adapt clinical practice to research findings. Issues within organizations, including agency resources, organizational culture, willingness to change, and characteristics of staff members, bear on how research can be translated into practice (Hartmann et al., 1995; Mullen, 2004; Simpson, 2002).

Marinelli-Casey et al. (2002) trace the reasons that development of new knowledge does not necessarily translate into changes in practice. Individual beliefs about the knowledge and its meaning, whether it is welcomed, shunned, or somewhere between, have to do with the background and training of substance abuse professionals. This can be the age-old self-help versus professional help debate in which some people believe that recovering alcoholics and addicts are uniquely qualified to treat substance abuse problems, whereas others argue that academic and licensing credentials are essential. Although Marinelli-Casey et al. (2002) describe the relationship between those providing the new information and those who will implement it as "critical" (p. 984), often there is a weak relationship or no relationship. Those who have worked in the field for many years may not be open to researchers who have no experience with actual clients. Other issues include financial and administrative constraints, rigid managed care funding policies, political considerations, staff members who are not supportive of change, and ineffective ways to disseminate the knowledge. Unless clinicians can see that specific types of treatment are effective, there is no incentive to do things differently.

Researchers and clinicians have made little effort to work together, and incentives do not exist for academics and clinicians to collaborate. Practitioners may not have an appreciation for research and science-based work. Academics and clinicians have different orientations and may go so far as to see each other's points of view as "fundamentally flawed" (Marinelli-Casey et al., 2002, p. 985). The training of researchers and clinicians does not typically bring them together (Sorensen & Midkiff, 2000). Researchers who support evidence-based practices bear the burden of demonstrating their fruits to clinicians (McGovern et al., 2004). Importantly, academic institutions may not value this kind of collaboration, and academics may not have interest because this kind of work does not help them advance their careers by supporting tenure and promotion (Eliason, 2007). Although we want to consider research as objective, researcher "allegiance" or bias can be reflected in observed differences in comparing treatments (Imel, Wampold, Miller, & Fleming, 2008).

Some counselors maintain positive attitudes toward integrating research and practice (Campbell, Catlin, & Melchert, 2003). However, other clinicians are not motivated to learn new tools and techniques, believing that the treatment they offer is already effective (Addis, Wade, & Hatgis, 1999; Carroll et al., 2002).

In the Clinical Trials Network study, practitioners felt they were already using motivational enhancement therapy and motivational interviewing techniques. Yet trainers found that this was not the case and that clinicians may not have a good grasp of motivational interviewing techniques (Carroll et al., 2002).

Research outcomes and trends often remain out of the sight of substance abuse clinicians. Professional journal articles can be dense and complicated, and readers may not have sufficient understanding of research methods and statistics to grasp the findings (Kerwin, Walker-Smith, & Kirby, 2006). This seems to be increasingly the case as research methods become even more complex and involve new technologies. Importantly, counselors have acknowledged they do not have the skills and preparation for understanding published research material on substance abuse treatment (Campbell et al., 2003).

To close the gap, efforts can be made to bring together researchers, clinicians, policy makers, and recipients of treatment through meetings, conferences, and other formats that permit the exchange of ideas (Marinelli-Casey et al., 2002). The information must be disseminated to all types of professionals working in substance abuse treatment, including medical providers and regulatory agencies. More research needs to be done to examine the experiences of treatment professionals and their willingness to adopt evidence-based practices (McGovern et al., 2004). What are the incentives to change and adopt evidence-based practices, especially in the absence of compelling arguments that clinicians can understand? If clinicians feel they are communicating well with their clients, incentives to change do not exist for them.

OBSTACLES TO TREATMENT

Obstacles to treatment can be numerous for those with substance abuse and addiction problems. There are system barriers such as lack of insurance, barriers of the specific programs, and client barriers. Unfortunately, problems within the system create obstacles to treatment access and quality issues and may be blamed on clients rather than the organization and the system for the delivery of care (Broome, Simpson, & Joe, 1999; Ford et al., 2007). It is easier for staff members and administrators to blame clients than to sort out competing bureaucratic and systemic issues. Clients who have criminal justice involvement face further bureaucracy in obtaining treatment. Also, little is known about how to increase admissions to treatment programs, including the process of applying for treatment, the medical review process, insurance or funding verification, and then ensuring the client actually shows up for treatment (Ebener & Kilmer, 2003).

Treatment depends on the willingness of the client to stay, participate, and therefore have a chance for the treatment to work (Meier, Donmall, McElduff, Barrowclough, & Heller, 2006). All of this assumes that the client is fortunate enough to have health insurance to cover the cost of outpatient psychotherapy or to have private funds to pay. There is little use to offering many types of treatment if prospective clients cannot gain access.

Other obstacles to seeking help include concerns for privacy such as confidentiality issues and the potential for stigma (Tucker, Vuchinich, & Rippens, 2004). The denial that is a hallmark of addiction can keep alcoholics and addicts from acknowledging their problems and can delay entry into treatment. Another obstacle is the feelings of alcoholics, such as the perception that they can recover on their own, that their problem is not serious enough to warrant professional help, or that treatment would not be helpful. George and Tucker (1996) found that those who entered treatment received feedback about the need for help from friends and family. Some substance abusers may not have the support and assistance of family members.

SUMMARY AND CONCLUSION

The substance abuse treatment field is still trying to figure out what effectiveness means and how to adequately measure it. In the meantime, there has been progress within the past 10 years to bring alcohol treatment within health care, especially routine health appointments. The financial incentive for physician offices to screen for substance abuse is upon us, and it will take time to see how deep the inroads will be. Tucker and Simpson (2011) recommend a "consumer-informed process" among a range of treatment options, rather than a "one size fits all" treatment system.

Overall, research findings lean toward the importance of early identification and intervention and the need to reduce treatment dropouts. Research supports continuing care networks and consistent monitoring once treatment has been completed. Relapse intervention and recovery education and support with links to local recovery communities are also important. However, treatment systems that offer access and high quality still leave many without treatment.

No nation or culture can solve drug problems through treatment alone or through incarceration or prevention efforts. Treatment reduces health problems, including HIV infections and crime concerns, and for individuals it improves employment. In the words of Reuter and Pollack (2006): "Treatment is generally acknowledged to be useful, frail, and incomplete" (p. 342).

TREATMENT GOALS: ABSTINENCE AND HARM REDUCTION

W ho sets treatment goals for clients? How do you arrive at treatment goals? How do you determine success in treatment? These are some of the questions that are critical to determining appropriate treatment plans for clients. Treatment planning includes long-term goals and short-term objectives. Abstinence has been the primary short- and long-term goal and the mainstay of American treatment, yet perspectives have changed over time. The substance abuse treatment field initially perceived abstinence and harm reduction as mutually exclusive categories. However, the definitions are not necessarily distinct, and there can be overlap rather than competition in treatment goals. At its simplest, the "Just Say No" slogan of First Lady Nancy Reagan in the 1980s is an example of an abstinence-based model—that is, no drug use. *Harm reduction* refers to reducing alcohol and drug use and the negative consequences associated with substance abuse. Prime examples of the harm reduction approach include needle cleaning and exchange programs, known as "bleach and teach."

This chapter examines goals of treatment for people with addictive disorders and examines the move from abstinence-based treatment approaches to a greater recognition of the value of harm-reduction approaches for people with drug and alcohol problems. See Box 2.1 for an illustration of treatment goals developed in 1994 and their current applicability. Today the list of goals for clients might replace "maximize motivation for abstinence" with "maximize motivation for treatment and reduce harm from alcohol and drug use."

From the 1880s into the 1990s there has been consensus that abstinence was the most appropriate treatment goal and that anything less than abstinence did

---

BOX 2.1 Goals of Treatment by Dr. Marc Schuckit

Schuckit's treatment goals were written more than 20 years ago and are still important today.
  Goals for work with clients:

1. Maximize motivation for abstinence
2. Rebuild a substance-free lifestyle
3. Optimize medical functioning
4. Identify and treat psychiatric symptoms and disorders
5. Deal with marital and family problems
6. Enrich job functioning and financial management
7. Address relevant spiritual issues
8. Deal with homelessness
9. Prevent relapse

  Goals for programs:

1. Consider fiscal and political realities
2. Carefully use financial and staff resources
3. Clearly state the philosophy of the staff (eclectic and specific models)
4. Remember that no treatment is totally safe—start with the least restrictive treatment option
5. Determine that treatment approaches being considered are more effective than chance alone

_____
Source: Schuckit (1994).

---

not constitute recovery (White, 1998). The abstinence model has been firmly entrenched in American history and is a fundamental tenet of the disease concept of alcoholism and Alcoholics Anonymous (AA), which began in 1935.

The abstinence model has been widely accepted in both the professional and the academic worlds. In the 1970s it was commonplace for recovering alcohol and drug counselors to say, "I'm just a drink (or drug) away from losing everything," referring to the widely held belief that a taste of alcohol would surely return the person to drinking and the inevitable loss of family and professional lives. Today this view is not universally accepted, and there is room to consider continued use while reducing the consequences of alcohol and drug use.

Even though we expect a definition of abstinence to be clear and simple, that is not necessarily the case. For example, *abstinence* can be defined as no illegal drug use, no use of medications that have not been prescribed by a doctor, or no drug use (McKeganey, Bloor, Robertson, Neale, & MacDougall, 2006). Abstinence can be defined for a specific period from weeks to months to years or within a lifetime.

An exclusive focus on abstinence as the treatment goal can be problematic if it means that any drinking or drugging is deemed failure (Gastfriend, Garbutt, Pettinati, & Forman, 2007). Failure at abstinence can lead alcoholics and addicts to find recovery harder to pursue. Also, clients who are not interested in abstinence can be viewed as "resistant" to treatment (MacMaster, 2004; Miller & Rollnick, 1991). There is general agreement, however, that abstinence is critical for pregnant women, because no safe level of alcohol has been determined and there is risk for fetal alcohol spectrum disorders, resulting in permanent brain damage for the child.

For people with alcohol use disorders, some support abstinence-based treatment, whereas others may be open to controlled or moderate drinking, as it has become known. People who advocate abstinence from alcohol express concern that controlled drinking cannot be maintained over longer periods and that there can be more negative medical, psychological, and social consequences for those who are trying to achieve controlled drinking than for those who choose abstinence (Walters, 2000). Some take issue with the abstinence orientation of AA, finding in *The Big Book of AA*, published in 1939, an acknowledgment that moderate drinking may be possible:

> If anyone, who is showing inability to control his drinking, can do the right-about-face and drink like a gentleman, our hats are off to him. Heaven knows we have tried hard enough and long enough to drink like other people! (*The Big Book of AA*, as cited in White, 1998, p. 232)

Professional attitudes toward abstinence and harm reduction can also be a reflection of education and training. People steeped in the abstinence model, popular through the 1970s and into the 1980s, may find it especially hard to consider espousing the benefits of controlled drinking. However, these individuals may have retired or may no longer be working in the field.

PRINCIPLES OF HARM REDUCTION

Overall, harm reduction is a controversial topic in the substance abuse treatment field. It has been perceived differently over time (Erickson, 1995; Lenton & Single, 1998; Marlatt & Witkiewitz, 2002; Witkiewitz & Marlatt, 2006). The term *harm reduction* refers to the reduction in health, social, or economic consequences of substance abuse, both legal and illegal. It has different meanings in different settings and therefore is not a "precise" concept (Kleinig, 2008, p. 3). Although it seeks to reduce harm to individuals, their family, and their community, it does not necessarily require a reduction in substance use (Einstein, 2007). It is an acknowledgment that some people want to reduce the consequences of heavy drinking yet may not want to stop drinking altogether (Marlatt & Witkiewitz, 2002). See Box 2.2 for a review of the principles of harm reduction.

Harm reduction has a number of advantages over the traditional abstinence orientation. Harm reduction can assist more people with substance abuse

---

BOX 2.2 Typical Principles of Harm Reduction

1. Avoid exacerbating the harm caused by the misuse of drugs.
2. Treat drug users with dignity and as normal humans.
3. Maximize intervention options.
4. Prioritize achievable goals.
5. Hold a neutral stance toward legalization or decriminalization of drugs.
6. Distinguish between the harm-reduction approach and the "war on drugs" approach that typically results in criminal justice rather than treatment responses for drug users.

Source: Lenton and Single (1998).

---

problems in accessing treatment and can even reach clients at an earlier point because it does not require abstinence (Snow & Delaney, 2006). It is a useful approach when clients are in earlier stages of their drug use and before clients have come to acknowledge the severity of their problems with alcohol, drugs, or both. Harm reduction is a humanistic approach that focuses on collaboration with the client to reduce harmful consequences (Marlatt & Witkiewitz, 2010). It also offers the opportunity to work on other issues, including housing and parenting issues.

Harm-reduction approaches can provide intermediate goals rather than overwhelming clients with an abstinence goal they may not feel is realistic at the point of entering treatment. Harm reduction can emphasize reducing the types of drugs used as well as using decreased amounts (Ackerson & Karoll, 2005). Importantly, it provides an alternative to the abstinence model and zero-tolerance approach by having drinking goals that are accepted by the drinker (Marlatt & Witkiewitz, 2002; Rosenberg, 1993).

Harm reduction serves as outreach to the most difficult and challenging addicts and offers them the opportunity to see that resources for recovery are available to them. Thus, it serves as an effort to engage addicts in the treatment system (Einstein, 2007). It gives the addict the opportunity to move forward in smaller and seemingly less painful ways rather than abruptly stopping use of drugs, alcohol, or both. Harm-reduction approaches are also flexible and individualized rather than one size fits all (Marlatt & Witkiewitz, 2010).

The best known examples of harm reduction are substitute medications such as methadone and needle exchange programs. Needle exchange programs have received the most public attention (MacMaster, 2004). Harm reduction provides the opportunity to test for HIV/AIDS, hepatitis, and other sexually transmitted diseases and can offer primary care to people in need, as well as overdose prevention. It can provide referral to legal and social services and opportunities for sex education (Drucker, Lurie, Wodakt, & Alcabes, 1998;

Einstein, 2007). Convenience is an important factor—harm reduction can happen in mobile vans, on the streets, and even in the homes of substance abusers (Einstein, 2007).

The sharing of drug paraphernalia is one of the greatest health risks correlated with drug injection (Tomolillo, Crothers, & Aberson, 2007). Needle exchange programs reduce these risks, including bacterial infections at the injection site. Importantly, needle exchange programs are structured and receive oversight; programs must follow laws and guidelines on program location, client eligibility, and the number of needles that can be exchanged (Tomolillo et al., 2007).

HISTORICAL PERSPECTIVE

Harm reduction is not a new concept. Early examples of this principle in action are the prescription of heroin and morphine for opiate addiction in England in the 1920s (Rhodes & Hedrich, 2010). In the United States between 1919 and 1923, morphine clinics treated patients for opiate addiction. Through the work of endocrinologist Dr. Vincent Dole and psychiatrist Dr. Marie Nyswander, methadone maintenance was developed in the 1960s (White, 1998). In the United Kingdom opiates were given to small numbers of addicts who were functioning members of society.

In the United States in the 1980s, HIV and AIDS were just becoming known (Einstein, 2007). The first syringe and needle exchange program was developed in Amsterdam in 1984 with government support (Marlatt & Witkiewitz, 2010). In the Netherlands, harm reduction developed to reduce HIV/AIDS and hepatitis, acknowledging that these illnesses are more critical than drug use. Similar programs were developed in the United Kingdom, Australia, Canada, and Switzerland in the 1980s and 1990s.

Since the late 1980s, needle exchange programs have received government funding in Europe, Australia, Canada, and the United States. More recently, harm reduction has provided the basis for substance abuse policies in Western European countries (MacMaster, 2004). Needle exchange programs are the best known harm-reduction approaches, and their effectiveness was evident from the early 1990s (Marlatt & Witkiewitz, 2010; Wodak, 2009).

On the global stage, harm reduction is accepted for several reasons: (a) successful efforts to curb the HIV epidemic, (b) research findings showing effectiveness of harm-reduction strategies, and (c) supply-control strategies that are costly and ineffective (Wodak, 2009). Needle exchange programs have consistently been shown to be successful in reducing the transmission of HIV/AIDS (Drucker et al., 1998; Finlinson et al., 2006; Strathdee & Pollini, 2007; Van Den Berg, Smit, Van Brussel, Coutinho, & Prins, 2007).

Today harm reduction represents a global change from the abstinence model popular in the United States (Snow & Delaney, 2006). Harm reduction is on the way to being an accepted mainstream practice (Rhodes & Hedrich,

2010; Witkiewitz & Marlatt, 2006). Harm reduction can be incorporated into both social policy and specific strategies for alcohol and drug abusers. From a strategic perspective, harm reduction is likely to be more focused on working with active drug users rather than waiting for addicts to seek assistance on their own (Lenton & Single, 1998). The European Monitoring Centre for Drugs and Drug Addiction (EMCDDA, 2013) sees harm reduction as a "combination intervention" that includes a number of interventions. These can include needle and syringe programs, methadone maintenance, safe places where drugs can be consumed, and counseling for addicts, as well as advocacy for policy change. From a policy perspective, abstinence can be a policy goal. Not surprisingly, it is harder to measure a reduction of harm than it is to measure abstinence; however, reductions in harm are clearly seen in the reduced number of new cases of HIV/AIDS (Marlatt & Witkiewitz, 2010).

People who may benefit the most from harm-reduction strategies regarding alcohol are those in late adolescence and young adulthood, the heaviest drinking years in the life course (Marlatt & Witkiewitz, 2002). In applying harm reduction to college drinking, Fromme and Orrick (2004) state: "Reducing high-risk behaviors is not incongruous with a goal of abstinence. Abstinence is the ultimate form of risk reduction" (p. 336). Reducing drinking among college students also reduces other negative behaviors, including violent behavior.

Harm-reduction strategies have been extended to include the operation of safe injection facilities, where drug users inject their drugs with clean equipment and under the supervision of health care professionals (Marlatt & Witkiewitz, 2010). These programs are operating in the Netherlands, Switzerland, Germany, Norway, Australia, Canada, and Spain. These programs have been shown to reduce needle sharing and drug overdoses, as well as public injection and discarding of paraphernalia. Regarding alcohol, candidates for harm reduction are typically those who do not have physical dependence and feel that they can learn to drink in moderation (Marlatt & Witkiewitz, 2002).

Examples of harm reduction beyond substance abuse include condom distribution to specific populations such as high school and college students and prison inmates; required medical examinations for sex workers; and shelters specifically for lesbian, gay, bisexual, transgender, and questioning (LGBTQ) youth (Kleinig, 2008).

Although needle exchange programs have proved effective on their own, there is evidence that treatment for substance abuse enhances the effects of needle exchange. In a study comparing addicts in needle exchange programs with addicts also enrolled in treatment, treatment-enrolled addicts reported reduced opioid and cocaine use and fewer, as well as reduced, legal offenses with lower rates of incarceration (Kidorf, King, Pierce, Kolodner, & Brooner, 2011). In their study of harm reduction in Amsterdam, the combination of methadone and needle exchange programs proved more successful than either intervention on its own. These programs together significantly reduced the incidence of HIV and hepatitis C infection (Van Den Berg et al., 2007).

Therapeutic communities for drug addicts, where clients live in the treatment setting for several months or longer, have typically focused on an abstinence model. However, with the rise of HIV/AIDS, some therapeutic communities in Australia have been willing to offer HIV education, as well as sterile needles and syringes, to clients (Larney, Corcoran, Wodak, & Dolan, 2006).

ETHICAL CONSIDERATIONS

Can harm reduction be value neutral? Value neutrality implies that addicts and alcoholics are treated rather than judged or punished for their addictions. If the stigma of addiction is removed, or reduced, this supports more willingness to seek help. Some researchers believe that harm reduction can be ethically neutral, whereas others vigorously disagree, feeling that values are inherent in how policies and strategies are developed. According to Einstein (2007), "harm reduction is a nonjudgmental approach that meets substance abusers where they are at" (p. 258). Keane (2005a, 2005b) agrees it is important to be as neutral as possible. However, Hathaway (2005) does not believe value neutrality can be achieved. Loff (2006) describes value neutrality in terms of harm reduction as a "fictional proposition" (p. 371). Kleinig (2008) states that harm reduction is not value neutral and that it is misleading to think so.

A limitation of harm reduction is a lack of an agreed-upon moral code (Fry, Treloar, & Maher, 2005). Keane (2005b) supports the view of Fry et al. (2005) regarding a moral framework, saying that "ethical engagement" (p. 551) should guide the policy and practice of harm reduction. Keane (2005a, 2005b) argues that lack of moral judgment has served as an important basis of harm-reduction strategies. A public health approach can reduce stigma and develop a culture that supports treatment rather than punishment. According to Kleinig (2008), "Harm reduction confronts as many ethical issues in the matter of its delivery as in the determination of whether to support it" (p. 8), yet it is hard to determine the specific strategies that are "ethically legitimate" (p. 11). From a philosophical point of view, harm reduction operates from the notion that humans have choice and that human rights must be respected.

Although harm reduction offers many benefits, it is not without challenges. In addition to the previously mentioned ethical issues, there are a number of other issues of concern. For example, child protection issues pose challenges to harm reduction when abstinence is the expected goal (Ackerson & Karoll, 2005). Legal issues, such as charges of driving under the influence, often lead to the expectation of abstinence rather than a decreased use of alcohol.

One of the controversies surrounding harm reduction is whether it supports and even encourages illicit drug use and underage drinking and can serve as a "gateway" to more extensive drug involvement (Cadogan, 1999). Some believe that mitigating the negative consequences of addiction allows the addict or alcoholic to remain longer in the addiction. Using the pleasure-or-pain principle, when the pain is greater than the pleasure, the addict is more likely to seek abstinence. By Cadogan's thinking, reducing the consequences means the substance abuse problem is more likely to continue.

Trace (2005) addresses how hard it is to recover from addiction and advocates a "needs-led" approach. For Trace, the important issue is when to encourage clients who are doing harm reduction to become abstinent, acknowledging that dual diagnosis (co-occurring disorders) exists and some other clients will continue to need medication. Trace recommends a "menu" of services and professionals who encourage and support clients in feeling that they can become independent. Clients should be able to get the services they need at the time and should have awareness that their needs can change.

Miller (2005) expressed concern that harm-reduction efforts are aimed at drug users without acknowledging and dealing with environmental inequalities. That is, harm reduction may be forced onto drug users as a way to address public health issues and does not focus on helping drug users address personal goals.

Importantly, harm reduction does not focus solely on policies; it also focuses on strategies to address the implementation of policies, confidentiality, and type and quality of services delivered. This includes where the services are delivered, such as in poor, high crime areas, and the risks to clients and staff members when it comes to law enforcement and legal issues (Kleinig, 2008).

POLITICS OF HARM REDUCTION

Harm-reduction approaches can have political connotations and are hindered when substance abuse issues are politicized. For example, the "war on drugs" is generally acknowledged to be a highly politicized and punitive effort to address drug problems (Kleinig, 2008). The drug trade is a global problem (Marlatt & Witkiewitz, 2010). However, many important public policy issues are affected by politics. Around the world more effort has gone into dealing with issues of supply and demand of drugs from a law enforcement perspective than into focusing on prevention and treatment (Kerr, Wood, Betteridge, Lines, & Jurgens, 2004). This has resulted in a considerable rise in the prison population internationally. The opportunity for politics to bear heavily on a significant social and policy issue is a reminder of the importance of evidence-based practices (Rhodes & Hedrich, 2010).

Some researchers object to the term *harm reduction* because they feel it is not an appropriate goal or because they choose to associate strategies for reducing harm with drug legalization (Leshner, 2008; Weatherburn, 2009). Leshner (2008), the former director of the National Institute on Drug Abuse, finds harm reduction is associated with decriminalization or legalization and "it has become distorted into a euphemism for policies and programs that could increase drug use" (p. 513). *Decriminalization* removes legal sanctions for drug use, typically seen as falling between drug prohibition and drug legalization. *Legalization* removes all criminal and civil penalties for drug use.

DuPont (1996) also sees harm reduction as an alternative to drug legalization and drug prohibition. He sees it as protecting prohibition policies because it keeps drugs illegal but reduces the consequences of prohibition policies.

DuPont predicts that sanctions such as decriminalization will increase marijuana use, but others such as Erickson (1996) argue that is not the case. Erickson views the United States as the country most opposed to harm-reduction policies and strategies and that prohibition in the United States, because of the significant legal consequences, is a "punishment maximization system" (p. 1968).

Some people associate harm-reduction approaches with efforts to legalize drugs. Harm reduction can be confused with legalization, but is not a policy framework (MacMaster, 2004). Harm-reduction approaches are not inherently supportive of either legalization or prohibition efforts (Erickson, 1995; Marlatt & Witkiewitz, 2002).

Weatherburn (2009) maintains it is not possible to determine which harm-reduction programs and policies are best. He explains there is "no metric" (p. 345) to compare and "harms" are difficult to measure. If one type of harm is reduced, another can be created.

The United Nations (UN) General Assembly adopted a political declaration in 1998 to address the global drug problem. This was an effort to take action against manufacturing, trafficking, and abuse, and it included developing cooperation on judicial issues and eradication of drug crops. This effort was considered a failure because drug production increased. In 2009 the UN put forth a revised political declaration, and despite the European Union's support of harm-reduction strategies, the zero-tolerance approach supported by the United States, Japan, Russia, and Italy won out (Marlatt & Witkiewitz, 2010).

The UN and the United States have played important roles in international drug control efforts, and there is a close relationship between legislation of the UN and U.S. policies (Bewley-Taylor, 2004). They support zero-tolerance efforts, but this does not always mean they are successful. Latin American countries and the Caribbean are more reliant on the United States for trade and therefore more concerned about U.S. reaction to drug policies than are Canadians (Bewley-Taylor, 2004). Thus, countries need to cooperate with U.S. antidrug strategies for their own benefit.

Today harm reduction is supported by all UN organizations, including the Joint United Nations Program on HIV/AIDS (UNAIDS), the United Nations Office on Drugs and Crime (UNODC), the United Nations Children's Fund (UNICEF), and the World Bank. The Red Cross and the Global Fund for AIDS, Tuberculosis, and Malaria also support harm-reduction policies and strategies (Wodak & Cooney, 2006).

Acceptance of harm-reduction policies and strategies is more likely to be found among political liberals than among political conservatives, who may have a greater need for order and structure and may prefer less ambiguity (MacCoun, 2013). The attitudes favoring zero tolerance in the United States have resulted in lack of interest in and slow adoption of harm reduction (Wodak & Cooney, 2006). Despite the support of the UN and the World Health Organization, overall the United States continues to oppose harm-reduction strategies, preferring that most government funding go to reducing the supply of drugs (Marlatt & Witkiewitz, 2010). Importantly, supply-reduction efforts in the United States redirect significant resources away from drug treatment and prevention, including harm reduction (Strathdee & Patterson, 2009). This is despite compelling international evidence that needle exchange programs work and are cost-effective, safe programs (Wodak & Cooney, 2006).

There is a bleak picture for harm reduction in prisons that emphasize security and abstinence over harm-reduction policies (Kerr et al., 2004). High-risk drug injection is more likely to take place in correctional institutions than in other places. There has been a special concern about bleach distribution in prison that can be seen as condoning illicit drug injecting coupled with the fact that bleach puts corrections officers at risk of harm (Godin, Gagnon, Alary, Noel, & Morissette, 2001; Kerr et al., 2004). However, Jurgens (1996) found that bleach distribution did not present security risks in correctional facilities.

In a rebuke of American policy, Lurie and Drucker (1997) chastised the federal government for ignoring the findings of six government-funded studies supporting needle exchange programs and for failing to provide a national needle exchange effort. The authors calculated the disturbingly high number of HIV infections among intravenous drug users, their sexual partners, and their children. We see here an example of a public policy with a clear negative effect on thousands of people for the failure to take prevention seriously.

A strong case can be made for the integration of harm reduction and abstinence-based treatment (Futterman, Lorente, & Silverman, 2004). This can be especially meaningful in the effort to engage clients in treatment—continued use does not require that treatment be terminated. From the harm-reduction view, clients are engaged and encouraged to remain in treatment and are given a supportive environment within which they can deal with recovery issues. The goal of abstinence provides a more structured framework and a clearer purpose.

No sizable, well-organized U.S. political lobby addresses harm-reduction approaches, especially needle exchange programs (MacCoun, 2009). Increased lobbying efforts can prove the effectiveness of harm-reduction approaches to policy makers and to the U.S. public, especially in the decline in rates of HIV/AIDS around the world.

The historical perspective on alcohol and controlled drinking has had an even rockier start compared with the harm-reduction efforts focused on drugs. Harm-reduction strategies for people with alcohol problems come up against firmly entrenched views over many years that abstinence should be the sole goal. Although harm-reduction strategies for drugs have shown dramatic success in reducing HIV/AIDS, no similar claim can be made for controlled or moderate drinking.

THE CONTROLLED DRINKING CONTROVERSY AND MODERATION MANAGEMENT

In the 1950s, some evidence that it may be possible for alcoholics to return to social drinking began to appear. James Shea (1954) was one of the first to document abstinence followed by a return to social drinking. Dr. Melvin Selzer and

William Holloway's study of alcoholics at Ypsilanti State Hospital in Michigan in 1957 found that 13 alcoholics were able to become social drinkers. In 1962 D. L. Davies, a psychiatrist in the United Kingdom, found that 7 of 93 patients were able to return to moderate drinking some 7 to 11 years after inpatient treatment for alcoholism (Hersey, 2001). Arthur Cain's *The Cured Alcoholic*, published in 1964, also claimed some alcoholics could return to social drinking. The term *controlled drinking* was coined by Reinert and Bowen in 1968.

In the United States harm reduction was placed in the limelight by the 1970s controversy over controlled drinking, considered one of the most important controversies to exist in the substance abuse treatment field (Walters, 2000; Witkiewitz & Marlatt, 2006). The National Institute on Alcohol Abuse and Alcoholism funded research to examine the effectiveness of substance abuse treatment by following up with clients discharged from treatment centers across the United States. Known as the Rand Report, this study, published in 1976, offered evidence that alcoholics could return to social drinking (Hersey, 2001). At this time the author was working in an alcohol detoxification and rehabilitation program and saw how easily clinicians were willing to dismiss the notion of returning to controlled drinking. One effect was to fuel the dichotomy between the views of researchers and those of clinicians, as discussed in Chapter 1.

Mark and Linda Sobell (1973, 1978), in the quest to develop "individualized behavior therapy," found evidence for the ability to return to controlled drinking and that people who were controlling their drinking had more "days functioning well" than those who received treatment aimed at abstinence (Hersey, 2001). The Sobells were accused of professional misconduct in their research by Pendery, Maltzman, and West (1982), who claimed that respondents were not able to reduce and control their drinking and that the Sobells' results were fraudulent. The Sobells survived their professional attack, and a committee of independent scientists exonerated the Sobells (Marlatt, Larimer, Baer, & Quigley, 1993).

The Sobells (1995) addressed the profound effect of challenging the entrenched abstinence model: "Controlled drinking, in particular, threatened an entire culture based on the philosophy of Alcoholics Anonymous (AA)" (p. 1149). They acknowledged that for people who are alcohol dependent, abstinence is the focus, whereas those who do not have severe dependence are more likely to be successful in drinking less.

In one early study of controlled drinking, clients who were successful in achieving moderation had less severe symptoms and a less severe family history of drinking problems (Miller & Joyce, 1979). However, other variables are important in determining treatment goals, especially clients' beliefs about the nature of their drinking problem, self-assessment, and goals (Heather & Dawe, 2005; Miller, Leckman, Delaney, & Tinkcom, 1992). It is difficult to determine the appropriate goals regarding alcohol use during the initial assessment; this needs to unfold over time in treatment (Orford & Keddie, 1986).

The severity of the drinking problem is most likely to set the clients' goals, with the more severe cases likely to aim for abstinence (Cox, Rosenberg,

Hodgins, Macartney, & Maurer, 2004; Heather & Dawe, 2005; Marlatt & Witkiewitz, 2002; Miller et al., 1992). Some research supports the return to controlled drinking for people who are problem drinkers and even those who are considered physically dependent on alcohol (Orford & Keddie, 1986, 2006). Controlled-drinking approaches typically use behavior modification techniques and today can be known as *behavioral self-control training* (Lloyd & Salzberg, 1975; Walters, 2000). This can include limiting the number of drinks in a day, as well as limiting the number of days in a week in which an individual drinks alcohol. In a meta-analysis of 17 studies, Walters (2000) found that behavioral self-control training designed to reduce alcohol can be equally effective for alcohol abusers and those who are physically dependent. Walters (2000) concluded that "the extent, severity, and chronicity of problem drinking appears to have little bearing on who will and will not profit from enrollment in a program of behavioral self-control training" (p. 145).

One effort to provide support for people seeking to return to controlled drinking is the program known as Moderation Management (MM). Research has shown that those who attend MM would not seek treatment for alcohol problems in other programs (Kosok, 2006; Witkiewitz & Marlatt, 2006). Overall, the typical MM member is White, is female, has a college education, is over the age of 35, and has a mild to moderate alcohol problem. To reflect the lack of clarity regarding drinking goals for clients, Kosok (2006) found 19% came to MM with the hope of receiving help in deciding a more appropriate goal. See Box 2.3 for a description of MM and its founder, Audrey Kishline.

This debate over controlled or moderated alcohol and drug use is more entrenched regarding drinking alcohol than it is regarding illegal drugs because it has a significantly longer history. We are left with the impression that some people can moderate their alcohol and drug use and others cannot. Further research needs to consider more clearly the characteristics of people who can and those who cannot moderate their alcohol and drug use.

SETTING TREATMENT GOALS

Who chooses substance abuse treatment goals? In many treatment settings the assumption is made that abstinence is the goal, and a choice of goal may not be offered to clients (Adamson & Sellman, 2001). Yet, offering clients a choice of goals may bolster motivation for change and smooth the way for moderate drinking or abstinence (Marlatt & Witkiewitz, 2002; Walters, 2000). In practice, clients do not typically follow the recommendations of professionals if they do not agree with those recommendations. Whether a client is offered a treatment goal of abstinence or one of controlled drinking is determined by the client's behavior. The goal of abstinence or of moderation should be the client's choice, although the client may seek a therapist's advice and can chose a goal the therapist does not agree with (Heather & Dawe, 2005). When the

BOX 2.3 Audrey Kishline and MM

MM, developed by Kishline (1994), began as a self-help program in the early 1990s with the goal of helping problem drinkers moderate their drinking. Kishline felt that she had personally achieved the ability to become a moderate drinker. This belief was controversial, but the controversy became closer to a fury when in 2000 Kishline caused a terrible car accident while drunk, resulting in the deaths of 38-year-old Richard Davis and his 12-year-old daughter, LaSchell. Kishline was unconscious with an alcohol blood level of 0.26. Pleading guilty to vehicular homicide, Kishline served 3½ years in prison.

Humphreys (2003) found that MM members are more likely to be problem drinkers than to have physical dependence on alcohol. Humphreys deemed the program to be "dangerous" (2003, p. 622) for those with severe alcohol dependency if it dissuaded alcoholics from getting into treatment or if it supported MM for all people with drinking problems regardless of severity. However, he acknowledged the importance of the program for problem drinkers who have an interest in the MM program. In May 2014 the Moderation Management Wikipedia entry estimated the program's membership to be at 500.

Sources: Kishline (1994), Humphreys (2003), and Peele (2000).

treatment provider determines the goals, there is less influence on the longer term outcomes for clients (Sobell & Sobell, 1995). As stated earlier, although there is not definitive agreement, moderation strategies support treatment for people with less severe alcohol problems.

There is confusion about the appropriate goals of abstinence and harm reduction and who should make treatment goal decisions. For example, in the Drug Outcome Research in Scotland study, 56.6% of 1,033 respondents stated that abstinence was their only goal (McKeganey, Morris, Neale, & Robertson, 2004). The study found that 19.8% of respondents wanted harm reduction and abstinence and 19.6% wanted harm reduction. The study's authors argued that policy and practice in Scotland have given priority to harm reduction over abstinence but that drug users want assistance in becoming abstinent.

In a United Kingdom study of drinking goals, 54.3% chose abstinence as their goal and 45.7% chose nonabstinence (Heather, Adamson, Raistrick, & Slegg, 2010). Those who chose abstinence were more likely to be female, unemployed, drinking more heavily but not as often, and to have been treated in a detoxification program within 2 weeks of entering the study.

In a study of health care providers, recommendations for abstinence or controlled drinking depended on client characteristics such as severity of the alcohol problem, gender, and social support, as well as cultural factors (Cox et al., 2004; Rosenberg, 1993; Rosenberg & Davis, 1994). Abstinence was most often recommended for severe alcohol problems and for people with greater social support. In comparing attitudes toward drinking goals, health care providers in the United States were more likely to recommend abstinence and those from the United Kingdom were more accepting of controlled drinking: In a study of acceptance of moderate drinking by treatment providers in the United States, only 25% found this an acceptable treatment goal (Rosenberg & Davis, 1994).

Treatment goals change over the time the clients are in treatment. Hodgins, Leigh, Milne, and Gerrish (1997) found that at initial entry into treatment, 46% of clients stated abstinence was their goal but that by the fourth session 65% sought abstinence as their goal. There is also evidence that outpatient agencies are more likely than inpatient or residential programs to offer moderate drinking as a goal. In one study of alcoholism treatment services in Canada, 62% of outpatient programs accepted the goal of moderate drinking as opposed to only 16% of halfway houses (Rosenberg, Devine, & Rothrock, 1996). Again, it is the severity of the drinking problem that determines whether the client is referred for outpatient or inpatient treatment.

Professional recommendations regarding abstinence versus harm reduction create issues for professionals. For example, the social work ethical standard of client self-determination can be a gray area if the social worker thinks nonabstinence poses a risk to the client. A social worker who overrides the wishes of the client can be seen as paternalistic (MacMaster, 2004). Ideally, the social worker assists the client in determining appropriate goals. An initial goal of reduced use can change over time to an abstinence goal if efforts at moderation are not successful.

Stanton Peele (1987), a long-standing critic of conceptualizations of addiction and treatment, makes the important point that the cultural framework bears on the abstinence versus moderation debate. Inherent here are individual and ethnic beliefs toward alcohol attitudes, changes in professional attitudes, and development of research technologies over time. Overall, a shared goal at the start of treatment between client and therapist supports a positive therapeutic relationship (Gastfriend et al., 2007).

Harm reductionists generally do not have a problem with clients wanting abstinence, but advocates of abstinence tend to have issues with harm reduction (Roberts, 2005). Newman (2005), considered a leader in harm reduction in the United States, refers to the distinction between harm reduction and abstinence as a "false dichotomy" (p. 265). Some researchers ask why professionals cannot see harm reduction and abstinence as a continuum rather than as competing paradigms (McKeganey, 2005; Trace, 2005). Glatt (1995) concluded that the debate has subsided and people have returned to their original positions. That is, AA and substance abuse clinicians espouse abstinence, and researchers, psychologists, and sociologists espouse that moderation is possible and perhaps even preferable.

SUMMARY AND CONCLUSION

Over time the debate in the treatment field has evolved beyond merely choosing abstinence versus nonabstinence. Today the debate is how to bring drinking and drug-use goals into treatment in appropriate ways. An increase in the range of treatment goal options can encourage more people with substance problems to enter treatment. As we have seen, broader and more recent definitions of harm reduction can include abstinence goals.

Like all treatment, harm-reduction programs need to be evaluated. Considerably more research is needed on the effects of harm reduction policies globally, as well as for specific clients in treatment. Policy considerations and the needs of clients should not be in competition. Multicultural and global comparison studies are needed to learn more about for whom and when harm-reduction and abstinence programs are effective.

For now we continue to grapple with some important questions: Should harm reduction be available because it is cheaper rather than because it helps individuals? Should participation in harm reduction be voluntary or required? Should clients be part of this discussion? The processes need to be considered, in addition to the outcomes. Overall, high-quality research needs to compare and contrast abstinence and moderation models.

MOTIVATION FOR TREATMENT

What happens to alcoholics and addicts to bring them to treatment and supports their recovery from addiction? Each story is unique, but one thing is certain: Alcoholics and addicts remember what made things different for them and how they came to walk the road of recovery. These tales of addiction and recovery are the subject of many fascinating memoirs (Hamill, 1994; Knapp, 1996; Zailckas, 2005). In this chapter we review types of client motivation, as well as the more recent efforts of professionals to search for ways to enhance client motivation for successful treatment.

We are all familiar with the expression that describes people who are unmotivated to do the things we want them to do: "You can lead a horse to water but you can't make him drink." Alcoholics Anonymous (AA) turns this on its head: "Bring the body (to self-help meetings) and the mind will follow." Immersion in a program in which others are motivated can rub off. Much attention has been paid to understanding the concept of motivation, and the treatment field has long considered client motivation a cornerstone of successful treatment. Yet a number of factors can stand in the way of client motivation for treatment and recovery. For example, denial, resistance, and lack of motivation are considered normal parts of treating clients with substance abuse problems (Center for Substance Abuse Treatment, 1999; Mignon, Faiia, Myers, & Rubington, 2009). Family members and friends can "enable" alcoholics and addicts by excusing their behavior, providing money that goes toward drugs and alcohol, and generally cleaning up the physical and emotional messes addicts can leave in their wake. The classic case is the wife who phones the boss to say her husband has the flu when he is too hungover to go to work. This means that family and friends can also be in denial about the severity of the problem. Rather than expressing concern for the addiction and acting in ways that support getting help, family and friends can fall into patterns of enabling.

What are the reasons people abuse substances? According to Dodes (2002), "No addiction is fundamentally motivated by a search for pleasure.... Addictions are fundamentally driven whether they lead to pleasure or not, and are determined by deeper factors than pleasure-seeking" (p. 206). There are many answers to why addictions develop, but they are not likely to lead toward recovery. As a clinician, the author learned that the reason someone becomes an alcoholic or addict is not important; instead, the reasons to recover need to be the focus.

The process of recovery from addictions can be a long road and can include relapse and multiple treatment experiences. According to Dodes (2002), people who are successful in treatment need to have the "capacity to be thoughtful about themselves" (p. 232). Dodes (2002) states that treatment failures occur when clients are not truthful with therapists about their addictions. Although that can be the case, active alcoholics and addicts may also have a limited capacity for knowing the truth. Alcoholics and addicts may know something is wrong, but there are different levels of clarity about the problem (Nace & Tinsley, 2007). Dodes (2002) also points out that treatment may not be successful if clients have angry feelings toward others. This anger can be related to underlying fear, including the fear of success in treatment. Finally, clients may not be successful because they drop out before they finish the program (Dodes, 2002).

Clinicians can look at a variety of client characteristics to assess motivation: self-efficacy, the readiness to change, and the capacity to make good decisions (Center for Substance Abuse Treatment, 1999). The perceived severity of the substance abuse problem by the substance abuser can be what brings the person into treatment (Cosden et al., 2006; Finney & Moos, 1995). Health problems are likely to motivate alcohol abusers to reduce their drinking (Cunningham, Wild, Koski-Jannes, Cordingley, & Toneatto, 2002). Cunningham et al. (2002) found that people who had more "costs of change" were not as likely to want to reduce their drinking. It is hardly a surprise that people who had not experienced negative consequences chose to continue using at that point. Matzger, Kaskutas, and Weisner (2005) also found a correlation between alcohol use and health concerns. Thirty-one percent in a general population sample and 58% in treatment samples reduced their drinking because it caused health problems. Involvement in the criminal justice system can also contribute to motivation for treatment and recovery.

Higher treatment retention rates are more likely when clients are highly motivated, receive help from a highly motivated staff, and are offered longer term treatment in convenient settings (McKay & Hiller-Sturmhofel, 2011). Simple ideas such as telephone follow-up with clients can be cost-effective supplements to agency-based care and convey interest in supporting client success.

Level of intelligence can also bear on motivation for treatment. At times, low intellectual abilities can be mistaken for a lack of motivation for treatment. Fifty percent of offenders in one study had below-average intellectual abilities (Vandevelde, Broekaert, Schuyten, & Van Hove, 2005). However, among these drug offenders in the Belgian criminal justice system, those with low to average intellectual abilities were more likely to be motivated for substance abuse treatment than those with high intellectual abilities (Vandevelde et al., 2005). Reasons for this remain unclear, and further research is needed.

DEFINITIONS OF MOTIVATION

Historically, motivation has been conceived of as an all-or-nothing proposition—a substance abuser either was motivated for treatment or was not. Many professionals felt their hands were tied and they could not, and were not expected to try, to motivate clients (Beckman, 1980). Today there is a more nuanced approach that reflects the abilities of others around the substance abuser to encourage, support, and perhaps even coerce motivation through family or legal intervention, discussed later in this chapter.

Motivation can work in ways other than solely quitting or reducing alcohol or drug use. It may be not just motivation for treatment but also motivation for life changes that brings an alcoholic or addict into treatment. Desires for a better job and improved family relationships can lead addicts and alcoholics to give up drugs. Yet it is possible to stop drug and alcohol use without professional intervention. In a study of 46 alcoholics and addicts who stopped alcohol and drug use without professional help, respondents were employed and had the support of family members and friends (Granfield & Cloud, 1996). This evidence contradicted previously held notions that alcoholics and addicts had to "hit bottom" by losing everything—family, job, and self-respect—before reaching the point of seeking recovery.

Motivation is most often characterized as coming either from within the alcoholic or addict, known as internal or *intrinsic motivation*, or from external environmental pressures, known as external or *extrinsic motivation* (Battjes, Gordon, O'Grady, Kinlock, & Carswell, 2003; Rosen, Hiller, Webster, Staton, & Leukefeld, 2004). These two types of motivation work from different perspectives and are reviewed in the following section.

Intrinsic Motivation

Internal factors include cognitive and emotional factors, level of emotional distress, physical problems, acknowledgment of the role substance abuse plays in the individual's life, and the desire for a better life (Rosen et al., 2004). Internal motivation is linked to a deeper commitment to treatment and can be linked to better outcomes if treatment is deeply desired by the alcoholic or addict (Rosen et al., 2004). A highly motivated client often translates into a client who is an active participant in a treatment program and who is more likely to achieve success, however success is defined—this can include abstinence or reduction in alcohol or drug use. Intrinsic motivation in the field is often related to Prochaska and DiClemente's stages of change, as described in the following section (Fickenscher, Novins, & Beals, 2006; Miller & Rollnick, 1991).

In a study of 220 male prison inmates with substance abuse problems, greater intrinsic motivation was correlated with deeper engagement in treatment that can be associated with a style of counseling known as *motivational interviewing* (Miller & Rollnick, 1991; Rosen et al., 2004). Older offenders were also found to be more likely to have a greater commitment to treatment for reasons that were unclear.

Extrinsic Motivation

Extrinsic motivation is attributed to external circumstances or other people who can bring about pressure for treatment (Fickenscher, Novins, & Beals, 2006). External factors include consequences of substance abuse or addiction, including loss of profession or job, divorce, loss of or restricted involvement with children, and legal factors such as a driving-under-the-influence arrest (Rosen et al., 2004). Efforts can be made to engage family members in providing support to the individual alcoholic and addict to get into treatment while helping family avoid "enabling" behaviors that support substance abuse (Smith & Meyers, 2004). It can be difficult to distinguish between internal and external pressures, especially among substance abusers with criminal justice involvement (Rosen et al., 2004).

Attention to adolescent motivation for treatment developed later than research interest in adult populations (Battjes et al., 2003). External or extrinsic pressures are more likely than internal or intrinsic factors to bring adolescents into treatment. In adolescent substance abusers, severe health effects may not have developed as they have in older alcoholics and addicts. Adolescents are likely to have more limited coping skills and the brain is still developing. In one study, it was not the severity of the substance abuse problem but rather the negative consequences the adolescents experienced that determined the level of motivation (Battjes et al., 2003). Seventy-six percent of the adolescent sample indicated they had been pressured into treatment by family, the legal system, or the school system. Importantly, the length of treatment was also a predictor of success at follow-up. Battjes et al. (2003) were especially struck by the low levels of motivation found among an adolescent sample in outpatient treatment. Another study found that adolescent motivation for entrance into a therapeutic community was higher than adolescent motivation for outpatient services (Melnick, De Leon, Hawke, Jainchill, & Kressel, 1997). For Native American adolescents, legal issues were associated with completion of treatment (Fickenscher et al., 2006).

At Phoenix House, an inpatient therapeutic community, client motivation was a huge issue regarding program admission (Ebener & Kilmer, 2003). In their review of all 16 adolescent clients, the counselors cited lack of motivation and lack of parental permission as the most important barriers to treatment. For adult clients, more than half were considered by counselors to lack motivation. Delays in the admission process contributed to not entering treatment—it gave potential clients time to change their minds and relapse. Delays in the availability of treatment have long been known in the field to make recovery more difficult and potentially contribute to relapse.

HISTORY OF MOTIVATION

As early as the 1950s and 1960s, motivation was considered an important concern in the alcoholism treatment field. According to Sterne and Pittman (1965), "Probably in no other illness is so much verbal concern manifested for the patient's motivation to recover as in alcoholism" (p. 41). In their study of alcoholism treatment professionals, Sterne and Pittman (1965) used the Motivation Questionnaire, and half the respondents agreed with the statement: "It is absolutely essential that the alcoholic want to be treated in order for treatment to succeed" (p. 45). Forty-eight percent of respondents agreed that alcoholics could be divided into two categories: those who are motivated for recovery and those who are not motivated. Yet, for all the concern about motivation, we are still debating whether the motivated succeed in treatment and the unmotivated fail at treatment.

An alcoholic who is not successful in treatment can be blamed for having "inadequate motivation" (Sterne & Pittman, 1965, p. 54). Sterne and Pittman (1965) argued that this does not move forward our understanding of what happens before a client becomes motivated and that motivation can thus be seen as "closer to judgment than to explanation; it is a summary way of stating that the alcoholic succeeds or fails in conforming to the expectations of the treatment agent, without attempting to understand why this is so" (p. 47). Today we have a better understanding of the issue and recognize that "blaming the victim" is problematic and not useful in helping alcoholics and addicts recover.

Yet in the 1960s it was recognized that blaming the alcoholic could hold back the search for other reasons clients are not successful in their treatment and keep professionals from examining the issues they have control over. For example, the factors associated with clinician characteristics can be associated with client response to treatment. These clinician characteristics can include education, attitudes toward alcoholics and addicts, and philosophy of addictions. The importance of traits of clinicians appeared in the literature as early as the 1960s. Treatment professionals need to reach out and do more to engage alcoholics in treatment and to develop trusting relationships. As Sterne and Pittman (1965) conclude, "The motivation concept, as frequently applied to alcoholics, serves as a convenient rationale for unwillingness to review and modify current policies and practices so as to encourage the alcoholic to seek treatment and stay with it" (p. 56).

Within the last 30 years much has been done to encourage professionals and family members to become more proactive in engaging alcoholics and addicts in treatment. For example, the Johnson Institute method of family intervention is described later in this chapter.

STAGES OF CHANGE MODEL

Change is more of a process than an outcome in substance abuse treatment (Center for Substance Abuse Treatment, 1999). Prochaska and DiClemente's (1984, 1992) work is a stages of change model to conceptualize substance abusers' readiness for treatment and change focusing on five stages: precontemplation, contemplation, preparation, action, and maintenance.

Precontemplation means substance abusers are likely to be in denial about the problem and give no thought to changing behavior or attitudes. They may have yet to experience the negative consequences of substance abuse. *Contemplation* refers to the beginning of awareness of the substance abuse problem, and substance abusers may consider using less or quitting. Substance abusers can spend years in this stage (Center for Substance Abuse Treatment, 1999). *Preparation* refers to thoughts about trying to reduce substance use, and individuals may begin to set goals. This includes determining what type of treatment is appropriate. *Action* refers to engaging in a strategy for change, including reduction in use or quitting, time of self-reflection, and figuring out how to get treatment. *Maintenance* refers to trying to hold on to positive changes from the action stage. This includes relapse prevention, an important part of a treatment plan. Although envisioned as stages for clients to move through, clients also move between these stages.

Efforts to reduce the subjectivity in determining motivation resulted in instruments developed to assess level of motivation for treatment. The best known scales were developed in the 1990s, although they do not seem to have achieved widespread use. The Circumstances, Motivation, Readiness, and Suitability scale was developed for drug addicts treated in inpatient therapeutic communities (De Leon, Melnick, Kressel, & Jainhill, 1994). The Stages of Change Readiness and Treatment Eagerness Scale (SOCRATES) was developed for people with alcohol problems (Miller & Tonigan, 1996). The Texas Christian University Treatment Motivation Assistance scales examine recognition of the drug problem, desire to receive assistance, and readiness for treatment (Joe, Simpson, & Broome, 1998). These scales are important in assessing the motivation for treatment for individuals and are important because they allow comparisons among respondents.

EPIPHANIES AND SPIRITUAL AWAKENINGS

Some people who choose to recover can do so after a variety of experiences, including a period of self-reflection, traumatic events or hitting bottom, interventions by others, moments of revelation known as "epiphanies," and spiritual experiences. These do not have to be mutually exclusive experiences (Matzger et al., 2005). Matzger et al. (2005) found that 10% of people in their general population sample had hit a bottom compared with 67% in the treatment sample. For some, this experience is described as a "spiritual awakening" that led them to become abstinent from alcohol and drugs, a major reason a large sample of adults gave for reducing their drinking (Matzger et al., 2005). Yet it is hard to know how many have this experience, and although written about, few efforts have been made to analyze these experiences in the literature (Green, Fullilove, & Fullilove, 1998). This section shares the stories of a number of alcoholics and addicts and their recoveries.

Research shows that people who have spiritual experiences related to their substance abuse recovery are more likely to have grown up with religious or spiritual training (Heinz et al., 2010). AA, developed in 1935, cultivated the spiritual rather than the religious approach still used today. Staff of the Willmar Hospital, which opened in Minnesota in 1912 as an "inebriate asylum," encouraged spiritual awakening as a way to combat alcoholism (White, 1998). The importance of spiritual awakening was touted by psychiatrist Dr. Carl G. Jung and others. See Box 3.1 for a description from 1960.

In correspondence between Bill Wilson, a cofounder of AA, and Jung in 1961, Bill W. recounted his meeting with Roland H., who had been treated by Jung. Bill W. wrote, "You recommended that he place himself in a religious atmosphere and hope for the best" (*AA Grapevine*, 1994, pp. 49–50). Bill W. then wrote of his own "utter despair" and crying out, "'If there be a God, will he show himself.' There came to me an illumination of enormous impact and dimension" (p. 51). In part, Jung responded:

> The only right and legitimate way to such an experience is that it happens to you in reality, and it can only happen to you when you walk on a path which leads you to higher understanding. You might be led to that goal by an act of grace or through a personal and honest contact with friends, or through higher education of the mind beyond the confines of mere rationalism. (p. 53)

See Box 3.2 for the experience of Stephen Levine, who became one of the best known spiritual teachers in the United States.

Others experience some form of crisis, injury, or flash of insight that leads them to change their behavior without a spiritual component. Harry Crews wrote several works focused on what was widely considered a wild life, including his experiences as a boxer and a drinker. He wrote 17 novels and a number of articles in the 1970s for *Playboy* and *Esquire* and acknowledged that he had problems with alcohol: "Alcohol whipped me. Alcohol and I had many marvelous times together. We laughed, we talked, we danced at the party; then one day I woke up and the band had gone home and I was

---

BOX 3.1 The Importance of a Spiritual Awakening

The treatment of alcoholism is a long and arduous process. It is also one that usually involves a multiplicity of ministrations. An occasional alcoholic, to be sure, achieves his own release. But not through his own exertions—not through "will power" or "self-analysis." When such manumissions occur, they are almost always the unbidden and unexpected result of a deep spiritual experience that has reshaped the personality.

Source: Roueche (1960, p. 143).

> ### BOX 3.2 The Experience of Renowned Spiritual Teacher Stephen Levine
>
> One night, sick-addicted on my way to get dosed and disappear into my couch, I became enraged at a long stoplight in Mexico City. Pounding on the steering wheel, nauseous and drenched in sweat, I knew I had to do something right then or I would be sick the rest of my life. It was agonizingly clear that heroin could kill the pain, but not the suffering. And that even such understandings were not enough to open the closed fist of addiction.
>
> I knew I wanted God and clarity more than anything. Weeping, I pulled off the road and stayed there soaked in perspiration and tears with my head in my hands for perhaps an hour. A sweet voice repeated slowly and without the nervous urgency of the body, "You have to want something more than this to be free of it. You must choose between God and heroin!" And it was over! And so it has been ever since.
>
> *Source:* Levine (2002, p. 29). Reprinted with permission.

lying in the broken glass with a shirt full of puke and I said, 'Hey, man, the ball game's up'" (Associated Press, 2012, p. B11). See Box 3.3 for writer Jeanne Darst's description in her memoir of when she knew she had to stop drinking.

The case of Joe B. in Box 3.4 offers another example of opening one's eyes to the terrible reality that has become the addict's life.

> ### BOX 3.3 The Case of Writer Jeanne Darst
>
> The thing is, I had no other options. A few days later I said out loud, "I'm an alcoholic." And it felt like it was the first honest thing I had said in my life. Like the last thing I ever wanted to say. It made me nervous but I knew it was something I had been looking for my whole life. Not sobriety of course, but the truth.
>
> I thought, Well, if I'm considering killing myself here, maybe I'll give this sobriety a chance. I always thought I would drink less, drink better, stop slugging people when I got my shit together. I drank because of my problems and once those went away I wouldn't drink so much. But I agreed to reverse the logical order of things and quit drinking first in order to get a handle on those problems. Not for a lifetime. Just to solve my problems with a clear head, and then I could drink normally again ... or, you know, for the first time.
>
> *Source:* Darst (2011, pp. 223–224).

BOX 3.4 Joe B.'s Story of Recovery

People often report that they entered the process of recovery after "hitting bottom." I found this to be bullshit for myself. Although I often report at self-help meetings that I in fact hit bottom to enter the process of recovery, this simply is not accurate. In reality I had stolen a fellow resident's vehicle from the parking area of the SRO (single room occupancy) that we were both residing at, a filthy dump really. I took the vehicle so that I could go shoplifting in order to earn enough money to purchase heroin. I took the vehicle full of merchandise to my fence and then proceeded to acquire the heroin for that day and the next. Unfortunately, I became so high that I do not remember driving the vehicle into a brick wall at over sixty miles per hour. I am still not sure if the action was intentional.

After several days and extensive surgery, I informed the physician that I would need to go to a detox in order to avoid the likely confrontation with the individual whose car I had stolen, but not for the purpose of getting healthy; I knew he would kick my ass! I was transported to a detox center from the community hospital.

While I was at the detox I began to hear things that I had never heard before in my life. Probably the most influential statement that I heard from the counselor was the fact that I "never had to do what I was doing ever again in my life." Initially I rejected the statement, now I realize what was transpiring in those early counseling sessions was for the first time my denial defenses were being attacked and there was no logical justification for my previous behavior that made any sense even to me. Basically hearing the above statement meant that denial would no longer protect me from myself. Due to the fact that I could not walk and required either a wheel chair or crutches to move about, I was allowed to stay at the detox for a couple of days beyond what the insurance was willing to cover. Eventually, however, I was informed that I would either have to find someplace to be discharged to or I would need to find a homeless shelter. Being naturally pessimistic about the possibility of living a life of recovery I informed the staff that "it was in my higher power's hands now," a way of living one's life advocated by the staff at the treatment facility. I did not have much hope of finding further treatment since I was disabled and about to receive Social Security; most halfway houses require people to work in order to participate in their programming. Quite frankly, I was being sarcastic when I said that my higher power would handle it; I thought for sure I would be homeless. Amazingly, however, within forty-eight hours I was told of an opening at a halfway house that had four disability beds. The next day I was on my way to the halfway house and the beginning of a new chapter in my life. All the stars seemed to have aligned.

Source: Joe B., story written for this book, 2012.

INTERVENTIONS BY FAMILY

Family involvement in encouraging substance abuse treatment has a rich history in the United States. Vernon Johnson, known as the "father of intervention," was an Episcopal priest and a recovering alcoholic who began his work in the 1960s and founded the Johnson Institute in 1966, specializing in intervention and employee assistance for people who had drinking problems. Johnson went on to write six books, including his best known, *I'll Quit Tomorrow* (1973), and *Intervention, How to Help Some Who Doesn't Want Help: A Step-by-Step Guide for Families and Friends of Chemically Dependent Persons* (1986).

Johnson did not believe that family members had to wait until the alcoholic or addict had a spiritual awakening or a flash of insight. He felt that family members could create the motivation for treatment. Johnson's confrontational method used a professional counselor to plan a client meeting with family and friends during which the participants spoke of their concern, read letters they had written to the alcoholic, and typically supported immediate entrance into an inpatient alcoholism treatment program. The underlying rationale is that alcoholics and addicts can be so deep in their denial that this confrontation is necessary to get them to see the dismal reality of their situation. The intervention is seen as the beginning of recovery for the alcoholic and the family, although it is not used often in the field (Farber & Keating-O'Connor, 1991).

One test of the Johnson Institute method compared it with two other counseling approaches in a randomized trial: Al-Anon (the 12-step support group for families and friends of alcoholics) and a community reinforcement and family training (CRAFT) approach that teaches behavior skills training (Miller, Meyers, & Tonigan, 1999). The CRAFT approach was found to be the most successful by engaging 64% of the initially unmotivated sample in treatment; the Johnson method engaged 30% in treatment, and Al-Anon engaged only 13% of unmotivated drinkers in treatment. In fairness, Al-Anon is a support group for family and friends and therefore is not designed to be a treatment for alcoholics.

The Johnson method has been criticized as aggressive, confrontational, and potentially uncomfortable for family members engaging in this level of forceful intervention. In one study of the Johnson method, only 29% of family and friends pursued the actual intervention (Liepman, Nirenberg, & Begin, 1989). A Relational Intervention Sequence for Engagement (ARISE) intervention was developed as a response to the Johnson method; it cultivates a far less confrontational approach and focuses specifically on outpatient rather than inpatient treatment as a goal (Garrett et al., 1998).

There are also a number of books aimed at family members to assist them in getting the alcoholic or addict into treatment. Some book titles available today are *The Intervention Book: Stories and Solutions from Addicts, Professionals, and Families* by Kathy L. (2011); *Love First: A Family's Guide to Intervention* by Jeff Jay, Debra Jay, and George McGovern (2008); and *Family Interventions in Substance Abuse: Current Best Practices* by Oliver J. Morgan and Cheryl H. Lizke (2007).

Other research reveals that interventions from a physician or family member may not be successful and may even be associated with continued drinking, because such interventions can be perceived as strong emotional pressure (Weisner, Delucchi, Matzger, & Schmidt, 2003). In their treatment sample, Matzger et al. (2005) found that a physician intervention within a 1-year follow-up was not associated with reduced problem drinking. In their general population sample, pressure from partners or spouses correlated with the continuation of alcohol abuse This serves as an important reminder that nagging the alcoholic or addict is not likely to be helpful. Matzger et al. (2005) reported that drinking less was correlated with the person experiencing a trauma, hitting bottom, or having a spiritual awakening.

LEGALLY MANDATED AND COERCED TREATMENT

As we have seen, motivation can come from the client or from outside sources. Mandatory or *coerced treatment* involves pressure to enter substance abuse treatment when clients are not interested or refuse treatment, and this approach is increasingly used with offender populations (Parhar, Wormith, Derkzen, & Beauregard, 2008). Inherent in the definition is that these clients risk losing something important to them, such as their personal freedom. External motivation, especially from the criminal justice system, can include the threat of further sanctions such as jail time as a motivator to participate in outpatient drug court programs. There are different levels of coerced treatment. A client can be ordered by a court into an outpatient treatment program, a relatively mild intervention. At the most extreme, in some states clients can be remanded into locked substance abuse treatment units because their problems are so severe. Known as a Section 35 in Massachusetts, family members or police departments can seek a court order for inpatient treatment, clearly at a point when the alcoholic or addict is unable to make a personal decision to seek help. Clinicians sometimes report that seeking a Section 35 intervention can be an overreaction on the part of parents who are frustrated and do not know what else they can do.

There are positive results associated with legal pressure, including obtaining needed treatment, reduced time in a correctional facility, or transfer to a preferred correctional facility for that treatment (Center for Substance Abuse Treatment, 2005). Clients who are coerced into treatment by the legal system may still be in the precontemplation stage, unlike those who are seeking treatment on their own (Vandevelde et al., 2005). The likelihood of reduced criminal sanctions can be an important motivator.

One study found that both internal motivation and legal pressure factors can make clients less likely to drop out of treatment (Knight, Hiller, Broome, & Simpson, 2000). Those with greater internal motivation, known as *treatment readiness,* stayed in treatment longer whether legal pressure was present or not. Clients with internal motivation showed more engagement in the therapeutic process. Those under legal pressure also stayed longer in treatment whether internal motivation was present or not. Another study found that offenders with less serious substance abuse problems, less serious criminal histories, and a good work history were more likely to benefit from treatment and that less severe substance abuse problems were better predictors of treatment outcomes than the attitudes of clients (Cosden et al., 2006).

Mandated treatment continues to be controversial, bolstered by results that both support and undermine its importance. Methodological differences and differing definitions of the terms *involuntary, coerced, legal pressure*, and *mandated* can also affect research findings, a reminder that it is important to understand the definitions of these terms used in studies. In a meta-analysis of treatment effectiveness for coerced offenders, a review of 129 studies found "mandated treatment was ineffective, particularly when the treatment was located in custodial settings, whereas voluntary treatment produced significant treatment effects sizes regardless of setting" (Parhar et al., 2008, p. 1128).

A national survey of public programs found that legal coercion reduced the risk of dropping out of treatment (Perron & Bright, 2008). The most significant effect was found for short-term inpatient substance abuse treatment; long-term inpatient treatment had a moderate effect, and outpatient treatment had the smallest effect. Although this study focused on length of stay in treatment, this cannot be compared with the Parhar et al. (2008) study that focused on treatment outcomes. Overall, it is not clear whether clients are just "putting in their time" or are genuinely working on recovery.

It has been established that strong client participation in treatment is associated with positive treatment outcomes. That is, the more involved the client is in the individual and group therapy (intensity) and the longer the client stays in treatment (duration), the more likely the client is to stay clean from drugs and alcohol (Fiorentine, Nakashima, & Anglin, 1999). Although we have typically seen more emphasis put on the client investment in treatment, this view is not without contradictory evidence. Treatment programs can provide the impetus for clients to engage more deeply in treatment. This is important because rather than simply looking at client characteristics and background, treatment programs can be improved and be more deeply encouraged to engage clients (Fiorentine et al., 1999).

THE CLIENT AND COUNSELOR RELATIONSHIP

Some professionals think it is important to wait for the addict or alcoholic to "become sick and tired of being sick and tired," a way of saying they have had enough of drinking, drugging, or both and then have become motivated toward sobriety and entering treatment. As indicated, some people stop drinking and drugging on their own, whereas others seek professional help. Today we know that the therapist or treatment program can strongly encourage the client to become motivated.

A strong relationship between the counselor and the client is correlated with greater success in treatment (Meier, Donmall, McElduff, Barrowclough, & Heller, 2006; Simpson, Joe, Rowan-Szal, & Greener, 1997; Smith, Thomas, & Jackson, 2004). Known as the *therapeutic alliance*, this speaks to the importance of the client–counselor relationship (Zuroff et al., 2000). Research over the previous 20 years found that an early therapeutic alliance predicts that clients will engage and continue in treatment (Meier, Barrowclough, & Donmall, 2005). However, although we know that empathy and trust are important, there is insufficient knowledge about how to define and understand the quality of the relationship between counselors and clients.

Future research needs a greater focus on examining the relationship and interactions between clients and clinicians (Imel, Wampold, Miller, & Fleming, 2008). Although the focus has been on standardization of treatment, Imel et al. (2008) remind us to look at the therapists and their qualities and that clinicians with "higher working alliance scores" (p. 541) are more effective as therapists.

Research has yet to determine the relative importance of the roles of patients and therapists in the therapeutic alliance, that is, which role carries more weight (Baldwin, Wampold, & Imel, 2007). Baldwin et al. (2007) found that therapist characteristics more than patient characteristics predicted the outcome. They recommend that therapists receive training and feedback on how to develop strong alliances. We associate positive alliances with building trust in the therapist and having the client view the therapist as competent and interested in helping. Although positive therapeutic alliances can help clients with poor motivation, the reasons for this may not yet be clear from the current state of research (Ilgen, McKellar, Moos, & Finney, 2006). It was reported that the quality of the relationship, as determined by the therapist, rather than the type of intervention was more helpful (Ilgen et al., 2006).

Meier et al. (2006) found that counselors with the most experience were able to keep clients in drug treatment longer. The rating of the counselors regarding the therapeutic alliance predicted clients who would drop out. It is not a surprise that clients who expected treatment to be helpful were more willing to stay longer in treatment.

This expectation is reminiscent of a story frequently shared in detox programs. A client is anxious to leave the detox program against medical advice. The counselor may not be able to persuade the client to stay and resorts to telling the client that he or she has to stay until the next day when the head counselor will speak with him or her about his or her important complaints about the program. This strategy is designed to provide the client with another day of treatment in the hopes that the client will change his or her mind and reengage in the treatment process. This also serves as a reminder that there is no proven strategy for keeping patients in a detox program or other type of treatment.

Do other things matter to recovery? Is recovery dependent only on behavior change such as level of alcohol or drug use, illegal activity, or job retention? One study reported that quality therapeutic interactions and client attendance in the first 2 months of treatment mutually support each other and improve treatment success (Simpson et al., 1997). Overall, Simpson et al. (1997) found three important factors: positive therapeutic relationship, engagement in treatment, and motivation for treatment. In reality, for individuals it can be a combination of timing, internal motivation, level of support from family and friends, and ready availability of treatment with an engaging therapist.

In the 1970s confrontational and hard-line approaches to treatment were readily available. Many counselors were themselves in recovery and relied on the strategies that helped them to recover to engage with their clients. (The picture of the substance abuse workforce has changed considerably over the years to include the importance of education, certification, and licensure—and is still changing, as discussed in Chapter 12.) In a substance abuse treatment program in which the author worked in the 1970s, one counselor in particular relished the confrontational approach he used with his clients. At staff meetings he discussed the clients he intended to "hit hard" in their denial. The counselor's statements were often made while he vigorously slammed one fist into his other open hand. The author later learned that the counselor had been a professional boxer earlier in his life, accounting for his frequent boxing metaphors. Although appreciated for his confrontational approach by some clients and counselors, others sought to avoid him. Forman, Bovasso, and Woody (2001) found that counselors who had fewer years working in the substance abuse treatment field tended to be more supportive of confrontational approaches. These authors suggest that may be because they are not aware of therapeutic alternatives. This serves as a reminder that there is no substitute for experience in the substance abuse treatment field.

Less confrontational and direct approaches taken by therapists can be associated with less drinking (Karno & Longabaugh, 2005b). For patients who had a lot of anger, the more direct approach taken by the therapist correlated with more frequent drinking after the end of treatment (Karno & Longabaugh, 2005a). Conversely, for patients who were considered low in anger, a more direct approach correlated with less drinking after the treatment ended.

Read, Kahler, and Stevenson (2001), following Lambert and Bergin (1994), found that common factors, rather than specific treatment types, may be involved. Lambert and Bergin (1994) found that specific therapists are more effective rather than specific therapies, lending support to the importance of the therapeutic relationship. Read et al. (2001) support the idea that treatment providers can be most effective if they encourage client motivation and reinforcing variables, avoid confrontational approaches, focus on acquisition of specific skills, support coping skills, encourage the setting of goals, and enhance socioenvironmental factors such as support networks, including family, friends, and 12-step programs. Clients must find the treatment manageable and convenient, participate in setting goals, and perceive the assistance as useful (McKay, 2005).

No studies compare the outcomes for various treatment professionals, such as physicians specializing in addiction, psychiatrists, social workers, and bachelor's and master's level clinicians, to determine which groups have greater success in treating addictions (Gitlow & Gold, 2007).

Motivational Interviewing

Motivational interviewing, developed by Miller and Rollnick (1991), is "designed to help clients build commitment and reach a decision to change" (p. x). Motivational interviewing is a client-focused counseling style that supports behavioral changes by resolving ambivalence, an obstacle to recovery (Center for Substance Abuse Treatment, 1999; Thyrian et al., 2007). *Ambivalence* refers to wanting to continue drinking or drugging while also wanting to quit. Motivational interviewing was developed to address a variety of health issues, including alcoholism, drug addiction, and smoking, and has been expanded to include a variety of other problems, including sex addiction.

The principles of motivational interviewing include careful and empathic listening on the part of the counselor, steering clear of confrontation, and working with the resistance of the client rather than trying to break it down. The principles also include assisting the client to see that behavior is out of line with personal values and goals, supporting the client's ability to change, and encouraging optimism for the future (Center for Substance Abuse Treatment, 1999). Although some clinicians see motivational interviewing as a specific approach to treatment, other clinicians view these characteristics as important in any treatment approach. Motivational interviewing is discussed in Chapter 6 as one of the most effective counseling styles in the substance abuse treatment field today.

Importantly, motivational interviewing has been found to be helpful in assisting patients to stay in treatment (De Leon, Melnick, Thomas, Kressel, & Wexler, 2000). In a sample of 423 substance abusers in outpatient treatment, clinicians who received special training in motivational interviewing were found to receive higher ratings than other clinicians. Clients had better retention rates through a follow-up at 28 days, yet there were no significant effects of motivational interviewing after that and up to an 84-day follow-up (Carroll et al., 2006). Motivational interviewing was also more effective in retaining alcoholics than in retaining drug addicts in treatment.

SUMMARY AND CONCLUSION

The importance of motivation for substance abuse treatment has received considerable research attention with varying research results. Whereas in the early days of substance abuse treatment only client motivation was deemed an important factor, today we know that quality professional counseling and family and legal interventions can be helpful to addicts and alcoholics in their recovery. Legal pressure and the threat of incarceration can motivate adolescents and adults with substance abuse problems to get into treatment. The characteristics of therapists, rather than the specific style of counseling, can also be associated with positive outcomes.

There is no reason to declare that either internal or external motivation is preferable, and a melding of both is possible and reasonable. It is difficult to sort through the myriad research findings, but it is important to remember that although some approaches are better at keeping clients in treatment for longer periods, this does not necessarily mean that the treatment outcomes are more successful. Supportive approaches, such as the motivational interviewing style, have been found to be more successful overall, yet there are clients who prefer a confrontational style. The difficulty is to figure out what kinds of clients can be most helped by what kinds of interventions.

THE SUBSTANCE ABUSE
TREATMENT INDUSTRY

*T*he substance abuse treatment field has grown and changed enormously through the years, with the current treatment system evolving since the 1950s (Rawson & Obert, 2002). The history of substance abuse treatment has its roots in a combination of sources, including Alcoholics Anonymous (AA), the rise of the acceptance of the disease concept, and informal and more formal approaches to treatment, all bolstered by the quest for what works and what does not. Informal counseling approaches offered to clients by recovering alcoholic counselors popular in the 1970s have given way to a variety of evidence-based approaches to treatment and recovery provided by highly educated and credentialed substance abuse professionals.

The current system of private and for-profit alcohol and drug treatment today developed through federal legislation and public funding provided over the years (Roman, Johnson, & Blum, 2000). It is significant that the substance abuse treatment field has developed independently of medical practice, with few physicians seeking addiction medicine as a specialty (Miller, Sorensen, Selzer, & Brigham, 2006). This chapter provides a chronology of major developments in substance abuse treatment from the 1920s to the present.

The substance abuse field began with a focus exclusively on alcoholism. It began to expand to include addiction to other drugs, including heroin and cocaine, in the 1970s. The disease concept of alcoholism morphed into the disease concept of chemical dependency or disease of addiction as people abusing substances were drinking alcohol, as well as increasingly using other drugs (Mignon, Faiia, Myers, & Rubington, 2009).

THE 1920s THROUGH THE 1940s

The Prohibition years of 1920 to 1933 were tumultuous political times filled with opposing messages of the evils of "demon rum" and a huge bootlegging business and speakeasies (clubs where illegal alcohol was served) that were an integral part of big city life. Prohibition banned the manufacture, sale, and transportation of alcohol but not its consumption (Burnham, 1968). Some view Prohibition as a historic failure in curbing alcohol use that fueled the rise of organized crime. Some evidence points to a reduction in alcohol use through the Prohibition years, although assessments of Prohibition are difficult because the experiences of people in large cities were different from the experiences of those in rural areas (Burnham, 1968). The effects of Prohibition are still debated. See Hall (2010) for a comprehensive discussion of Prohibition and social policy. The interest once paid to alcohol use, its negative effect on families, and the politics surrounding Prohibition were greatly reduced after 1933. The Great Depression and the repeal of Prohibition "left most people bored with the topic of alcohol—they were tired of hearing about it" (Kurtz, 2002, p. 7).

Although many people are aware of the development of AA, which began in 1935, few are aware of the road paved for it by the Oxford Groups. The Oxford Groups developed in the 1920s and 1930s and provided support groups that included a religious focus (Sadler, 2003). It was the "religiosity and rigidity" (Sadler, 2003, p. 6) of this organization that led to a split and the subsequent development of AA by cofounders Bill W. and Dr. Bob. See Box 4.1 for a description of the Oxford Groups.

In the late 1930s and early 1940s an informal treatment system of alcoholics helping one another developed out of AA (Yalisove, 1998). These programs, known as "AA farms," were retreats, not medical treatment programs, for recovering alcoholics. The first was High Watch Farm in Connecticut that opened in 1940 when the farm was given to Bill W. a cofounder of AA. Pioneer House opened in 1948 and then Hazelden opened in Minnesota in 1949. The alcoholism rehabilitation treatment centers and halfway houses of today developed out of these programs. The alcoholism rehabilitation treatment centers became intensive inpatient programs, whereas halfway houses developed into longer term living situations where clients were usually required to work (Yalisove, 1998). These inpatient and sober housing options are described in Chapter 5.

In the 1940s, hospital-based treatment was typically available in the form of public mental hospitals for alcoholics. These programs emphasized short-term detoxification or long-term institutional care for what was likely Wernicke-Korsakoff's syndrome or "wet brain," brain damage attributed to long-term alcoholism that results in the deterioration of cognitive abilities (Roman et al., 2000). Some available treatments were drugs to suppress the craving for alcohol, including mixtures with quinine, glycerin, and a combination of atropine and strychnine (White, 1998). Today our culture has again embraced legal drugs, such as naltrexone and acamprosate, as appropriate treatments

BOX 4.1 The Oxford Groups

The Oxford Groups developed in the 1900s as a spiritual movement that grew through the 1930s and then declined in the 1940s. The Oxford Groups did not specifically require abstinence from alcohol but gave alcoholics hope with the promise of a better life. It laid the groundwork for AA by encouraging a personal spiritual transformation. The Oxford Groups promoted a good life focused on "four absolutes": absolute honesty, absolute unselfishness, absolute purity, and absolute love.

The cofounders of AA, Bill W. and Dr. Bob, both had experience with Oxford Groups. While continuing to drink, Smith had attended meetings of the Oxford Groups for more than 2 years. Wilson was encouraged to attend a meeting on December 11, 1934, but he attributes his admission for detoxification to the Charles B. Towns Hospital in Manhattan, New York, to his spiritual awakening and subsequent decision to found AA.

Wilson (1957) wrote about his connections with the Oxford Groups:

> The Oxford Groups had clearly shown us what to do. And, just as importantly, we also learned from them what not to do as far as alcoholics were concerned. We had found that certain of their ideas and attitudes simply could not be sold to alcoholics. For example, drinkers would not take pressure in any form, excepting from John Barleycorn himself. They always had to be led, not pushed. They would not stand for the rather aggressive evangelism of the Oxford Groups. And they would not accept the principle of "team guidance" for their own personal lives. It was too authoritarian for them. In other respects, too, we found we had to make haste slowly. When first contacted, most alcoholics just wanted to find sobriety, nothing else. They clung to their other defects, letting go only little by little. They simply did not want to get "too good too soon." The Oxford Groups' absolute concept—absolute purity, absolute honestly, absolute unselfishness, and absolute love—were frequently too much for the drunks. These ideas had to be fed with teaspoons rather than by buckets. (pp. 74–75)

Sources: White (1998) and Wilson (1957).

for alcoholism and drug addiction, especially to reduce cravings and block the high associated with some illegal substances. These medications are further discussed in Chapter 6.

A significant development in the research and treatment of alcoholics was the inception of the *Quarterly Journal of Studies on Alcohol* in 1940. It was founded by Dr. Howard Haggard of Yale University, a physiologist who studied the effects of alcohol on the body and promoted the dissemination of research on the effects of alcohol and alcoholism (White, 1998; Wiener, 1981). In 1975 it became the *Journal of Studies on Alcohol* and since 2007 it has been known as the *Journal of Studies on Alcohol and Drugs* to reflect the loss of distinction between alcohol and drug problems, now known as substance abuse problems. This journal was critical in recognizing that alcoholism was an important field deserving of research; it remains the most prestigious journal in the substance abuse field.

The National Council on Alcoholism was founded in 1943 by members of AA, including Marty Mann, one of the first female members of AA. The organization is now known as the National Council on Alcoholism and Drug Dependence (NCADD). The mission remains the same—to remove the stigma of alcoholism and drug addiction and to promote the view that alcoholism is a treatable disease that should be treated within the health care system (Roman et al., 2000). See Box 4.2 for a description of the contributions of Mann.

This interest in alcoholism, especially of people involved with AA, including Mann, developed into the founding of the Center of Alcohol Studies at Yale University (now located at Rutgers University). The first Summer School of Alcohol Studies at Yale was offered in 1943. In 1944 the Yale Plan Clinics were founded as the first "modern" outpatient clinics for the treatment of alcoholism; their services included individual psychotherapy, AA, and "religiotherapy" (based on religious beliefs; Yalisove, 1998). The clinics used the AA approach, and treatment was designed specifically for middle-class alcoholics rather than the "skid row bums" typically associated with alcoholism (Roman et al., 2000). In these early years a few private psychiatric facilities also offered treatment to alcoholics.

BOX 4.2 Story of Marty Mann (1904–1980)

Mann attended her first AA meeting in the home of Bill W. and his wife, Lois, in 1939. She was one of the first women to join AA. Her alcoholism developed at an early age, supported by heavy partying in elite social circles. Her drinking dragged her down until she became a charity patient at Bellevue Hospital in New York. In her recovery Mann embraced the disease concept and worked tirelessly to reduce the stigma of alcoholism and to define it as a public health problem. She worked to start the Yale School of Alcohol Studies and became the first director of the National Council on Alcoholism. Alcoholism had been seen primarily as a problem affecting men, and Mann brought needed attention to the alcoholism of women.

Sources: Miller (1963) and White (1998).

THE 1950s AND 1960s

Mental hospitals provided institutional care for alcoholics in the late 1940s and 1950s, although there was little formal treatment (Yalisove, 1998). The moralistic and negative views of alcoholics and alcoholism were still alive and well, despite the intense efforts of members of AA.

Disulfiram (Antabuse), the prescription drug that makes a drinker sick within a few minutes of ingesting alcohol, was the first medication approved in the United States to deter alcoholics from drinking (Saxe, Doughtery, Estey, & Fine, 1983). It was initially developed by a drug company in Denmark to treat parasites. Antabuse's interaction with alcohol became known in 1948. Antabuse was prescribed through the 1950s and continued into the 1970s as an adjunct to other forms of alcoholism treatment.

Although the American Medical Association in 1956 acknowledged that alcoholism is an illness and that alcoholics need hospital treatment, it was not until the 1970s that medically supervised detoxification programs were developed (Yalisove, 1998). This is further evidence that physicians have remained on the periphery of substance abuse treatment.

The Hazelden Foundation was established in 1949, the same year the National Institute of Mental Health (NIMH) was established. At the time Hazelden was an inpatient facility for "curable alcoholics" (Hazelden, n.d., p. 2). Today Hazelden remains the most prestigious, well funded, and influential of all substance abuse treatment programs, offering many treatment and educational services. The Minnesota Model developed in the late 1950s and 1960s through the Hazelden Foundation, incorporating professionals and paraprofessional recovering alcoholic counselors using the principles of AA. It focused on the disease concept and a 28-day inpatient treatment model (Anderson, McGovern, & DuPont, 1999). This included adherence to the disease concept and a holistic approach to recovery incorporating involvement of family, alcoholism education for patients and family, and an aftercare program that included continued involvement in AA.

In the 1960s, the National Council on Alcoholism continued to seek development of alcoholism treatment programs through government funding. The council was responsible for the efforts to reduce stigma and the "medicalization" process that redefined alcoholics from "bad" people to "sick" people and culminated in referring alcoholics for treatment if they were considered public inebriates. Although this was successful in the early 1970s, it did not move NCA ahead into treating working- and middle-class alcoholics.

The mid-1960s to the mid-1970s offered much federal legislation aimed at the treatment of alcoholism and drug addiction; 13 pieces of legislation were enacted between 1963 and 1974 (White, 1998). The federal system of treatment has its roots in the national Narcotic Addict Rehabilitation Act (NARA) of 1966, which allowed some addicts to enter into treatment rather than into the criminal justice system and offered supervision for addicts released from prison. In 1966 the National Center for Prevention and Control of Alcoholism was founded as part of NIMH. The Alcoholic and Narcotic Addict Rehabilitation Act of 1968 followed and provided money to establish community treatment programs (White, 1998). The 1963 Community Mental Health Act expanded in 1986 to include support for the provision of alcohol and drug treatment in these centers.

In the 1960s Dr. Vincent P. Dole and Dr. Marie E. Nyswander developed methadone maintenance as a treatment for heroin addiction, and in 1967 they published "Heroin Addiction: A Metabolic Disease" in the *Archives of Internal Medicine*. Their model consisted of intensive inpatient treatment, unlike the outpatient methadone maintenance programs of today (White, 1998).

THE 1970s

The Comprehensive Alcohol Abuse and Alcoholism Prevention, Treatment, and Rehabilitation Act of 1970, commonly known as the Hughes Act, established the National Institute on Alcohol Abuse and Alcoholism (NIAAA) within NIMH. Senator Harold E. Hughes, a recovering alcoholic, used his considerable political capital in the passage of this Act, which is widely considered the most important piece of legislation in alcohol and drug treatment history. NIAAA had the responsibility of making the public more aware of alcoholism and therefore created the opportunity for greater local and state government funding of programs (Wiener, 1981). The Institute created a network of alcoholism treatment centers and provided money for alcoholism research and education. "Formula" grants provided the basis of public programs, such as detoxification programs where patients received medical treatment to assist in withdrawing from alcohol and drugs. In addition, the NIAAA established grant money for graduate training in substance abuse treatment (The author received one of these NIAAA grants, provided to social work graduate students at the Washington Center for Addictions in Jamaica Plain, Massachusetts, in the mid-1970s). NIAAA also supported nonprofit agencies by offering funds to lobby for mandatory health insurance coverage for alcoholism treatment (Roman et al., 2000).

NIAAA established the National Center for Alcohol Education (NCAE) in the mid-1970s to develop curricula for public education programs and develop training programs for clinicians (Wiener, 1981). In 1972 the Drug Abuse Office and Treatment Act established the National Institute on Drug Abuse (NIDA) within NIMH. In the mid-1970s, NIDA launched the National Drug Abuse Training Center to develop counselor-training programs (White, 1998). Overall, this was a time of great excitement, with much interest in and funding for the treatment of substance abuse problems.

In September 1973 the Alcohol, Drug Abuse, and Mental Health Administration (ADAMHA) was established; it brought together NIAAA, NIDA, and NIMH. ADAMHA was renamed the Substance Abuse and Mental Health Services Administration (SAMHSA) in July 1992.

The 1970s were also a time of development and expansion of employee assistance programs that provided outpatient counseling, as well as a source of referrals to inpatient treatment centers (Roman et al., 2000). Insurance coverage for employees and their families contributed to the development of private treatment centers from the middle of the 1970s until the late 1980s. The 1970s also saw the development of alcoholism and drug counselor professional associations.

The year 1976 saw the release of the Rand Report (Armor, Polich, & Stambul, 1976), which was to have a critical effect on the substance abuse treatment field. This involved a grant from NIAAA to study the alcohol treatment centers by examining the client monitoring system (Wiener, 1981). For 6-month client follow-up, 44 alcohol treatment centers were reviewed, and 8 centers were chosen for an 18-month follow-up. The findings provided support for the controversial view that some alcoholics could return to social drinking and have no greater risk of relapse than alcoholics who choose to abstain from alcohol. The report found that abstinent clients were as likely to return to alcoholism as people who drank at "normal levels" (Wiener, 1981, p. 207). The Rand Report concluded that only 10% of the sample was abstinent from alcohol at the 6-month follow-up. This sent shock waves through the substance abuse treatment world, with recovering alcoholic counselors shaking their heads about how researchers did not know what they were talking about.

Importantly, the 1970s also saw the development of national surveys of alcohol use that would allow comparative national research. The National Household Survey of Drug Abuse began in 1971. Today, known as the National Survey on Drug Use and Health (NSDUH), it provides national data on patterns of legal and illegal drug use, including tobacco, alcohol, and specific types of drugs, and identifies groups at high risk for substance abuse. This national survey is one of the most important sources of data for substance abuse researchers.

In the 1970s efforts to review and summarize the state of treatment research mostly concluded that it was preferable to have treatment rather than no treatment. Problems in methodology made it difficult to compare treatment types; therefore, it was not possible to determine whether specific treatments were preferable to others (Saxe et al., 1983). The call for research supported by the federal government was described as "the best hope for providing objective and unambiguous data about treatment effectiveness" (Saxe et al., 1983, p. 53).

THE 1980s

The 1980s were a time of increasing coverage for substance abuse treatment and an increase in inpatient treatment, mostly based on the Minnesota Model of 28 days of inpatient treatment (Barnett & Swindle, 1997; Roman et al., 2000). This was also a time of competition for patients among private treatment providers—and among organizations' "community service" workers who recruited private-paying patients into the programs. These inpatient programs were typically staffed by recovering alcoholic counselors and, as indicated previously, had minimal input from physicians (Roman et al., 2000).

Substance abuse treatment was developed by borrowing from the mental health field. A respondent in Wiener's (1981) study said:

> Among service providers there is an egalitarian notion that all philosophies of treatment should be given equal consideration. This is fair to the philosophers, but many of the techniques (TM [transcendental meditation], gestalt, psychodrama) are modalities that were not designed for alcoholism. Alcoholism is a step-child—you have to fit somebody else's clothes. Helping professionals are not trained in alcoholism but in psychosis and neurosis, and those are the tools they use. If the alcoholic goes away and stays sober, *we* succeeded; if he goes away and gets drunk, *he* failed. (p. 81)

Importantly, substance abuse developed into a field separate from mental health only to be brought back with mental health under federal regulations in 1992.

The late 1970s and early 1980s brought considerable media attention to celebrities entering treatment. According to White (1998):

> Going to treatment and participating in some type of Twelve-Step recovery program became something of a fad. Programs like the Palm Beach Institute, Betty Ford Center, Hazelden, Edgehill Newport, Fair Oaks Hospital, Regent Hospital, and Sierra Tucson found themselves catering to the addicted rich and famous, whose entrance and ongoing status in treatment was regularly reported in newspapers, popular magazines, and the tabloids. (p. 277)

At that time few anticipated that some of the expensive and posh treatment programs based on the Minnesota Model of Hazelden would not survive both the competition and the changes in insurance reimbursement.

A study by Saxe et al. published in 1983 challenged the notion that the Minnesota Model was the best approach: It was expensive, and evidence was lacking that inpatient treatment was superior to outpatient treatment. Saxe et al. (1983) pointed out that insurance and reimbursement systems, especially Medicare and Medicaid, paid for expensive treatment, apparently without complaint. Estimates are that in 1982 Medicare paid $150 million for alcoholism treatment. It was the cost and the lack of proof of effectiveness that brought challenges to the lucrative inpatient treatment approach (Roman et al., 2000).

Managed care brought more extensive review of the records of patients rated for substance abuse and resulted in shorter stays in inpatient treatment (Barnett & Swindle, 1997). In addition, according to Roman et al. (2000), these relatively new private centers were vulnerable to ambivalent attitudes toward alcoholism and did not offer the "quick fix" (p. 330) desired as a response to medical, as well as social, problems. In comparison to AA, which requires no payments or dues, these private treatment centers seemed especially expensive. Alcoholism treatment centers also did not form a national organization that could have lobbied on their behalf, the result of which was each organization fending for itself. Thus, the quick and unplanned increase in the number of programs resulted in significant problems, and between 1989 and 1991 at least 20% of these private centers closed (Roman et al., 2000).

Roman et al. (2000) remark, "The transformation from a fledgling self-help group into a nationwide complex of relatively expensive and highly visible programs offering a 'one size fits all' treatment modality gave way to large-scale abandonment of that modality replicated by considerable diversification of services" (p. 341). What began as the development of inpatient programs to help alcoholics and addicts in their recovery became a lucrative enterprise that could not be sustained.

THE 1990s

The Alcohol, Drug Abuse, and Mental Health Administration (ADAMHA) was abolished and SAMHSA was created in October 1992; the latter is now part of the U.S. Department of Health and Human Services (HHS). The research arms of NIAAA, NIDA, and NIMH became a part of the National Institutes of Health, whereas the service parts became part of SAMHSA (National Institutes of Health, 2013). SAMHSA is the federal agency charged with improving access to substance abuse treatment and prevention and mental health services. It provides leadership, grant funding, policies, programs and research data, and regulation and oversight of substance abuse (SAMHSA, 2011). Today there are four components of SAMHSA that focus on dissemination of research, prevention efforts, and the development of treatment services for addiction and mental illness. See Box 4.3 for a review of the major components of SAMHSA.

Overall, SAMHSA has sought greater visibility in providing leadership to address substance abuse and mental health problems and has an ambitious agenda in these next years. See Box 4.4 for a description of the 2012 SAMHSA initiatives.

BOX 4.3 Components of SAMHSA

1. Office of Applied Studies

   The Office of Applied Studies (OAS) collects and disseminates data on the prevention and treatment of substance abuse and mental disorders (SAMHSA, 2006). The primary system is the National Survey on Drug Use and Health, which yields an enormous amount of data on characteristics of people with substance abuse and mental health issues. OAS collects data on treatment programs and client treatment outcomes. OAS is responsible for the Drug and Alcohol Services Information System (DASIS), which provides primary data. OAS also manages the Drug Abuse Warning Network (DAWN), a system that keeps track of visits to hospital emergency rooms for treatment of drug-related physical problems and deaths because of drugs that come to the attention of coroners and medical examiners (SAMHSA, 2008).

(continued)

BOX 4.3 Components of SAMHSA (continued)

2. Center for Substance Abuse Prevention
   The Center for Substance Abuse Prevention (CSAP) aims to improve the quality of prevention services, as well as the accessibility of these services nationally. CSAP took the place of the Office of Substance Abuse Prevention (OSAP) created by the Anti-Drug Abuse Act of 1986 and helps states and communities to effectively use prevention information.

3. Center for Substance Abuse Treatment
   The goal of the Center for Substance Abuse Treatment (CSAT) is to bring effective alcohol and drug treatment services to communities across the United States.

4. Center for Mental Health Services
   The Center for Mental Health Services aims to improve advocacy on behalf of people with mental illness and to foster relationships between research and service organizations. It seeks to remove barriers to prevention and treatment of mental disorders.

Source: Substance Abuse and Mental Health Services Administration (2006; 2008).

BOX 4.4 SAMHSA 2012 Strategic Initiatives That Will Remain in Place Through 2014

1. Prevention of Substance Abuse and Mental Illness
   The prevention initiative focuses on reducing mental illness, substance abuse, and suicide and promoting mental health. This includes preventing or reducing consequences of underage drinking and adult problem drinking, as well as reducing prescription drug misuse and abuse. Special focus is placed on preventing suicides among high-risk populations, especially military families; lesbian, gay, bisexual, and questioning (LGBTQ) youth; and Native Americans (p. 5).

2. Trauma and Justice
   This initiative seeks the development of a comprehensive public health response to trauma and violence, as well as to reducing the effect of disasters on the behavioral health of individuals, families, and communities. This includes providing screening for trauma, early intervention and treatment for children and families, and trauma-informed treatment. In addition, the initiative addresses the needs of people with co-occurring disorders or a history of trauma in the criminal and juvenile justice systems (p. 6).

3. Military Families

   For military families this initiative seeks to develop a coordinated system of policies and programs at the local, state, and national levels. This includes greater coordination among federal agencies such as the U.S. Department of Defense and the Veterans Health Administration (pp. 6–7).

4. Recovery Support

   This initiative promotes human service systems and peer support for people in recovery from mental health and substance abuse problems. More specifically, this includes efforts to develop permanent housing and increase educational and work opportunities (p. 8).

5. Health Reform

   This initiative has the objective of ensuring integration of primary and behavioral health care. It ensures that behavioral health is included in all aspects of health care reform, the Affordable Care Act, and especially Medicaid and Medicare (pp. 9–10).

6. Health Information Technology

   This initiative addresses the importance of having up-to-date technology, including electronic medical records, emphasizing privacy, confidentiality, and data standards. It includes the provision of technical assistance to behavioral health and health providers, patients, and consumers. It also supports data analysis to evaluate quality of patient care and improve outcomes (p. 10).

7. Data, Outcomes, and Quality

   This initiative focuses on developing an integrated approach for SAMHSA's collection, analysis, and use of data and for the development of standardized data collection, quality of care, and outcomes measurement. This can result in improved quality in substance abuse treatment program evaluations and research (p. 11).

8. Public Awareness and Support

   This initiative supports efforts to remove stigma from and enhance knowledge of mental and substance abuse disorders by raising the visibility of SAMHSA. It includes how to access treatment for behavioral health problems (p. 12).

Source: Substance Abuse and Mental Health Services Administration (2011c).

Another critical development in the early 1990s was the formulation of the American Society of Addiction Medicine (ASAM) criteria for the treatment of addiction. ASAM provides advocacy for appropriate medical training for physicians and medical students and promotes prevention, research, and substance abuse treatment.

The ASAM criteria were developed to ensure that patients receive appropriate, high-quality treatment along a continuum of care, to encourage treatment to be both effective and efficient, and to ensure continuity of financial resources and access to care (Earley, 2013; Gregoire, 2000). A number of domains are assessed to plan for the appropriate length of stay and intensity of treatment The ASAM criteria address (a) the level of acute intoxication and potential for withdrawal symptoms; (b) biomedical conditions and complications; (c) cognitive, behavioral, and emotional conditions; (d) readiness and motivation for treatment; (e) the potential for relapse and continued problem use; and (f) the recovery environment, including family and community support (Mee-Lee, 2013). The specific levels of care are outlined in Chapter 5.

The use of the ASAM criteria became part of the effort to match patients to specific kinds of treatment. However, treatment matching, as we have seen in Chapter 1 with Project MATCH, did not score much success. The purpose of the ASAM criteria was to use assessment of a variety of categories and to be objective about patient needs and outcomes (Early, 2013). Subsequent research found the criteria of ASAM was broad and not all that useful, with a bias in favor of inpatient treatment (Gregoire, 2000).

We have seen funding for mental health and substance abuse services as a percentage of total health care costs erode over time. In 1991 total spending on mental health services and substance abuse treatment was $60 billion, and although this area of spending increased to $104 billion in 2001, its average annual growth rate of 5.6% is 1.1% lower (6.5%) than the growth rate for the total of all health care spending between 1991 and 2001 (Mark et al., 2005). For substance abuse treatment spending, it is estimated that $18 billion was spent on substance abuse treatment in 2001, accounting for 1.3% of all spending on health care. In 2003, spending increased by $3 billion to $21 billion spent on substance abuse treatment, still accounting for 1.3% of all spending on health care (Mark et al., 2007). These figures do not include what is called the "disease burden" (Mark et al., 2005, p. v) of treating medical disorders associated with substance abuse, such as liver disease, or social issues, such as federal housing subsidies and job training.

The substance abuse treatment system between 1979 and 1990 saw the public sector of treatment increase by only 11%, whereas the private system of care increased by 116%. There was a 604% increase in for-profit agencies, and nonprofits increased by 80% (Weisner, Greenfield, & Room, 1995).

State and local governments pay for most substance abuse treatment, accounting for 57% of substance abuse spending in 2001, including spending through Medicaid, state grants, and local resources (Mark et al., 2007). Overall, public payers for substance abuse treatment increased to 76% in 2001, a 15-percentage point increase from 62% in 1991. This increased to 77% of public sources of funding for substance abuse treatment in 2003.

The transition from inpatient to outpatient care is one of the critical changes in substance abuse treatment that began in the 1980s. Inpatient treatment has declined dramatically starting in the 1980s; length of stay in inpatient programs has also declined (Mark et al., 2005, 2007). Between 1993 and 2003, money spent on inpatient treatment was reduced from 41% to 21% of substance abuse treatment expenditures. During the same 10-year period outpatient treatment spending rose from 34% to 49% (Mark et al., 2007).

Starting in the 1980s and continuing into the 1990s "treatment on demand" developed. It was defined as immediate accessibility to substance abuse treatment. One critical purpose for treatment on demand for drug addicts was to slow the transmission of HIV (Friedmann, Lemon, & D'Aunno, 2003). This meant that as soon as a person indicated willingness to get help for a substance abuse problem, that individual would not have to be on a waiting list for days or weeks. Friedmann et al. (2003) found that private for-profit programs were twice as likely to offer treatment on demand, yet these profit-making programs were seven times more likely to refuse admission to some patients. The programs that served low- or no-income individuals were less likely to be able to provide treatment on demand but were far less likely to turn away clients seeking admission. Waiting lists for treatment entry are known to have potential clients drop from them (Friedmann et al., 2003). Although "treatment on demand" was a popular slogan, in reality it meant immediate treatment was available for people with excellent insurance and those who could pay privately rather than for all people in need of treatment.

During the 1990s further restrictions were added to treatment availability, and the field began to see a reduction in the 28-day inpatient rehabilitation programs (Gregoire, 2000). Payment for both public and private programs was typically based on a daily rate, so there were financial reasons for a long inpatient treatment experience. Morell (1996) stated that there was never an adequate number of programs to meet the needs of substance abusers and that managed care resulted in insurance companies reducing benefits and discharging clients from treatment before they were ready.

Managed care meant a close review of patient medical records, and if improvement was not shown, benefits were terminated. Typically it was a "utilization review" nurse who completed the medical record reviews and then discussed them with the physician overseer of the process. This was in keeping with the view that patients should receive the least restrictive, lowest cost, and most appropriate treatment for substance abuse (Gregoire, 2000). The utilization review process had a strong effect on hospital treatment for many patients with any major illness, and that effect is seen clearly in substance abuse treatment.

The advent of managed care led to a decline in spending on mental health care as a percentage of overall health spending in the 1990s (Sturm & Sherbourne, 2001). This is associated with the decline of health insurance benefits for substance abuse treatment and the growth of managed care. Etheridge, Craddock, Dunteman, and Hubbard (1995) reviewed two national studies, the Treatment Outcome Prospective Study (TOPS) from 1979 to 1981 and the Drug Abuse Treatment Outcome Study (DATOS) 1991 to 1993, and found a decrease in the number and types of resources offering drug abuse treatment.

Managed care has been successful in limiting the financial outlay for substance abuse services, yet this does not translate into improved services for clients (Gregoire, 2000). Although managed care greatly reduced inpatient rehabilitation, it did not necessarily show a corresponding increase in outpatient substance abuse treatment services (Friedmann et al., 2003; Galanter, Keller, Dermatis, & Egelko, 2000). One study found that managed care decreased the number of types of services that treatment facilities are able to offer, which could lead to poor client outcomes, increased crime, and unemployment (Olmstead, White, & Sindelar, 2004).

Whereas in 1995 32% of substance abuse treatment facilities had managed care contracts, by 1999 this increased to 54% (SAMHSA, 2001). This was accompanied by a 70% increase in the number of private for-profit treatment centers and a 39% increase in nonprofit treatment centers. Overall, in 1999 private nonprofits were 60% of the system, followed by for-profits at 26% of the system.

The American Society for Addiction Medicine (ASAM) found that managed care in substance abuse treatment caused a "drastic reduction in frequency and duration of inpatient hospitalization" (Galanter, Keller, Dermatis, & Egelko, 2000, p. 13). Addiction physicians felt managed care had negatively affected both detoxification and rehabilitation and impinged on their ability to offer ethically appropriate treatment.

The early 1990s also brought the development of the Addiction Technology Transfer Centers (ATTCs) with the goal of translating research findings into improved clinical practice. Although there have been a number of exciting projects, most research findings and the literature are read by other researchers rather than by clinicians and it is a concern that clinical settings have been slow to adopt practices developed by ATTCs (Brown & Flynn, 2002). One of the important things to come out the development of the ATTCs is *The Change Book: A Blueprint for Technology Transfer* (Addiction Technology Transfer Center Network, 2004). This book presents 10 steps for the planning, implementation, and evaluation of drug treatment systems. In their discussion of evidence-based practices and the use of manual-based psychotherapies, the authors state, "Dramatic changes in health care reimbursement have created an atmosphere of anxiety, fear, and anger in many practicing clinicians" (Addis, Wade, & Hatgis, 1999, p. 430).

THE 2000s

By the early 2000s much pressure was brought to bear on substance abuse treatment. There was the recognition that substance abuse problems were intertwined with public safety and law enforcement issues, as well as public health problems (McLellan, Carise, & Kleber, 2003). The Drug Abuse Services Information System in 2001 found that a remarkable 55% of people referred for substance abuse treatment nationally were involved with the criminal justice system. People in the welfare system represented 10% of those referred for substance abuse treatment.

McLellan et al. (2003) concluded that with closings of programs and with approximately one-third being reorganized, the administrative and organizational aspects of many programs should be considered "inadequate and unstable" (p. 120). In addition, the staffing of treatment programs suffers from high turnover among counselors and administrative staff. Finally, the authors recommend examining governmental and managed care requirements for paperwork that does not in reality monitor or improve care.

The Mental Health Parity and Addiction Equity Act of 2008 is another piece of critical legislation. This federal law requires group insurance plans to cover mental health and substance abuse problems at the same level they cover medical problems and surgery. Although the Act does not require insurance companies to cover substance abuse and mental health problems, if they do, it must be at the same level as other health issues (SAMHSA, 2013a). The law does not address people without insurance or those with minimal insurance that does not cover substance abuse and mental health treatment. The effect of the new federal health care insurance known as the Affordable Care Act remains to be seen.

COST-EFFECTIVENESS ISSUES IN SUBSTANCE ABUSE TREATMENT

In substance abuse treatment, as in any medical treatment, the desire is to provide the right amount of treatment—not too much and not too little. As we have seen, managed care has placed greater emphasis on financial restrictions, and this has translated into the quest for cost-effective treatment.

The cost-effectiveness of particular types of treatment has become an increasingly important issue, and research needs to address treatment effectiveness, as well as cost-effectiveness (Drummond, 2002; Kelly & Yeterian, 2011; Morgan & Crane, 2010). Cost and cost-effectiveness should not be confused. The cost of treatment refers only to the financial outlay. Cost-effectiveness reflects the costs of the treatment as related to the outcomes for clients, that is, whether they improve (Morgan & Crane, 2010). According to SAMHSA (2011), for each dollar spent on substance abuse treatment $7 are saved by reductions in health care costs, an increase in work productivity, and a reduction in crime.

Concern for cost is especially important at times of reduced public funding for treatment—it fuels the desire to prove that interventions and treatment are effective (Hartmann, Wolk, & Sullivan, 1995). It can be difficult, and perhaps not possible, to measure, because the benefits are well beyond the funding agency and relate to improved job, family, and overall social functioning (McKay, 2005).

Do new treatments save more money for governmental agencies and health insurance companies than they cost to implement? For example, why pay many thousands of dollars more for inpatient treatment if outpatient treatment is just as effective? That was the rationale for reducing access to inpatient treatment. Overall, more intensive and therefore more expensive treatment may not be the most cost-effective (Mojtabai & Zivin, 2003). However, substance abuse treatment can be more cost-effective than other health interventions for treatment of diseases stemming from substance abuse and addiction. Savings from treatment can then be used to treat more clients. Outpatient treatment is the most cost-effective professional treatment option, and AA has virtually no cost.

Kimberly and McLellan (2006) started the Center for Organization and Management in Addiction Treatment (COMAT) in 2005 to study the business aspects of substance abuse treatment. They point out that often substance abuse treatment is not considered to be part of the overall health care system. Kimberly and McLellan (2006) see addiction treatment as a "separate and unequal" (p. 215) system. Overall, even with improvements in assessing cost of treatment, more research is needed (Bray & Zarkin, 2006).

As indicated earlier, because more acute treatment is available, it is not a surprise that funding is typically put into acute care detoxification services, with limited coverage for longer term solutions (Scott, Dennis, & White, 2004). More needs to be done for "sustained recovery management" (p. 33).

Holder, Longabaugh, Miller, and Rubonis (1991) reviewed data from existing literature, examined 224 controlled clinical trials, interviewed research experts, and then ranked 33 treatment types by cost and by effectiveness. Holder et al. (1991) and Finney and Monahan (1996) both conclude that more expensive treatments are not necessarily better treatments.

Morgan and Crane (2010) state financial costs are often neglected in effectiveness discussions. Better choices and decisions can be made when cost is considered, especially in today's economy. They caution against seeing this as simple and warn that some treatments may be more cost-effective solely because of lower expenditures, not because the treatment has been found to be more effective.

The Drug Abuse Treatment Cost Analysis Program (DATCAP; French, Dunlap, Zarkin, McGeary, & McLellan, 1997) creates cost estimates for treatment and overhead. It also calculates losses of time and money related to work. DATCAP was devised by Dr. Michael French (French, 2003; French et al., 1997; French, Salome, & McLellan, 2002) of the University of Miami to provide a means to evaluate the cost of addiction treatment within inpatient and outpatient settings. DATCAP collects and organizes data on treatment resources and how much they cost. It can assess costs associated with staff, clients, program funding, supplies and equipment, and facilities. In one study, DATCAP was used with the Addictions Severity Index (ASI), a substance abuse assessment tool, and showed that combining economic and clinical data produces a good foundation for economic evaluation of substance abuse treatment (French et al., 2002). DATCAP is in the public domain, meaning that no special permission is required and no costs are associated with using it.

The integration of primary medical care with addiction treatment has been found to show improved treatment outcomes while demonstrating that this is a cost-effective way of delivering services (Weisner, Mertens, Parthasarathy, Moore, & Lu, 2001). In a large study of people receiving Medicaid health insurance benefits, those with mental health problems and substance abuse problems had significantly higher expenditures than those with only mental health issues (Clark, Samnaliev, & McGovern, 2009).

Some research has concluded that there is too little spending on substance abuse treatment in the United States (Meara & Frank, 2005). This conclusion was based on figures from 1997; whereas $294 billion was spent on estimated social costs associated with substance abuse, only $11.9 billion was spent on treatment. Although this treatment spending almost doubled in 2003, with an estimated $21 billion for treatment of substance abuse, as noted earlier, this still accounted for only 1.3% of all money spent on health care (Mark et al., 2007). Meara and Frank (2005) concluded that little is known about the few substance abusers who receive treatment, the type and quality of treatment services, and how these factors affect treatment outcomes.

Today treatment needs are complex, and treatments offered are complicated, but there is increased pressure for treatment programs to do more with less funding (Rieckmann, Fuller, Saedi, & McCarty, 2010). Innovations are hard to adopt when counselors and supervisors are overwhelmed with work and have not had appropriate training and education (Rieckmann et al., 2010). In Chapter 12 we review current concerns about the addiction workforce.

SUMMARY AND CONCLUSION

There is a long history in the United States of looking for what works to help addicts and alcoholics, and a variety of types of treatment have been developed. The history of substance abuse treatment started with alcoholics trying to keep one another sober, and over time the field transitioned into a quest for huge profits by corporations.

Many kinds of federal legislation regarding addiction were implemented, especially during the 1970s. The Comprehensive Alcohol Abuse and Alcoholism Prevention, Treatment, and Rehabilitation Act of 1970 and the creation of NIAAA are among the most important developments in the substance abuse field.

Some people think that addiction treatment is becoming increasingly subsumed within the field of mental health, preferring clinicians with mental health credentials to those with substance abuse counseling credentials. This is clearly a by-product of the organizing services for substance abusers and people with mental illness under the federal agency SAMHSA. This is discussed further in Chapter 12. As we see in the next chapters, inpatient treatment fell out of favor because of high costs and lack of proof that inpatient care was more successful than outpatient care.

INPATIENT SUBSTANCE ABUSE TREATMENT

*T*he previous chapter described the rise of the inpatient treatment centers in the 1980s that spawned a huge profit-making industry. In this chapter we describe the kinds of inpatient treatments that are available to addicts and alcoholics. Some are available to applicants without money, whereas others are restricted to people who can pay the high prices.

In this chapter and the next one on outpatient treatment, we examine the long debate over whether inpatient treatment is more effective than outpatient treatment and try to tease out the important factors that make one preferable to the other in specific circumstances. One study reported that 81.5% of inpatients in a hospital treating alcoholics in Switzerland made good progress and were deemed appropriate for that level of care, whereas 18.5% did not appear to benefit from the treatment offered (Rossegger, Keller, Odenwald, & Endrass, 2009). However, in their classic review of 26 controlled studies, Miller and Hester (1986) reported that overall there was no compelling evidence that inpatient treatment was more successful or effective than outpatient treatment. They concluded that treatment success is more likely to be affected by the content of the treatment rather than the treatment setting. Miller and Hester (1986) thus supported more cost-effective treatment rather than the extremely expensive inpatient programs available in the 1980s. This research also showed that inpatient treatment is not necessarily more effective, and these findings contributed to restrictions on expensive inpatient rehabilitation programs. Client motivation, as discussed in Chapter 3, is also an important factor.

As discussed in Chapter 1, many research studies rely on alcoholic or addict respondents to provide information on how they have fared since leaving specific treatment programs. This can be problematic because respondents may have memory issues that contribute to inaccuracy or a desire to present their recovery in a more positive light. Follow-up is not necessarily a measure of the treatment; it can be more a measure of the addict's or alcoholic's motivation, attitude, or depth of participation in treatment or self-help groups. (An adage from Alcoholics Anonymous that captures this is "But for the grace of God.") The type and quality of family support after discharge from inpatient rehabilitation is also an important factor.

Inpatient treatment programs are almost exclusively abstinence based and do not typically offer the option of harm reduction. Abstinence is a hallmark of inpatient programs. Clients who use drugs and alcohol are typically immediately discharged from the program. Of the many rules in any inpatient program, maintaining abstinence is by far the most important. If some clients or residents are allowed to drink or drug while others are trying to maintain abstinence, it creates a challenging treatment environment and puts people working on abstinence at greater risk of relapse. Safety of clients and staff members is an important consideration in all inpatient programs.

Clients in earlier phases of alcoholism or drug use may be successful in a harm-reduction program or in an abstinence-based outpatient program. This is in keeping with offering the least restrictive treatment that provides a client a good chance of success. If a client is in need of medical detoxification (detox), this can mean a short stay in an inpatient program or an intensive outpatient detox program, where the client spends the day in treatment and sleeps at home. If a client has had many detox treatments this provides good evidence that a longer term inpatient treatment may be appropriate. One detox program in Massachusetts in the 1980s presented a cake to a client on his 100th admission to that program. Although some found this humorous, others pondered the wisdom of this "revolving door" policy and whether the detox program enabled the client to stay in his addiction by always readmitting him on his request.

Overall, treatment completion is a good predictor of client success in recovery (Ravndal, Vaglum, & Lauritzen, 2005). A completion rate of 40% was found in a study of 13 programs in Norway with no difference between people new to treatment and those who had been through a number of previous inpatient treatments (Ravndal et al., 2005). It is difficult to determine who among the inpatients could have benefited from outpatient treatment instead. People with more severe substance abuse problems and difficulty functioning in the community are typically considered good candidates for inpatient programs.

DETOX PROGRAMS

Although controversy may swirl around the effectiveness of monthlong inpatient treatment, there is almost no controversy over detox programs, considered an essential part of substance abuse treatment. Detox services are designed to deal with the effects of alcohol and drugs and the potential for withdrawal symptoms, typically through the use of prescribed medications. Some substance abuse professionals consider detox a form of treatment; to others, it is an important "entrée into treatment" (Mignon, Faiia, Myers, & Rubington, 2009, p. 260).

Detox serves as the first step in determining the needs of a client. The essential components of detox are medical evaluation and stabilization, followed by making a plan to enter some type of inpatient or outpatient treatment (Center for Substance Abuse Treatment, 2006). Detox programs typically offer a 3- to 5-day stay during which the client is medically withdrawn from the drugs and alcohol to avoid withdrawal and, in extreme cases, delirium tremens (DTs). As discussed in Chapter 4, the American Society of Addiction Medicine (ASAM) developed recommendations for the appropriate level of care for substance abusers. The five levels of care for detox range from mild- or low-level outpatient care to intensive hospital-level care: Level I-D is ambulatory detox without extended onsite monitoring, Level II-D is ambulatory detox with extended onsite monitoring, Level III.2-D is clinically managed residential detox, Level III.7-D is medically monitored inpatient detox, and Level IV-D is medically managed intensive inpatient detox (Earley, 2013). These ASAM levels and the ASAM criteria given in Chapter 4 serve as guidelines for clinical practice.

One concern is whether clients completing detox will be willing to move on to some other kind of substance abuse treatment. One study of detox patients found that only 49.4% continued with some type of treatment within a 30-day period (Mark, Dilonardo, Chalk, & Coffey, 2003). Another study of inpatient detox found that clients were interested in undergoing individual counseling, attending meetings of Narcotics Anonymous (NA), and receiving help with finding a job (Tuten, Jones, Lertch, & Stitzer, 2007). However, on feeling physically better after detox, some clients decline further treatment and return to their substance abuse in a cycle known as a "tune-up" or a "spin dry." Some are attracted to having a clean place to sleep and regular meals, known as "three hots and a cot." Mark et al. (2003) conclude that not enough is being done to assist patients in connecting with follow-up services. Because relapse rates are high after detox, more needs to be done by professionals to encourage patients to continue in some form of treatment (Tuten et al., 2007).

The picture of clients in detox programs has changed over time. In the early 1970s government-funded detox programs sprang up as a response to the decriminalization of public drunkenness. This had the effect of keeping alcoholics out of the "drunk tanks" in local police stations and allowed police and others to bring alcoholics to detox for treatment rather than following the criminal justice response of punishment. Those served by detox programs in the 1970s were most likely to be older White male street alcoholics. In a study of public detox centers in Massachusetts, using data from 1984 to 1996, the picture of clients using the services was different from that in the 1970s (McCarty, Caspi, Panas, Krakow, & Mulligan, 2000). There was a decline of 25% in people seeking detox from alcohol, a twofold increase in cocaine users in detox, and a fourfold increase in heroin users in detox. There were also significant increases in women, African Americans, and Hispanics in detox programs. Today detox services are available in hospital-based programs, state-funded programs for low- or no-income individuals , and intensive outpatient programs.

STABILIZATION PROGRAMS

Stabilization programs grew up around the needs of very poor and homeless populations that need further inpatient treatment yet do not have the insurance coverage or financial resources for private inpatient rehabilitation. For people in publicly funded detox centers, stabilization programs are a good alternative because this group may not have other inpatient treatment options. A typical stay is 2 to 6 weeks. If the program is completed successfully, a client can go on to a halfway house or sober house. See Box 5.1 for an example of a stabilization program.

Although stabilization programs are an important service today, there is little research on their effectiveness. One reason is that these programs are often considered not a part of the treatment continuum but rather a "holding" facility while other treatment options are considered (Kertesz, Horton, Friedmann, Saitz, & Samet, 2003). In one study of homeless and nonhomeless people, 76% self-reported continued use of alcohol, drugs, or both after release from the stabilization program: 77% homeless and 75% nonhomeless (Kertesz, et al., 2003). The homeless individuals who participated in the study were typically older White males with no full-time employment, and half (50%) stated alcohol was their drug of choice. In contrast, nonhomeless participants were most likely to identify cocaine as their drug of choice (38%). The homeless group that used a stabilization program after detox was far more likely to enter a residential program such as a halfway house than those in the group that did not use a stabilization program (79% vs. 49%), a contrast not seen in the nonhomeless group. Even during the relatively short time that has passed since the Kertesz et al. study was completed, the homeless population has grown younger. This is compelling evidence for the importance of stabilization programs.

BOX 5.1 *Pine Street Inn Stabilization Program*

Pine Street Inn is a large human service organization offering shelter and a variety of services to homeless people in the Boston area. The stabilization program has 50 beds for men (age 18 and up) with addiction problems. It is a 28-day residential program after detox. This includes medical services, psychiatric evaluation, case management services, individual and group education and counseling, and aftercare planning.

The program serves clients with co-occurring disorders (substance abuse and mental illness), people living with HIV/AIDS, and those with other chronic health problems. Some medical insurance companies cover the cost of the program, and there are beds available for people admitted with no health insurance—they are immediately placed on the Massachusetts version of Medicaid, known as MassHealth.

Source: Pine Street Inn (n.d.).

INPATIENT REHABILITATION PROGRAMS

Many things have to align to bring about admission to a 28- or 30-day stay in a rehabilitation program. Clinical wisdom implies an important advantage in providing a respite from the daily grind that interrupts the usage pattern of alcohol, drugs, or both over a longer period. It provides the client with a break from work and family responsibilities and allows complete focus on recovery. Inpatient treatment provides a higher level of medical supervision than is available in the community and can help patients to increase awareness of the trigger or triggers that place them at risk of relapse (Weiss, 1994). A month of inpatient treatment can provide the family with an important respite from the stress of living with an alcoholic or addict and offers the opportunity to learn more about addiction. Elements that can foster healthy coping skills for people in residential treatment include participation in 12-step programs, life skills training, and cultivation of a network of supportive relationships (Forys, McKellar, & Moos, 2007). Although in the 1980s people with good insurance coverage had this opportunity for inpatient treatment, we saw in the last chapter that this type of treatment became more restricted in the 1990s and continues to be limited today.

During the 1980s, when insurance coverage was available for a monthlong stay in a rehabilitation program, it was not uncommon to see working-class clients with excellent health insurance coverage treated within the resortlike atmosphere of some programs. One inpatient program in Rhode Island provided luxurious living arrangements, including Oriental carpeting and huge chandeliers. Clients were treated to gourmet meals in these sumptuous and almost surreal surroundings. The author attended a "referral conference" at this rehabilitation program for a lecture on a substance abuse topic and found that Alaskan king crab legs and expensive grilled steaks were served for lunch. Professionals were regularly invited to these "referral conferences" so that they would be sufficiently impressed and refer potential clients to the program. At the time some substance abuse professionals relished these experiences; others of us wondered about the effect on clients who lived modestly at best. It can be a tough transition from this fantasyland treatment experience back to the reality of the hard work of recovery.

Today only people with significant private funds are likely to be able to afford 1-month or longer stays in rehabilitation programs. See Box 5.2 for a description of the Betty Ford Center, one of the most prestigious internationally known inpatient treatment programs.

There have been few studies of the effectiveness of substance abuse treatment offered by private for-profit treatment centers (McLellan et al., 1993; Stinchfield & Owen, 1998). These studies were mostly completed in the 1980s when inpatient rehabilitation was in its heyday, and they offered no comparison groups. In a follow-up of 181 clients who completed inpatient rehabilitation at Edgehill Newport, 61% were continuously abstinent and 72% were abstinent at the time of the study (Wallace, McNeill, Gilfillan, MacLean, & Fanella, 1988). Sixty-six percent of alcoholics with no other drug problems were continuously

---

BOX 5.2 The Betty Ford Center

The Betty Ford Center opened in 1982 after First Lady Betty Ford acknowledged and received treatment for her addiction problems and sought to
help others. The beautiful 20-acre campus offers a variety of programs to
the international community. The inpatient program offers clinical diagnostic evaluation, detox, and 30-day treatment services for people age 18
and older. The 30- to 90-day program for licensed professionals attracts
physicians, nurses, and other health care providers, as well as other professionals whose careers may be at risk because of addiction. A relapse
prevention track of 30 days is offered. A track for clients with pain management issues runs 45 days. The young adult track is for those age 18 to
25 and is 90 to 120 days long. A 5-day family program is offered, as well as
a children's program for those age 7 to 12. Outpatient and after-inpatient
care services are also provided.

The Betty Ford Center is an example of a high-quality treatment program that is well out of the range that most alcoholics and addicts can
afford. The prices on the center's website as of July 1, 2013, subject to
change, list a 30-day inpatient stay at a cost of $33,000. For people in the
professional track who stay at the center for 90 days, the cost is $58,000.
And for those in the young adult track who remain in the program for the
maximum of 120 days, the cost is $71,000.

Source: Betty Ford Center (2013).

---

abstinent over time and 77% were abstinent at the time of the study. McLellan
et al. (1993) compared clients and services in a sample of men referred for
treatment by their employee assistance program. After 6 months, 59% were
abstinent, 82% had returned to work, and only 8% required further treatment
provided by the employee assistance program. Programs that offered a greater
number of services were found to be more effective.

In a study of patients in the highly regarded Schick Shadel Hospital in
Seattle, 65% were abstinent by self-report 1 year after treatment (Smith &
Frawley, 1993). Of 1,083 men and women treated at Hazelden between 1989
and 1991, a study found that after 1 year, 53% were abstinent; an additional
35% said they had reduced alcohol and drug use in the past year (Stinchfield &
Owen, 1998).

Staff members of the treatment programs completed some of these early
program evaluations with little knowledge of research methods. Questions are
also raised about the ability to be objective when staff members of inpatient
treatment programs perform program evaluations. Today it is expected that
research professionals who have no vested interest in the outcomes perform
treatment program evaluations.

In response to the controversy over whether the outcomes are the same regardless of inpatient or outpatient treatment in the 1980s and early 1990s, one study compared cocaine abusers, 149 in inpatient treatment and 149 in outpatient treatment (Budde, Rounsaville, & Bryant, 1992). At treatment entry, inpatient cocaine abusers had more severe drug use, more severe social impairment, and more severe psychological problems. At 12-month follow-up, the severity of clinical symptoms was reversed for the two groups. That is, people who had inpatient treatment used less cocaine and had less severity in psychological problems than did those in outpatient treatment (Budde et al., 1992). Overall, these research results found better long-term success for people in the inpatient treatment group. A more recent comparison of inpatient and outpatient programs found that the relationship between the client and the therapist seems to be less important in inpatient treatment than in outpatient programs (Shin, Marsh, Cao, & Andrews, 2011). That is, outpatients with strong relationships with therapists stayed in treatment longer and reduced their substance abuse after treatment. Among the inpatients, length of treatment and reduction in substance abuse after treatment completion were not related to the quality of the client–therapist relationship (Shin et al., 2011). This could indicate that other variables in inpatient treatment, beyond the quality of the therapeutic relationship, affect clients in residential programs.

McKeganey, Bloor, Robertson, Neale, and MacDougall (2006) completed a follow-up of respondents in the 2004 Drug Outcome Research in Scotland study (McKeganey, Morris, Neale, & Robertson, 2004). At the follow-up 33 months after their recruitment, 9% of men and 5.9% of women had been drug free for 3 months before the interview. Although these numbers are low, people who went to an inpatient rehabilitation program were significantly more likely to attain the 3-month period of abstinence. In a study of 3,032 patients in 15 residential treatment programs, researchers examined the factors that predicted outpatient treatment after completion of residential treatment (Harris, McKellar, Moos, Schaefer, & Cronkite, 2006). Longer participation in outpatient care was associated with client motivation before residential treatment, lower use of alcohol, higher levels of stress, recent suicide attempts, and greater cognitive abilities. Patients with greater cognitive abilities may be more likely to understand the risks of their substance abuse and may be better able to benefit from treatment approaches that require abstract thinking (Harris et al., 2006).

Some research focuses on outcomes for women in residential treatment. In a study of an innovative residential program for cocaine-abusing women and their children, the mothers (and their children) who completed residential treatment had more positive outcomes compared with those who did not graduate (Connors, Bradley, Whiteside-Mansell, & Crone, 2001). Program graduates had reduced drug use and greater employment, self-sufficiency, and family interaction skills compared with those who did not graduate. In a study of 146 homeless addicted women in residential treatment, those with early trauma and abuse histories had poorer treatment outcomes (Sacks, McKendrick, & Banks, 2008). The abused women were more likely to have continued difficulties in psychological functioning, substance abuse problems, and reexposure to trauma. This speaks to the need to address the trauma and abuse histories of women in treatment (Sacks et al., 2008).

Individual experiences within rehabilitation programs vary. Some relish the amenities in posh programs, whereas some clients are more comfortable in less ostentatious surroundings. Some credit the inpatient rehabilitation experience with saving their lives, whereas others are less positive. Some clients heartily embrace the disease concept of addiction, whereas others still feel the full force of the stigma and self-judgment associated with addiction. Some people who have spent time in inpatient rehabilitation programs have not embraced the opportunity or considered it a great experience. See Box 5.3 for the experience of one writer in rehabilitation.

BOX 5.3 *Memories of Inpatient Rehabilitation*

In his memoir of recovery, Wilfrid Sheed recorded his lack of motivation during his stay in an inpatient rehabilitation program:

> All I wanted from Happy Valley was a little peace and quiet while I gently let the poison out of my system, and maybe also some tips on how to hurry it up. Beyond that, I was neither thinking straight nor snorting defiance as I checked into Happy Valley. My wildest hope was that somewhere on the premises might conceivably lurk a brilliant mechanic who could give me a jiggle and start things purring again just like that. That, on a less successful scale, was pretty much how it had worked with polio. I'd learned nothing from the doctors, but I'd met several good physiotherapists who seemed to have learned the machinery of polio from hanging around the shop, and I'd learned a bit more from other veterans; and the counselors at Happy Valley were alleged to be a bit of both—therapists and veterans. At any rate, the catalogue listed them all as graduates cum laude of the gutter, so I hoped that somewhere in the interstices of the party line one of them would actually let slip something useful.
>
> But whether they did or not, I knew that the only way to find out was to go along with them as far as I could. As Rilke said of criticism, you must open yourself to the work of art completely before you begin to judge it. And I knew I would get nothing out of Happy Valley if I entered the room arguing. Blue Cross or somebody was paying good money for this, and they wouldn't get their pennyworth if I recited my own opinions over and over, and stuck out my tongue.

Source: Sheed (1995, p. 95). Reprinted with permission.

For some, the inpatient rehabilitation model embodies far more than the opportunity for recovery; it connotes political ideology as well. According to Reznicek (2012), a psychiatrist in the substance abuse treatment field, "The medical profession has created a drug treatment industry that has received little scrutiny. Stripped to its core, rehabilitation is little more than ideological indoctrination into the disease model. At the margins, there are subtle appeals to practice sobriety" (p. 92).

RESIDENTIAL PROGRAMS

Therapeutic communities and halfway houses share the same philosophy and goals of abstinence, but therapeutic communities are more geared toward people with drug addiction and halfway houses are more geared toward alcoholics. Both types of residential programs have grown up within the self-help tradition (Wexler, 1995). Halfway houses tend to provide more of a transition into the overall community than therapeutic communities, which typically exist as a separate community (Reis & Laranjeira, 2008). The blurring of the distinction between therapeutic communities and halfway houses and the distinctions in types of therapeutic communities further complicates efforts to research which programs can be most beneficial for which clients (De Leon, 1995). At this point both kinds of programs offer individual and group therapy, support 12-step program participation, encourage clients to acquire or bolster vocational skills, and emphasize acquiring the skills needed to return to independent living in the overall community.

Therapeutic Communities

Therapeutic communities focus primarily on establishing a community that supports abstinence and recovery and embraces self-help and mutual-help approaches (National Institute on Drug Abuse, 2002). Synanon (founded by Charles Dederich, a recovering alcoholic) was the first therapeutic community; it opened in 1958. Synanon became well known for its harsh confrontational techniques that today have fallen out of favor. Therapeutic communities were mostly developed in the 1960s for male heroin addicts; at the same time, they developed as a new approach for treatment of people with mental illness (Messina, Wish, & Nemes, 2000; Reis & Laranjeira, 2008). See Box 5.4 for a description of Daytop Village, a well-known therapeutic community that began in the 1960s and has evolved into a community that serves a broader spectrum of people today.

There is variability in determining the amount of time residents need to stay in treatment. Research shows that longer stays in therapeutic communities are associated with better client outcomes (Messina et al., 2000; NIDA, 2002; Vanderplasschen et al., 2013). Men and women who stayed for the entire 1-year period in a therapeutic community had better outcomes than those who left the program earlier (Messina et al., 2000). Graduates had less drug use, less

BOX 5.4 Daytop Village

Daytop Village of New York offers a therapeutic community experience that is designed to help adolescents and adults build a "drug-free life through services that are individual, comprehensive, and multidisciplinary without regard to race, religions, nationality or socioeconomic status" (Daytop, 2012, p. 4). Daytop accepts clients with Medicaid health insurance, an important part of the public welfare system in the United States.

Daytop Lodge at Butler Manor on Staten Island, New York, was founded in 1964 to serve 22 men on probation from the Brooklyn, New York, correctional system. It developed into Daytop Village, serving both men and women on a voluntary or legally mandated basis. Today Daytop offers numerous sites and programs that serve inpatients who may remain in the program for 30 days or several months, depending on individual needs. Daytop has also developed a specialized program for veterans that pays specific attention to posttraumatic stress disorder.

Daytop uses an outcomes management system (OMS) to assess client satisfaction and treatment effectiveness. Clients complete questionnaires during treatment, and their progress is monitored through the 3-month period after graduation.

Source: Daytop (2012).

criminal activity, and fewer arrests, and they were more likely to be employed. Condelli and Hubbard (1994) found that the longer clients remain in the therapeutic community, the more likely they are to be successful in recovery.

In a study of five therapeutic communities a variety of factors predicted whether clients remained in the program (Condelli & De Leon, 1993). These included the initial evaluation of client motivation, whether the client had been incarcerated, and whether the client spent time with large groups of people. One strong predictor of whether clients would stay in the therapeutic communities was an initial staff assessment of client motivation to remain long enough to reap the benefit of treatment. Another strong predictor was that clients were more likely to be successful if they spent most of their time with large groups of people, rather than alone or with a few others. Condelli and De Leon (1993) conclude that both treatment variables and client variables need to be studied to further understand and improve retention in therapeutic communities and other types of substance abuse treatment.

A technique used by some therapeutic communities is known as the "pull-up." These are verbal reminders that residents are expected to share with one another, often during group therapy, about areas in which they feel other residents are lacking in their recovery work. This can include reduced motivation for recovery, lack of participation in specific programs, lack of respect for staff members or other residents, and myriad attitudes and behaviors that reflect that the resident is not fully engaged in moving in a positive direction in recovery (De Leon, 2000). For example, a resident may take another resident to task for failure to prepare a decent meal and not doing her share to keep the kitchen clean. Another example is one resident telling another that he is not being honest about the severity of past addiction experiences.

A contrasting technique is known as a "push-up." Push-ups are positive comments made by residents to one another to bolster their self-confidence. An example of a push-up is one resident telling another that she is admired for the hard work she is doing being honest with others.

One study found that people who give more pull-ups to other residents are more likely to graduate from therapeutic communities (Warren, Hiance, Doogan, De Leon, & Phillips, 2013). However, people who received more pull-ups from staff and other residents were less likely to graduate. This adds to the evidence that both program and client variables need to be considered in effectiveness research.

One effort to measure client perceptions of their experiences is to administer a questionnaire at regular intervals during their stay in a therapeutic community. The Dimensions of Change instrument considers treatment from the client's point of view and aims to predict client outcomes, understand the effective parts of treatment in a therapeutic community, and improve the overall quality of treatment (Miles, Mandell, & Wenzel, 2008). Miles et al. (2008) reported that scores on the instrument at each stage (at admission and then at 1, 3, 6, and 9 months) predicted whether clients would drop out within the next treatment period.

More recent research has focused on the personality characteristics of alcohol abusers and polydrug abusers in therapeutic communities. Research findings show significant differences between the two groups: Polydrug abusers were more likely to have lower levels of conscientiousness and agreeableness compared with alcohol abusers (Lackner, Unterrainer, & Neubauer, 2013). Polydrug abusers were also more likely to have a higher level of sensation seeking and a lower level of spiritual or religious well-being.

The most recent evaluation of therapeutic communities reviewed 30 published peer-reviewed journal articles based on 16 original controlled studies (Vanderplasschen et al., 2013). Vanderplasschen et al. (2013) found variance in the quality of the studies but noted that the research quality "was often poor due to high attrition rates, lack of objective verification of study findings, and a focus on one single study site" (pp. 3–4). Their review found that between 25% and 55% of clients relapsed after 12 to 19 months. Studies showing lower relapse rates typically had clients with longer stays. The authors concluded that "there is some evidence for the effectiveness of therapeutic community treatment" (Vanderplasschen et al., 2013, p. 18). This may especially be the case for drug addicts with mental illness, people who are homeless, and people who are incarcerated. It is not possible to say which programs are better than others, but future research must address client characteristics—who benefits most from which type of therapeutic community and at what point in recovery (Chan et al., 2004; Vanderplasschen et al., 2013).

Halfway Houses

Halfway houses are designed for people who need a place to live during the period of recovery. Halfway houses, typically supervised by a manager, provide a stable, safe, and structured living environment over several months and the opportunity for educational and vocational training, social skills development, and involvement in 12-step programs. This is a longer term commitment that is not for everyone, especially people who have family responsibilities. For example, a parent with two or three small children and no available family support is unlikely to be able to enter a halfway house. In this case, intensive outpatient treatment may be a better alternative for the parent and children. However, if a family is involved with state child protective services, a parent may have no choice but to accept halfway house placement as a condition of having children returned to the parent's care in the future.

A review of research found that halfway houses are successful in reducing the number of detox admissions, reducing admissions to hospital emergency rooms, and improving levels of abstinence (Reis & Laranjeira, 2008). In a comparison between male veterans living in halfway houses and those living in the community, 40% of those living at home dropped out of an aftercare program. Male veterans living in halfway houses stayed in the aftercare program an average of 60 days longer than those in the community (Hitchcock, Stainback, & Roque, 1995). Halfway houses have also been found to reduce the use of public welfare resources, including lower medical and legal costs, reduced criminal activity and incarceration, and improved opportunities for employment (Reis & Laranjeira, 2008).

Sober Houses

Sober houses are designed to offer both an alcohol-free and a drug-free living environment shared by people in recovery (Polcin, 2001; Polcin & Henderson, 2008). There is great variability in quality among individual houses, because there is no active oversight or treatment provided by professionals. For some people this opportunity is a lifesaver, especially those with few financial resources who may have lost their families because of addiction or otherwise have no place to live. Sober houses typically are not licensed or recipients of local, state, or federal funds; instead, residents bear the costs of sober house living through their earnings or through government payments they receive, such as Supplemental Security Income (SSI) through the Social Security Administration, regular Social Security, or some kind of disability payment (Polcin, Korcha, & Galloway, 2010).

Like therapeutic communities and halfway houses, sober houses share the commitment to abstinence from alcohol and drugs and a peer support system. Although they may have no set period for residence, the National Institute on Drug Abuse recommends a stay of at least 3 months (Polcin et al., 2010).

One well-known sober house model is built on that of the Oxford House, which was founded in 1975 (Oxford House, 2013). Today there are 1,200 Oxford Houses, although each is run independently by residents without professional management or supervision. These are mutual-help recovery homes of 6 to 10 residents committed to abstinence, yet there is no required type of treatment—residents are free to choose whether they participate in 12-step programs, professional outpatient substance abuse treatment, or both. The average stay is longer than 1 year; however, residents may stay as long as they choose. A study that compared residents in an Oxford House in Illinois with people in outpatient treatment or self-help programs found that Oxford residents had significantly lower substance use, lower incarceration rates, and significantly higher incomes (Jason, Olson, Ferrari, & Lo Sasso, 2006).

Originally, sober houses were opened by recovering alcoholics and addicts to pass on to others the help they received in their recovery. Although that is still true today, other sober houses are intended to make money for private corporations. In an abusive situation, the owners of a sober house may become the "representative payees" for people receiving Social Security benefits, using little of the funds on the clients' behalf while padding their own pockets. Some are poorly run and have little to no oversight to ensure they are functioning well. See Box 5.5 for an extreme example of what can go wrong in a sober house.

BOX 5.5 Woman Murdered in a Boston Sober House

A 43-year-old man was charged and held without bail in the brutal slaying of his 33-year-old former girlfriend in June 2013. The police located the woman's body in a sober house in South Boston. The boyfriend had a history of arrests for failing to register as a sex offender and driving while intoxicated, and he had been physically abusive to the girlfriend previously. During a hospital stay for substance abuse treatment following his drunk driving arrest, the boyfriend confessed to the murder.

The sober house was closed immediately, and officials expressed concern that these unregulated houses can create serious problems. The president of the neighborhood association told the *Boston Globe* newspaper that neighbors had been concerned about drug use and transients staying in the apartment building. Several local politicians, including the new mayor of Boston in 2014, Martin Walsh, have called for regulation of sober houses, and a legislative bill is pending in Massachusetts that would require licensure of sober houses. Although it is unclear whether this victim's life could have been saved, the need for oversight of sober houses is evident.

Source: Young (2013, pp. B1, B13).

Overall, sober houses can provide an opportunity to work on recovery within a supportive environment. However, despite their importance, little research attention has been paid to the role of the sober house in recovery (Polcin & Henderson, 2008). In addition, little has been done to ensure that sober houses maintain a high quality of support for their residents.

SUMMARY AND CONCLUSION

Inpatient treatment for alcoholism and drug addiction has changed a great deal since the 1980s with the advent of managed health care and a significant reduction in payments for monthlong inpatient treatment programs. Research suggesting that inpatient care is not more effective than outpatient treatment provided an additional impetus to sway the treatment field more heavily toward outpatient treatment, as discussed in Chapter 6.

Detox programs are the first point of contact for many seeking treatment so that they can be safely, medically withdrawn from substances. It is a problem that many choose not to seek additional treatment after detox and that other kinds of treatment are not available to detox clients. Stabilization programs meet the needs of low- or no-income individuals who do not have the option for inpatient rehabilitation. Inpatient programs, especially popular and lucrative in the 1980s, are far less common today because of their high costs.

Finances are a huge issue in determining the type of treatment a client receives. Lengthy inpatient treatment programs today are available only to the wealthy. People who must rely on publicly funded treatment programs have far more restrictions on treatment alternatives. Stabilization programs, therapeutic communities, halfway houses, and sober houses are good alternatives for people who do not have established family and community support.

OUTPATIENT SUBSTANCE ABUSE TREATMENT

As discussed in Chapter 5, the days of lengthy inpatient substance abuse treatment program stays are over and outpatient treatment continues to be the most common type of addiction treatment (McKay & Hiller-Sturmhofel, 2011). Outpatient treatment is typically recommended when there is support in the community, when there are no negative elements such as returning to a crime- and drug-infested neighborhood, when a client expresses a preference for outpatient treatment, and when the client is capable of participating in outpatient treatment (Rossegger, Keller, Odenwald, & Endrass, 2009).

It is challenging to take on the hard work of comparing and assessing outpatient treatments. Before 1960 there was little emphasis on research to study efficacy (how well types of treatment perform in research studies) of substance abuse treatment, and only four controlled studies had been done (Miller & Wilbourne, 2002). Today there are an overwhelming number of studies, spurred in part by cost-containment efforts (Brown, 2004). The abundance of information and research findings must be sorted through and made meaningful to researchers and clinicians alike (Heather, 2007). In this chapter we review the types of outpatient treatment and different styles and approaches to counseling. See Box 6.1 for some types of outpatient treatment.

In recent years human service agencies have focused on comprehensive or wraparound services to address the many needs of clients; however, some evidence shows these efforts may not reach people with alcohol and drug problems. Despite reports by clients that they have a variety of needs, at 3-month follow-up, one study reported only approximately 8% received any kind of service (Pringle, Emptage, & Hubbard, 2006). Basic needs such as housing, food, family services, and legal services were in the greatest demand, followed by medical, mental health, and vocational services. Case management can offer some modest help in substance abuse treatment in coordinating community resources for the

BOX 6.1 Major Types of Outpatient Treatment

1. Brief intervention: Typically includes a short screening tool and advice from a medical provider
2. Outpatient detox: Typically offered through a local substance abuse agency
3. Intensive outpatient program: Typically a program in which the client spends the day in individual therapy, group therapy, or both, as well as other activities such as psychoeducation
4. Traditional individual substance abuse counseling: Undertaken weekly, biweekly, or monthly and arranged through the client's employer, health insurance coverage, or the local mental health or community service agency
5. Group therapy: Typically offered through a local private or public agency that may have a specific client population, such as a men's group or a women's group
6. Family therapy or behavioral couples therapy
7. Methadone maintenance
8. Other pharmacologic interventions: Acamprosate, buprenorphine, or naltrexone

client and can foster a stronger connection between the client and the case manager (Vanderplasschen, Wolf, Rapp, & Broekaert, 2007). This serves as a reminder that substance abuse treatment services must be delivered within a broader context that can assist clients in locating other human services. Although recovery may start for some through alcohol or drug intervention, family and community resources to meet basic needs are a critical part of the recovery process.

PROJECT MATCH

In the 1990s, amid concerns about cost containment, Project MATCH pushed the field forward in comparing and contrasting treatment types to determine those with the greatest efficacy. This fueled the quest for the "best" treatment. Project MATCH was the largest and most expensive study to measure the efficacy of three alcoholism treatment approaches that tested 504 hypotheses (Cutler & Fishbain, 2005). The first of two study sites had 952 clients in five outpatient settings (Butler Center for Research, 2010). The second site followed up with 774 clients who completed either inpatient treatment or intensive outpatient treatment. All were randomly assigned to one of three groups: cognitive behavioral therapy (CBT), 12-step facilitation (TSF) based on Alcoholics Anonymous (AA) steps and principles, or motivational enhancement therapy (MET). In trying to determine whether types of alcoholics could be matched with specific types of treatment, research outcomes focused on the number of days respondents were abstinent, the days when respondents drank, and the number of drinks consumed. Despite disappointment that no significant differences were found among the three treatments, overall there was less drinking after 1 year. After 3 years, 36% of TSF clients were abstinent, whereas 27% of MET clients and 24% of CBT clients were abstinent (Project MATCH Research Group, 1997, 1998).

Perhaps the greatest disappointment of Project MATCH was that it was not possible to predict the kinds of patients who could show benefits from the three kinds of therapy (McLellan, 2002). Other limitations of Project MATCH included not having a control group and relying on self-reports of the volunteer alcoholics involved in the study (Reznicek, 2012). In their review of Project MATCH data, Karno and Longabaugh (2003) reported that patients with depression had a worse outcome when the therapist focused on material that was emotionally painful to the patient. The authors suggested that it might be better to match patients with therapist behaviors rather than treatment modality.

Miller (2006) pointed out that Project MATCH findings did not view addiction as a disease that needs long-term management. The author expressed concern over the idea that the field should ignore "clinical wisdom" and let study designs take over. This puts researchers and policy makers at risk of approving only types of treatment that are more easily studied rather than treatments that may improve client outcomes. Project MATCH did, however, have the positive effect of improving the quality of research in evaluating types of treatment (Drummond, 2002).

TYPES OR MODELS OF OUTPATIENT SUBSTANCE ABUSE TREATMENT

A variety of models for outpatient treatment have been developed, often with federal grant money, to implement and evaluate types of treatment. The following is a review of the treatment models that have garnered the most research attention and have been shown to improve client success.

Brief Interventions

Brief interventions are often associated with physicians and their medical office practices, where they administer a short screening tool, discuss the results, and provide the patient with recommendations. Historically, physicians have had little interest in treating alcoholics and addicts, and brief interventions offer physician practices the opportunity to engage the patient in discussions of substance use in ways that are clear, direct, and nonjudgmental (Mignon, 1995, 1996). Brief interventions offer a simple and quick method to determine whether a patient may need assistance with a drug or alcohol problem. Physicians, nurses, social workers, and psychologists working with physicians can quickly screen for a substance abuse problem using a variety of screening tools (American Public Health Association and Education Development Center, 2008). If a patient or client screens positive for substance abuse, then the person can be referred for an assessment, an in-depth evaluation to determine whether there is a substance problem, and then possibly for substance abuse treatment. See Mignon, Faiia, Myers, and Rubington (2009) for a discussion of screening and assessment of substance abuse problems.

The goal of brief interventions is to provide information on substance abuse, give advice to become abstinent or reduce use, and encourage the person to seek treatment if needed. The brief intervention component is a discussion between the professional and the patient of 5 to 30 minutes' duration in which the professional expresses concern about substance use. This short conversation can include feedback on how alcohol and illicit drugs can negatively affect a diagnosis or interact with prescribed medications. The advantage to the patient is that early intervention can prevent the problem from becoming worse. The advantage to medical settings is that professionals need only minimal training to recognize that a substance abuse problem exists, which contributes to cost-effectiveness. The referral to treatment is a critical piece, one that physicians have avoided in the past largely because of lack of knowledge of appropriate community resources (Mignon, 1995, 1996). Brief interventions in recent years have been covered by insurance such as Medicare and Medicaid, as well as private insurance, and this provides a greater incentive for primary medical care practices to complete these screenings.

The Screening, Brief Intervention, and Referral to Treatment (SBIRT) model is evidence based and the best known of the brief interventions (Substance Abuse and Mental Health Administration, n.d.-c). It includes the National Institute on Alcohol Abuse and Alcoholism (NIAAA) single-question screen: "How many times in the past year have you had X or more drinks in a day?" (where X is 5 for men and 4 for women and a response of 1 is considered positive). A study of patients in a primary medical care practice found this question successfully identified patients with alcohol problems with a sensitivity of 81.8% (Smith, Schmidt, & Saitz, 2009). The National Institute on Drug Abuse (NIDA) recommends asking patients about drug use in the past year and uses the NIDA-Modified Alcohol, Smoking, and Substance Involvement Screening Test (ASSIST) screening tool to determine the risk level and provide feedback to the patient (NIDA, 2012c).

A huge study that screened 459,599 patients using SBIRT asked whether the patient had five or more drinks at one time or any illicit drug use in the past 30 days (Madras, Compton, & Clark, 2009). It was found that 22.7% of participants screened positive for substance abuse concerns, ranging from risky behavior to addiction. Of these, 15.9% were rated at the lower level and recommended for a brief intervention, 3.2% were at a moderate level of substance abuse and recommended to receive brief treatment, and 3.7% screened at a more severe level and were referred specifically for substance abuse treatment. Overall, for people who had illicit drug use at initial screening, after 6 months drug use was lower by 67.7% and heavy alcohol use was lower by 38.6%.

Brief interventions for alcohol problems have been the subject of more research studies than have brief interventions for illicit drug use (Fiellin, Reid, & O'Connor, 2000; Madras et al., 2009; Maisto et al., 2001). Alcohol is more often used by adolescents and adults than are illicit drugs. Screening tools have been reported to be effective in a variety of settings, including general medical practices, emergency rooms, and college health services (Dawson, Goldstein, & Grant, 2012). It makes sense to use screening tools that can screen for alcohol and illicit drug use at the same time. NIDA's NIDAMED offers resources for medical professionals that can be used to screen their patients for tobacco, alcohol, and illicit drug use. The NIDAMED resources include an online screening tool, a quick reference guide, and a detailed resource guide for medical professionals. Today it is still typical for screening tools to address either alcohol or drugs, and more work needs to be done to develop single tools that screen for both.

For youth, both school-based screening and brief interventions can be quite useful. Adolescents who participated in a two-session intervention, either alone or with parents, were significantly more likely to reduce behaviors associated with drug use than were those in a control group (Winters, Fahnhorst, Botzet, Lee, & Lalone, 2012). However, a review of research on brief interventions of youth age 21 or younger found inconclusive evidence regarding the efficacy of brief interventions in hospital emergency rooms because of differing methodologies to assess outcomes and the general poor quality of the studies (Newton et al., 2013).

Overall, SBIRT and other screening and brief interventions represent a positive step forward in identifying substance abuse at an earlier stage than was possible in the past. They can be used quickly and easily at little cost in a variety of settings. They view substance use within the overall context of health and serve as a reminder that alcohol and drug abuse are linked with serious medical problems, such as cirrhosis of the liver and hepatitis. Screening and brief interventions can also be incorporated into evaluations of people who are involved in the court system, as discussed in Chapter 10.

Brief interventions are effective and may have outcomes as good as outcomes in extended treatment (Moyer, Finney, Swearingen, & Vergun, 2002). Several comprehensive reviews of treatment types found brief interventions to be among the most efficacious treatments (positive results in controlled research trials; Hester, 1994; Miller & Wilbourne, 2002; Miller et al., 1995).

Outpatient Detoxification

Outpatient detoxification (detox) refers to clients going daily to a program that monitors withdrawal from alcohol, drugs, or both. This can be part of an intensive outpatient program in which clients spend a considerable amount of time during the day participating in individual therapy, group therapy, or both, as well as other activities. Not all detox outpatients require medication; typically those with mild to moderate symptoms such as headache or nausea do not need medication (Fiellin et al., 2000). In a study of 108 clients with alcohol dependence, only 38% required medication (chlordiazepoxide) to aid with withdrawal symptoms and 92% of the clients completed the detox program with no medical complications (Wiseman, Henderson, & Briggs, 1998).

Potential clients must be screened carefully to determine whether their medical issues, severity of addiction, and potential for withdrawal symptoms require inpatient detox. People who require inpatient detox typically have moderate to severe withdrawal symptoms, have had previous seizures or delirium tremens (DTs), have medical problems that require hospitalization, cannot take medication orally, or have not been successful in previous out-patient detox efforts (Fiellin et al., 2000). In their study of outpatient detox, Soyka and Horak (2004) reported that of 557 patients initially screened, 40.6% required inpatient detox in a special alcohol unit or in a hospital setting.

A major goal of detox is to support continued treatment. In a sample of people receiving outpatient alcohol detox services in Germany, 94% completed the 5- to 7-day detox period (Soyka & Horak, 2004). Of people who completed the outpatient detox program, 91% went on to another alcohol treatment program. In the sample, 46% completed the 1-year outpatient treatment program. This is clear evidence of success in assisting clients to complete a detox program and then go on to further treatment.

Outpatient detox is not widely used, and there has been a call among professionals to further develop these programs (Fiellin et al., 2000; Soyka & Horak, 2004). A review of the research shows structured outpatient programs are safe, efficacious, and low-cost detox treatments for people with few medical problems (Blondell, 2005; Soyka & Horak, 2004).

Individual Therapy

Individual therapy is often an option for people who are newly in recovery, whether they needed detox or not. Clients can locate an addiction therapist in a variety of ways, including doing an online search, calling their local hospital social service department, or contacting their employee assistance program. For people who have health insurance coverage, the most direct path today is to contact their insurance company to obtain the list of addiction therapists with whom the company has a contract. For people without insurance, many communities have a local mental health center that can offer counseling on a sliding-fee scale.

Typically, individual therapy consists of meeting once a week for approximately 50 minutes to discuss the road to recovery and the addict's most pressing issues. The number of sessions is typically limited by the insurance company; approximately six to eight meetings may be covered by insurance. If the therapy takes place in a mental health or clinic setting, after the client has been evaluated by and had some sessions with the individual therapist, the client can be referred for outpatient group therapy. The evaluation of the client by the individual therapist includes a determination that a client will not be threatening or otherwise inappropriate with other clients in the group. The transition to the group can be helpful in reassuring clients that others share the same concerns. See Box 6.2 for an example of the transition from individual to group therapy.

It is difficult to assess individual counseling, often known as *general alcoholism or drug counseling*. Because this term is poorly defined, it is problematic to compare and contrast it with other types of more clearly defined treatment approaches (Brown, 2004; Miller et al., 1995). Some types of individual counseling, such as motivational interviewing, avoid confrontation and have other defined characteristics. General counseling may not have defined characteristics and may rely more on the personal and professional preferences of the counselor or therapist, variables that are hard to evaluate in a research study.

BOX 6.2   The Case of Joan

Joan was a 47-year-old married woman with two grown children. After a long drinking history she entered an inpatient alcohol detox program and was then referred to a small community mental health center in rural Massachusetts for follow-up. Joan came regularly for individual counseling for 1 month and then transitioned into the therapy group for substance-abusing women. During her therapy she worked toward continued abstinence and ultimately separation and divorce from her abusive husband. As the oldest member of the group, the younger women looked to Joan for support, which she freely gave. Joan drove other women to AA meetings and took them home. She came to be viewed by other clients as a reliable and helpful resource and a model for working hard toward recovery.

Source: Case reported by Sylvia Mignon, substance abuse clinician in a mental health clinic in southeastern Massachusetts

Group Therapy

Group therapy has long been the most frequently used treatment for substance abuse and has been considered more cost-effective than individual treatment because many clients can be treated at the same time (Panas, Caspi, Fournier, & McCarty, 2003). The underlying premises are that clients benefit from sharing with others in similar circumstances and that supportive relationships develop. Groups can help break a cycle of social isolation common among people with addiction problems.

There are many kinds of groups, typically focused around a specific issue or population. For example, there are groups specifically for men in recovery and groups specifically for women in recovery. There are mixed-gender groups and groups for gay men and lesbians. There are also groups for adolescents and for older people with substance abuse problems. Groups are also widely used and likely required for people with drunk-driving arrests who are under supervision of the courts. Group therapy is distinguished from 12-step groups by its professional facilitator. A study using data from Massachusetts found that people in group treatment had better outcomes and were more likely to complete treatment and achieve their treatment goals than those in individual therapy (Panas et al., 2003).

Group therapy can also use a variety of the treatment approaches that we review later in this chapter. It is especially used in combination with a contingency management model. Although group therapy is considered an effective treatment, research on groups has lagged behind research on other types of substance abuse treatment. This may be associated with difficulties in maintaining membership of the group over the study period and problems in assessing group members' individual responses to treatment (NIDA, 2003).

Family Therapy or Behavioral Couples Therapy

It took some time for the family therapy approach to come to the field of substance abuse treatment. In the 1970s greater emphasis was placed on individual recovery with the proviso that if alcoholics put their recovery as their highest priority, they would then be available to their family in more appropriate ways. Over time the field has made stronger efforts to incorporate the family into treatment and inpatient rehabilitation programs have supported family involvement, as well as support for participation in Al-Anon for family and friends of alcoholics. Family therapy is encouraged and supported by the Substance Abuse and Mental Health Services Administration (SAMHSA) because it improves communication and accountability and supports positive change within the family (Center for Substance Abuse Treatment, 2004). It provides a neutral place to examine and resolve problems where individual family members can voice their concerns and get their needs met. Overall, family therapy examines each family member's experience of the substance abuse and how each member's issues affect the family system.

In their review of eight studies of family-based substance abuse treatment that addressed cost-effectiveness, Morgan and Crane (2010) found evidence that family therapy can be an important treatment option. Family involvement has also been shown to extend the time substance abusers are willing to remain in treatment (Stupak, Hook, & Hall, 2007).

Behavioral couples therapy has received the most research attention of all family therapy approaches. Studies typically compare individual treatment with individual treatment plus behavioral couples therapy. One such study reported that 83% of husbands in behavioral couples therapy reduced their substance abuse, whereas only 60% in individual treatment did this (Fals-Stewart et al., 2000). Furthermore, 60% of the couples in joint therapy reported better relationship adjustment compared with 35% of couples in which the husband received only individual treatment. Fals-Stewart, O'Farrell, and Birchler (2001) reported that men in a methadone maintenance program who participated in behavioral couples therapy had fewer positive urine samples, greater relationship happiness, and better adjustment at the end of treatment than those receiving individually based methadone services. Behavioral couples therapy has been reported to reduce partner violence, improve functioning of children in the family, and be cost-effective (Fals-Stewart et al., 2005). Fals-Stewart et al. (2005), who have done the most work on behavioral couples therapy to date, state, "Among the various types of couple and family therapies used to treat substance abuse, Behavioral Couples Therapy (BCT) has the strongest empirical support for its effectiveness" (p. 229). Several comprehensive reviews of research studies have supported the effectiveness of behavioral couples therapy (Finney & Monahan, 1996; Holder, Longabaugh, Miller, & Rubonis, 1991; Miller & Wilbourne, 2002).

Overall, family involvement in treatment can support the substance abuser entering treatment, can encourage family members' understanding of one another, and can be helpful to individual family members (Copello, Templeton, & Velleman, 2006). Family therapy is not intended as the only treatment for substance abuse and is not applicable for people who may not have family or have lost their family because of addiction.

TELEPHONE- AND WEB-BASED COUNSELING

New technology, including "telehealth" approaches, offer access to online screening of alcohol and drug problems, as well as social support and health education (Tucker & Simpson, 2011). The reader can log onto Drinkerscheckup .com or Alcoholscreening.org for alcohol screening (Cunningham, Kypri, & McCambridge, 2011). AA is now offering online support groups through AA-intergroup.org for people who may not be able to attend meetings.

E-therapy consists of using e-mail or other electronic technologies to provide services to people who may not be able to receive them in other ways, especially for those who may live in remote areas. It can be used for various problems and can provide screening and assessment, treatment, education, and follow-up services. It has also received considerable support from SAMHSA (Center for Substance Abuse Treatment, 2009a).

A study that compared telephone-based brief counseling contacts with face-to-face contacts after the completion of a 4-week intensive outpatient program for alcohol and cocaine dependence reported that overall higher rates of abstinence were achieved with the telephone follow-up for people who had fewer risk factors, whereas those with high-risk factors did better in face-to-face treatment (McKay, Lynch, Shepard, & Pettinati, 2005). McKay et al. (2005) caution that the results do not suggest that telephone contacts can replace initial treatment but that they may be especially helpful as a follow-up to people who have been in treatment programs.

PHARMACOLOGIC INTERVENTIONS

A number of medications have been developed through the years to reduce cravings for drugs, to block the effect of drugs if they are ingested, or to detoxify patients from drugs. The best known is methadone, which has been used since the 1960s in the treatment of heroin and opioid addiction.

Methadone Maintenance

Methadone maintenance developed from the late 1960s into the 1970s and has been the subject of more research attention than any other treatment for opioid dependence (Doran et al., 2003). Methadone maintenance has been fraught with controversy and stigma as some question the appropriateness of substituting an illegal drug with a legal one. Ira Marion (2005) shared his insights into the changes over the 40 years he worked with methadone patients. Methadone patients of today tend to be sicker than in the early days. The picture has changed considerably with the HIV/AIDS and hepatitis C epidemics, increased polysubstance abuse, and a wider age range of people on methadone. In the 1970s patients taking methadone were almost exclusively heroin users. Today it is common for people taking methadone to abuse alcohol, cocaine, amphetamines, and marijuana. Methadone has the challenge of trying to address one of the most intractable substance abuse problems because of a high rate of relapse to opioid abuse: approximately 80% of methadone treatment in the United States ends with a higher dropout rate among young people (Marion, 2005; McHugh et al., 2013).

In examining the picture of people on methadone in New York State, patients are starting methadone at earlier ages and staying on methadone for longer periods than they have in the past (Marion, 2005). Today it is not unusual to consider a lifelong commitment to remaining on methadone. Today's patients are more likely to have co-occurring disorders (mental illness) than those in the early years of the treatment, although it remains unclear whether there is an actual increase in disorders or better diagnosis. Methadone maintenance has evolved to the point where the dosages are individualized to the needs of specific patients, making treatment even more complex. It is further complicated by concern about interactions for medication to treat HIV and hepatitis C (Marion, 2005).

One review of treatment effectiveness pointed out that overall people with drug problems have poorer outcomes than those with alcohol problems (Gerstein, 1994). The challenges of treating patients with methadone include entering treatment for reasons other than recovery, such as continued access to drugs; noncompliance with the program; and early treatment dropout. People who stay in methadone programs for the longest periods and have long-term stability have better outcomes (Gerstein, 1994).

Other Pharmacologic Interventions

In recent years a dramatic change has come over the field as newly developed medications have become more readily available for the treatment of substance abuse. These medications include acamprosate for the treatment of chronic alcoholism and buprenorphine for the treatment of opioid addiction. The Drug Addiction Treatment Act of 2000 allows qualified physicians to prescribe and dispense medications to treat patients in office-based outpatient settings. In 2002 the U.S. Food and Drug Administration (FDA) approved buprenorphine marketed as Subutex and a combination of buprenorphine and naloxone marketed as Suboxone, both taken orally for the treatment of opioid addiction. These newer medications are rarely used as sole treatments but rather are used in combination with other types of outpatient treatments, such as cognitive behavioral counseling (Copenhaver, Bruce, & Altice, 2007).

Acamprosate (marketed as Campral) for the treatment of alcoholism was approved by the FDA in 2004. It is prescribed to alcoholics when they have stopped drinking to decrease the craving for alcohol and restore balance to the brain. Naltrexone (marketed as Vivitrol), as an extended-release injection, was approved by the FDA in 2006 to treat alcohol dependence and in October 2010 to treat opioid dependence (SAMHSA, 2012b; Zindel & Kranzler, 2014). Instead of taking daily oral dosages of medications such as methadone or oral naltrexone, patients receive one monthly injection. A recent review of 345 private substance abuse treatment programs found that only 16% of the programs offered injectable naltrexone as a treatment option (Abraham & Roman, 2010). Factors associated with low usage include not having information about the medication and not having access to doctors who prescribe naltrexone, as well as the high cost of the drug. Because approval by the FDA is relatively recent, more time is needed to determine how well injectable naltrexone will be used by treatment programs.

Although acamprosate and other medications are typically used within a supportive treatment plan, De Wildt et al. (2002) reported that "psychosocial intervention" (p. 380) did not have a positive effect on the outcomes for patients taking acamprosate. However, Pelc et al. (2005) reported that support from a community nurse significantly aided retention in a clinical trial and abstinence from alcohol for patients taking acamprosate. Rubio et al. (2005) reported that naltrexone can be especially helpful to people with severe alcoholism—those with a family history of alcoholism, those who developed drinking problems before the age of 25, and those who have abused other drugs, in addition to alcohol.

Buprenorphine, developed as a pain medication, can be used for detox, as well as for short- and long-term treatment of opioid addiction. This new medication has been more extensively studied than other medications. Research comparisons have been made between the use of buprenorphine and the use of the older medication methadone. Doran et al. (2003) reported that patients taking methadone in clinic treatment in Australia stayed in treatment longer than those treated with buprenorphine, although this did not reach the level of statistical significance; the authors concluded that buprenorphine is a "viable alternative" (p. 301) to methadone. Buprenorphine was reported to be better than methadone in a study of completion of inpatient detox: 89% of patients taking buprenorphine completed treatment compared with 78% of those taking methadone (Blondell, Smith, Servoss, DeVaul, & Simons, 2007).

Although initially used mainly in private treatment programs in the early 2000s, buprenorphine is now used in public sector programs as well. In more recent years buprenorphine education has been supported by NIDA, SAMHSA, and Addiction Technology Transfer Centers (ATTCs; Knudsen, Ducharme, & Roman, 2006). This speaks to a national effort to support the use of buprenorphine.

Counselor attitudes toward the use of medications can be an important factor in their use. In data collected between 2002 and 2004, substance abuse counselors had little awareness of the effectiveness of buprenorphine

(Knudsen, Ducharme, Roman, & Link, 2005). Some older alcoholism counselors, especially those in recovery, may not be supportive of medications because of messages they received that medications could compromise their own recovery.

The National Association of Alcoholism and Drug Abuse Counselors (NAADAC) recently surveyed its members about the use of medications for their clients (DiClemente & Tuohy, 2010). Although no numbers were reported, counselor attitudes ranged from enthusiastic to ambivalent. Counselors expressed concern about abuse potential of these medications and relative ease of availability, including an active black market for these drugs. Overall, these medications are best used "in the context of a comprehensive, multidisciplinary treatment plan" (DiClemente & Tuohy, 2010, p. 20).

COUNSELING STYLES AND APPROACHES

In addition to different types of treatment, there are different philosophical approaches that consider level of client motivation, incentives for recovery, support from family and friends, and community resources to support recovery. These styles or approaches can be used in both inpatient and outpatient settings. The following is a brief review of the best-known approaches. See Box 6.3 for a list of counseling styles and approaches.

Motivational Interviewing

Motivational interviewing is one of the most studied current substance abuse treatment approaches. It developed from the motivational enhancement therapy (MET) approach, as measured in Project MATCH. It works with intrinsic motivation and takes as its premise that it is up to the client to achieve recovery. It helps

---

BOX 6.3 Major Approaches or Styles of Counseling in Substance Abuse Treatment

1. Motivational interviewing cultivates internal motivation to change and increased personal responsibility.
2. CBT addresses thoughts about alcohol and drugs, cultivates refusal skills, and attempts to avoid potential relapse situations.
3. Contingency management uses the earning of incentives such as prizes for meeting goals in treatment.
4. Community reinforcement stresses learning new coping behaviors, making better choices, and relying on others for support.
5. Adjunct therapies such as yoga, meditation, music therapy, and art therapy add a relaxation component to reduce the stress of early recovery.

people with drug problems, homeless populations, and people with the severest alcohol problems (Strang & McCambridge, 2004; Vasilaki, Hosier, & Cox, 2006). Miller and Rollnick developed motivational interviewing in the 1980s: the first edition of their book, titled *Motivational Interviewing*, was published in 1991 and is now in its third edition. They describe the "spirit" of motivational interviewing as focusing on cultivating clients' motivation to change by examining their values and goals. It is a collaborative relationship between the client and the counselor in which the client maintains the autonomy for self-direction.

Motivational interviewing operates from four guiding principles for counselors: (a) express empathy for the client; (b) work to develop the discrepancy between client attitudes and behaviors and client goals, including working with client ambivalence; (c) tolerate resistance, do not oppose clients, and avoid arguments over the need to change; (d) support client self-efficacy—the client is responsible for determining the needed change and following through with change. Miller and Rollnick (2002) acknowledge that "there is little that is truly original in motivational interviewing" (p. xvi).

In a meta-analysis of 30 clinical trials of the efficacy of motivational interviewing, Burke, Arkowitz, and Menchola (2003) reported a 56% reduction in client drinking and that 51% of clients improved at follow-up compared with 37% receiving other or no treatment. Carroll et al. (2006) reported that motivational interviewing resulted in substance abuse clients remaining longer in treatment than those in a comparison group, although there were no significant effects after a 28-day follow-up. Overall, there is considerable research attesting to the effectiveness of motivational interviewing; however, how and why motivational interviewing works needs further exploration (Brown, 2004; Miller & Rose, 2010).

Cognitive Behavioral Therapy

CBT developed in the 1970s out of the behavior modification tradition. It tends to be short term and can be used with a variety of populations. In cognitive behavioral approaches, clients learn to identify thoughts, feelings, and circumstances that occur around the substance use (Budney & Higgins, 1998). By reflecting on these, clients can learn to make better choices and cultivate healthier habits and coping skills. It is an approach that can be used in inpatient and outpatient programs, as well as with individuals and groups (Budney & Higgins, 1998). It can also be used with the variety of medications available today to reduce cravings or block effects of illicit drugs, including acamprosate and buprenorphine.

CBT has been reported to be effective in treating alcoholism, cocaine addiction, and amphetamine abuse (Baker et al., 2005; Budney & Higgins, 1998). In a meta-analysis of 53 randomized controlled trials with alcohol and drug users, CBT was reported to be especially effective with women and people using marijuana (Magill & Ray, 2009). This study also found that the effects of CBT are especially apparent early in the treatment and diminish over time.

Morgenstern and Longabaugh (2000), in their review of 10 studies of CBT, agreed that it is effective but that little is known about how it works: "A strong theoretical base, impressive efficacy data and weak evidence for effective alternative treatment have led to the ascendency of CBT as the dominant paradigm for treating alcohol dependence within the research community" (p. 1476).

Relapse prevention therapy is a form of CBT that began as a treatment for alcoholism. Before the 1970s, a relapse, no matter how brief, was considered the loss of all gains made while in recovery. As the subfield of relapse prevention developed in the 1980s, it became clearer that relapse should be considered a "normal" part of the recovery process rather than the cause of shame. The relapse prevention model focuses on learning effective coping skills, evaluating and avoiding high-risk situations, and developing self-efficacy and self-confidence (Larimer, Palmer, & Marlatt, 1999; Neff & MacMaster, 2005). Research has shown relapse prevention therapy to be successful in reducing both the number of relapses and the intensity of each relapse (Irwin, Bowers, Dunn, & Wang, 1999).

Overall, comprehensive reviews of research on CBT have found it to be one of the best treatment approaches for substance abuse problems (Brown, 2004; Miller et al., 1995).

Contingency Management

Contingency management, developed in the 1990s, focuses on clients earning a variety of rewards from the treatment program as a way to provide incentives for recovery. When the appropriate behavior occurs, the client can earn rewards; when the client does not meet the treatment goal, the incentives are not given (Petry, 2000). Contingency management has been reported to be effective in samples of clients with alcoholism, with cocaine abuse, and with clients on methadone maintenance (Higgins, Wong, Badger, Ogden, & Dantona, 2000; Lewis & Petry, 2005; Petry, Martin, & Simcic, 2005).

Contingency management can be implemented in a variety of ways. Clients can earn cash or prizes to reinforce their recovery, such as a watch, television, phone card, or bus tokens (Petry, Cooney, & Kranzler, 2000). Vouchers allow for individual preferences and can be used to request things such as movie tickets, a radio, or sports equipment (Petry, 2000). A study by Petry et al. (2000) reported that 84% of alcoholic veterans receiving contingency management treatment stayed for 8 weeks in the program compared with only 22% of those receiving the standard treatment offered. At the conclusion of treatment, 69% of people in the contingency management group were abstinent compared with 39% abstinence among those receiving standard treatment.

A rich literature attests to the effectiveness of contingency management, and the federal government through SAMHSA has provided considerable financial resources to its development, implementation, and evaluation. This treatment approach has been found to reduce alcohol and drug use, improve attendance in treatment programs, extend the amount of time that clients stay in treatment, and bolster compliance in taking prescribed medications. Furthermore, it can support obtaining a job and can improve family relationships (Higgins & Petry, 1999; Lewis & Petry, 2005). A meta-analysis of 30 studies using voucher-based contingency management found that it had better outcomes than control treatments and that better outcomes were associated with quick delivery and greater financial worth of vouchers (Lussier, Heil, Mongeon, Badger, & Higgins, 2006). Other comprehensive reviews of research attest to the effectiveness of contingency management (Hester, 1994; Miller & Wilbourne, 2002). Yet for all the research that speaks to the usefulness of contingency management, "dissemination of this intervention has been rare in the U.S." (Petry et al., 2013, p. 5). A project to disseminate contingency management nationwide through the U.S. Department of Veterans Affairs (VA) met with success in training and implementation in 113 VA settings. This project is the largest training using evidence-based treatments for substance abuse problems in the VA system (Petry et al., 2013).

Acknowledging the positive effect of contingency management on client outcomes can be troublesome. Clinicians who have devoted their careers to helping substance abusers can be disconcerted to find that earning a prize is perhaps more useful to a client's recovery than a strong therapeutic relationship.

Community Reinforcement

The community reinforcement approach developed in the 1970s and has been used primarily in the treatment of alcoholism. The overall goal is for clients to achieve abstinence by eliminating positive reinforcement for drinking alcohol, taking drugs, or both and by enhancing positive reinforcement for sobriety. Simply put, the goal is to make a sober life more rewarding than the drinking or drugging life. Like motivational interviewing, it encourages the development of intrinsic motivation. It also includes analyzing the client's pattern of alcohol use, learning new coping behaviors, and cultivating family support during recovery (Miller, Meyers, & Hiller-Sturmhofel, 1999). The community reinforcement approach is similar to cognitive behavioral approaches in encouraging clients to make better choices to reinforce sobriety and to rely on others for support in this recovery process.

The community reinforcement approach has been shown to be effective with drug addiction and for homeless populations, as well as for both inpatients and outpatients (Meyers & Squires, 2001). The community reinforcement approach is consistently found to be effective in coping with life each day and matching client abilities to the requirements of the environment (Finney, 2000). Wolfe and Meyers (1999) found the community reinforcement approach cost-effective for people with alcohol problems. Overall, comprehensive reviews of research studies attest to the efficacy of the community reinforcement approach (Brown, 2004; Miller & Wilbourne, 2002; Miller et al., 1995). Meyers and Squires (2001) note that although studies show strong scientific evidence for its efficacy, few clinicians use community reinforcement.

This aforementioned review focused on the major types of treatment and approaches. Other approaches have not fared as well when evaluated. Treatment approaches that provide little support in the literature include confrontational approaches in counseling, insight psychotherapy, general counseling, aversion therapies (to create distaste for alcohol or drugs), relaxation training, and educational programs (Brown, 2004; Hester, 1994; Miller & Wilbourne, 2002). Brown (2004) laments that ineffective treatment approaches are often used in the United States and that a "common theme among ineffective approaches is their vague and imprecise description" (p. 14).

Adjunct Therapies

A variety of adjunct or complementary approaches exist to assist alcoholics and addicts with recovery. These are not recommended as primary or sole treatments but can help clients as they work on their recovery and rebuild their lives. Many people benefit from massage and yoga for stress relief (Osborn, 2003). Yoga can assist in developing the discipline it takes to do the hard work of recovery, and there is evidence of its effectiveness in the treatment of depression (Ricchuito, 2012). The reading of self-help materials, known as bibliotherapy, has been shown to be of some assistance in decreasing alcohol consumption for at-risk drinkers (Apodaca & Miller, 2003). Unfortunately, little attention has been paid to nutritional counseling for substance abusers. A study of nutrition education found improved treatment outcomes related to emotional and physical health after receiving nutrition education as part of their substance abuse treatment program (Grant, Haughton, & Sachan, 2004). Overall, adjunct therapies, including music and art therapy, support recovery. Although more research is needed, adjunct therapies can help reduce stress, support positive emotions, and provide structure to the day for people early in recovery.

As we have seen, there are various treatment alternatives and approaches, and it is not unusual to combine several approaches to treatment. McLellan, McKay, Forman, Cacciola, and Kemp (2005) state that there is an overemphasis on acute treatment and that more needs to be done in follow-up with clients. They devised *concurrent recovery monitoring,* a blending of traditional evaluation that looks at outcomes after treatment with performance monitoring practices and patient-focused models of evaluation that can be used in outpatient treatment settings. It offers a consistent relationship over time between the client and the clinician, including the physician. At the start of each session clients complete a questionnaire to report their symptoms since the last session. If this is computerized, the client and the clinician can immediately see the results in a graph. The measures are generally based on actual drug and alcohol consumption, how much time is spent at work, and improvement in personal health and social functioning.

Irrespective of the specific treatment approach, Read, Kahler, and Stevenson (2001) state that treatment is most effective if it encourages client motivation, uses a counseling style that is nonconfrontational, teaches particular skills to clients, encourages setting of appropriate goals, and addresses factors in the community that can support sobriety.

SUMMARY AND CONCLUSION

There are many types and approaches to substance abuse treatment. Project MATCH provided an important impetus to try to find the most effective outpatient treatments of today. The job of comparing and determining the most effective treatments reflects complicated research methodologies. As we have seen, there can be overlap in types and styles of treatment. Another complication is that at times different treatment approaches are used simultaneously.

Clients with substance abuse problems treated in an outpatient setting can receive detox services, individual therapy, group therapy, and family therapy. Medications to block the effects of drugs and to decrease cravings for alcohol and drugs continue to gain popularity in the treatment field.

Overall, there is strong evidence for the effectiveness of brief interventions, motivational interviewing, contingency management, CBT, and community reinforcement. Brief interventions can be helpful in bringing a substance abuse problem to the attention of a patient seen within a health care setting and in offering advice to reduce substance use. Motivational interviewing relies on a strong, empathic relationship with a counselor and avoids confrontation. CBT supports clients in identifying thoughts and feelings that relate to substance use and encourages better choices and healthier habits. Contingency management uses a system of earning rewards to provide incentives for recovery. The community reinforcement approach encourages clients to find ways to make a sober life more appealing and rewarding than the life of the active alcoholic or addict. A veriety of adjunct therapies can assist with stress relief and overall improved emotional and physical health. Therapists are also known to use an "eclectic" style that combines a variety of approaches or to feel they have developed successful approaches that have not been subject to evaluation.

SELF-HELP GROUPS

Self-help groups play a critical role in the field of substance abuse treatment. Self-help programs are considered by some people to be treatment, whereas others consider a self-help program or mutual-help group to be a support network for people in recovery, that is, a "fellowship" or a system of "informal care" (Moos & Timko, 2008, p. 511). It is difficult to determine the effects of self-help programs (Kelly, 2003), and some people believe it is not even appropriate to try to evaluate Alcoholics Anonymous (AA) and other self-help groups because they are "programs of attraction." Self-help group members self-select, a way of saying that members attend because they want to attend, even though court orders to self-help programs are not unusual. All of this adds to the challenges of assessing effectiveness (positive results from treatment) and efficacy (proof that treatment works through controlled research trials), as discussed in Chapter 1.

This chapter examines the evidence for the effectiveness of self-help groups, paying special attention to AA and Narcotics Anonymous (NA). AA, started in 1935 by Bill W. and Dr. Bob, was the first of the self-help groups and has spawned many other self-help groups. The chapter includes a discussion of the personality traits of people who choose to become members of AA. In addition, the chapter examines the relationship between professional treatment and self-help groups.

Overall, many research studies support that self-help programs are effective in reducing substance abuse, although this is not without some controversy, as we explore in this chapter (Cunningham, Koski-Jännes, Wild, & Cordingley, 2002; Johnsen & Herringer, 1993; Kelly & Yeterian, 2010; Moos & Moos, 2007; Tonigan & Beatty, 2011). Self-help meetings are readily available and free, whereas professional treatment services have become less available, more expensive, and of shorter duration (Humphreys, Huebsch, Finney, & Moos, 1999; Kahler et al., 2004; Sharma & Branscum, 2010). As we have seen, people with insurance coverage and financial resources have many more treatment options, and self-help programs can fill the gap for those unable to pay (Humphreys, Kaskutas, & Weisner, 1998). Because AA has no cost, it can be especially appealing to people with low socioeconomic status (Humphreys et al., 1998; Kelly & Yeterian, 2011). The basements of churches and schools are places where self-help meetings are often held. Self-help groups can also make up for the lack of services within the treatment system and can therefore decrease the demand for professional treatment (Humphreys et al., 1998; Humphreys & Moos, 2001; Moos & Timko, 2008). In 2012, only 10.8% of Americans in need of substance abuse treatment received it in a substance abuse treatment program (Substance Abuse and Mental Health Services Administration, 2013b). Clearly the needs are great, and self-help groups can assist in filling a treatment void.

Self-help groups have other advantages as well. Self-help meetings are available when professionals typically are not—on nights, weekends, and holidays (Kelly, Magill, & Stout, 2009). Although treatment programs have admission criteria and expectations for motivation and continued participation in treatment, these requirements do not apply to AA—no one has authority to bar others from participation (White & Kurtz, 2008). Self-help groups are available long after the termination of professional treatment, and people who become members can participate for as long as they choose. In increasing available support networks for people in recovery, self-help groups add to the addict's number of friends, especially those who are abstinent from alcohol and drugs (Humphreys & Noke, 1997; Moos & Moos, 2004a).

RESEARCH ISSUES

AA has received the most research attention of any self-help program. AA is often recommended by health professionals and laymen alike, yet its effectiveness and efficacy had infrequently been studied until the 1990s (McCrady & Miller, 1993; Miller et al., 1995). As discussed previously, *effectiveness* refers to positive results from treatment and *efficacy* refers to proof of positive results in a controlled experimental research trial. A number of things make it hard to determine the efficacy of AA, including difficulty in establishing appropriate research designs, membership that is typically voluntary, and members who are typically self-selected for participation or for whom attendance is coerced (Kaskutas, 2009; Kownacki & Shadish, 1999; Miller & Kurtz, 1994; Montgomery, Miller, & Tonigan, 1995; Tonigan, Toscova, & Miller, 1996). Client characteristics such as the severity of alcohol and drug problems and personality traits are also important in assessing the effects of self-help groups.

Studies of AA typically use randomized assignment to experimental groups, compare AA to other forms of treatment, or are follow-up studies of clients after AA participation over specified periods, usually several months to 1 year. A meta-analysis of AA examined 21 studies (approximately 7,000 individuals) of AA based on controlled experiments and was highly critical of the quality of the methodology of many studies (Kownacki & Shadish, 1999). Research challenges included studying the differences between people who attend voluntarily and those who are coerced by the courts into going to AA meetings.

To encourage research on AA, Tonigan, Connors, and Miller (1996) developed the Alcoholics Anonymous Involvement (AAI) Scale, a 13-item self-report instrument, shown to be reliable for assessing attendance and level of involvement in AA. However, treatment samples tend to focus on early participation in AA rather than long-term involvement, and these processes may be different (Kelly et al., 2009).

In their examination of the effectiveness of AA, McKellar, Stewart, and Humphreys (2003) reviewed three hypotheses. The first hypothesis is that participating in AA is effective in reducing alcohol consumption and associated problems. The second hypothesis is that lowered alcohol consumption leads people to affiliate with AA. McKellar et al. (2003) point out that these are not mutually exclusive categories; that is, reduced drinking can lead someone to attend AA meetings, and AA attendance can reduce drinking further in a pattern of mutual reinforcement. A third hypothesis is that a third variable, "good prognosis" (McKellar et al., 2003, p. 302), is responsible for attendance. This means that the person has a high motivation for recovery and implies that AA looks effective because it attracts people motivated toward recovery. In their study of 2,139 alcoholic males, McKellar et al. (2003) concluded that AA involvement was responsible for reductions in drinking (hypothesis 1) but did not support that reduced drinking led men to AA (hypothesis 2). Affiliation with AA (hypothesis 3) was neither explained by the level of motivation nor explained by the presence of co-occurring disorders.

Research findings regarding the effectiveness and efficacy of self-help groups tend to be inconsistent (Mueller, Petitjean, Boening, & Weisbeck, 2007). Earlier efforts in the 1980s to evaluate AA did not result in positive findings. Miller and Hester (1986) reviewed 26 controlled studies and reported that AA works no better than other approaches, including no treatment. In further research, Miller et al. (1995) found little research on self-help groups and, almost a decade later, that findings were still not positive.

A number of studies have specifically found no benefit of participation in self-help groups. In a study that followed alcoholics over an 8-year period, people who received professional treatment or participated in AA did better than those who did not receive help, yet there was almost no difference between the type of treatment and the outcome (Timko, Moos, Finney, & Lesar, 2000). A study of German patients who chose to attend self-help meetings or chose no support found that those attending the self-help groups showed a lower relapse rate after 1 month, although there were no significant differences between the groups within 1 year (Mueller et al., 2007).

The Cochrane Collaboration compared 12-step programs with no intervention and with professional interventions such as motivational enhancement therapy, cognitive behavioral therapy, and relapse prevention therapy. A total of 117 studies were initially identified for possible inclusion; ultimately eight randomized controlled studies were reviewed in depth (Ferri, Amato, &

Davoli, 2009). Ferri et al. (2009) reported that "there is no conclusive evidence to show that AA can help patients to achieve abstinence, nor is there any conclusive evidence to show that it cannot" (p. 11). The authors bemoaned the lack of experimental research and recommended large-scale studies that compare one AA or self-help group intervention with a control group over longer periods (Ferri et al., 2009). Ferri et al. (2009) also recommend qualitative studies with patients and families that can help to identify future research issues.

A lengthy stay by individuals in self-help groups and other treatment tends to correlate with greater success in recovery and is often used as the measure of effectiveness (Laudet, 2003). However, the high attrition rate affects the effectiveness of self-help groups and makes them harder to study (Laudet, 2003). The best studies of self-help groups are well designed and use large patient samples (Tonigan et al., 1996b). Although the methodological quality of studies has improved considerably since the 1990s, as noted by Humphreys (2006b), more research attention is needed on the subjective experience of involvement in AA and other self-help groups (Laudet, 2003; Tonigan, Miller, & Connors, 2000). When it comes to research on the effectiveness and efficacy of self-help groups, these are concerns primarily for researchers and are not typically shared by individual self-help group members. The members' personal experiences and bearing witness to the recovery of others are sufficient to convince members of the success of self-help groups.

ALCOHOLICS ANONYMOUS

AA is the most widely used program for alcohol problems, and the effectiveness of AA has been debated through the years. AA has received considerably more research attention than NA and other self-help programs we review in this chapter. A huge part of the appeal of AA is the support network available from members to one another, where deep friendships can develop (Humphreys & Noke, 1997; Longabaugh, Wirtz, Zweben, & Stout, 1998; McCrady, Epstein, & Kahler, 2004). See Box 7.1 for the 12 steps of AA.

The story of Dr. Bob and Bill W. is well known, and the development of AA in 1935 is a compelling story of alcoholic individuals trying to help one another. AA developed when there was still considerable stigma attached to alcoholism and when few treatment options were available (Laudet, 2003; Magura, 2007). AA members, such as Marty Mann, described in Chapter 4, were instrumental in developing the professional treatment system for alcoholic patients. AA was so highly valued in the 1950s that Harrison Trice (1957) stated, "This nonprofessional group has apparently achieved a success as great, if not greater, than the efforts of medicine, psychiatry, and psychology" (p. 39). The considerable public support for AA and its status as a highly regarded program for recovery from alcoholism has been maintained over many years and led to the following description by Emrick (1994): "Its success as a social movement is indisputable, exercising considerable influence on the professional community, government agencies and programs, as well as the general public" (p. 351).

BOX 7.1 The 12 Steps of AA

1. We admitted we were powerless over alcohol—that our lives had become unmanageable.
2. Came to believe that a power greater than ourselves could restore us to sanity.
3. Made a decision to turn our will and our lives over to the care of God *as we understood Him*.
4. Made a searching and fearless moral inventory of ourselves.
5. Admitted to God, to ourselves, and to another human being the exact nature of our wrongs.
6. Were entirely ready to have God remove all these defects of character.
7. Humbly asked Him to remove our shortcomings.
8. Made a list of all persons we had harmed, and became willing to make amends to them all.
9. Made direct amends to such people wherever possible, except when to do so would injure them or others.
10. Continued to take personal inventory and when we were wrong promptly admitted it.
11. Sought through prayer and meditation to improve our conscious contact with God *as we understood Him*, praying only for knowledge of His will for us and the power to carry that out.
12. Having had a spiritual awakening as the result of the Steps, we tried to carry this message to others, and to practice these principles in all our affairs.

Source: Alcoholics Anonymous World Services (1952). (Italics in the original.)

Many scholars attribute the promotion of the disease concept to AA, and "its members did have a large role in spreading and popularizing that understanding" (Kurtz, 2002, p. 5). AA established the idea of the threefold disease—physical, mental, and spiritual—and the Hughes Act of 1970 gave the federal government's "blessing" (Kurtz, 2002, p. 35) to the disease concept. Although the disease concept is no longer as hotly debated as it once was, a recent study reported that substance abuse treatment professionals who are in recovery are more likely to embrace the disease concept if they are abstinent and attend 12-step groups for their own personal recovery (Russell, Davies, & Hunter, 2011).

The 2011 membership survey of AA states that there are 114,000 AA groups all over the world today, an increase from 97,000 in 2001 (AA World Services, 2012). Membership surveys have been conducted every 3 to 4 years since 1968. The picture of AA today in the United States and Canada is that 65% of members are men and 35% are women. Whites make up 87% of the membership, followed by Hispanics at 5%, African Americans at 4%, Native Americans at 2%, Asians at 1%, and other groups at 1% of the membership. The average length of sobriety in 2011 was 10 years, up from 7 years in 2001 (AA World Services, 2002, 2012). In 2011 members attended an average of 2.6 meetings per week, an increase from 2 meetings per week on average in 2001. In 2011, 63% received some type of professional counseling or treatment before AA, and 74% of these members felt treatment encouraged their AA affiliation. See Box 7.2 for an experience of attending a first AA meeting.

A number of studies support both the effectiveness and the efficacy of AA. In an early meta-analysis of 107 previously published studies, greater involvement with AA could "modestly predict" reduced alcohol consumption (Emrick, Tonigan, Montgomery, & Little, 1993). Emrick (1994) summarized the positive

---

BOX 7.2 The First AA Meeting for John K.

March 27, 1986, is one of the most significant days in my life. Not only was this my 39th birthday, it was my first day of sobriety and my first AA meeting. I had been going to counseling for several weeks and tried on my own to cut back on drinking as I had many times in the past, switching substances to eventually abuse all of them. All to no avail. I went to counseling at 9 a.m. that day and for whatever reason the counselor confronted me. More importantly, I was ready that day to really listen and accept what he was saying about my long history of drinking and drugging. I knew down deep inside that there were problems but I was still blaming people, places and things in the past for why I was full of anger, regrets and remorse.

The gig was up on that day—no more blame games. I heard that the problem was alcohol and drugs, connecting me with the truth for the first time. I stood up and faced the window and had a deep cry. The counselor strongly suggested I go to AA and continue with outpatient counseling and if I couldn't stop, detox and inpatient treatment were the next options.

I was willing to do what he suggested and went to my first meeting at noon that same day in a nearby town. I had never thought before of trying AA to completely stop or deal with my drinking. I didn't know what to expect but as I walked into that first meeting I don't recall feeling overly anxious or uncomfortable. I felt welcomed but most importantly, safe, and free of the obsession of drinking. I didn't fully understand what they were sharing but what I did hear was not to drink that day. I also went to another meeting the evening of my first day of sobriety and a couple of men were standing at the door; one reached out to shake my hand with a smile and said, "Welcome." I proceeded to sit in the back of a large meeting in a church basement and listened to a few people share their drinking stories and how they didn't drink anymore. I have kept coming back to thousands of meetings all over the U.S. and Canada for the last 27 plus years and have not found it necessary to pick up that first drink.

Source: John K., story written for this book, 2013.

aspects as follows: the support of a sponsor and engaging in 12-step work, that is, bringing the program to others in need, chairing AA meetings, and becoming more involved with AA than in the past, especially after professional treatment. Montgomery et al. (1995) examined the efficacy of AA and followed patients after 28-day inpatient treatment to see whether there was a relationship between participation and outcomes. AA attendance did not predict better outcomes—it was the degree of active involvement that was "significantly predictive of positive outcomes" (Montgomery et al., 1995, p. 245).

The length of AA attendance is also correlated with the number of months of abstinence (McBride, 1991). It is not surprising that people who attend AA meetings frequently (weekly or more often) are more likely to reduce alcohol use and increase abstinence (Gossop et al., 2003). In a study of 150 patients in inpatient treatment in London, Gossop et al. (2003) reported that patients who attended many AA meetings during their inpatient treatment were more likely to attend AA during the follow-up period. People who attended AA meetings regularly reported less drinking than those who did not. Yet AA support may not be sufficient for people with psychiatric problems, and those with significant life problems may need more comprehensive care than AA can provide. Although today there is acknowledgment of the effectiveness of AA, the mechanisms that support recovery in AA are not well understood (Kelly et al., 2009).

AA and Personality Traits

One research focus for evaluating AA is based on individual personality traits that promote or discourage participation in self-help groups (Kelly, Stout, Tonigan, Magill, & Pagano, 2010; Reigle & Dowd, 2004). Trice (1957) observed at an early date that the following are necessary to become a member: defining oneself as a person who shares emotional experiences with other people, not adhering to behavior models of willpower, giving up friends who drink, and accepting the sincerity of members of AA. One analysis described the appeal of AA as attributing alcoholism to outside forces rather than personal characteristics of the alcoholics; it "enables alcoholics to develop a positive self-image, redirect blame and assuage guilt" (Beckman, 1980, p. 714).

For clients in early recovery (3 months or less), some gravitate toward AA and others have a hard time affiliating with the program. People who are able to share their feelings and are more comfortable with intimacy can have an easier time (Caldwell & Cutter, 1998). A study of personality types and attendance at self-help meetings among 62 recently detoxified alcohol and drug patients suggested that people who are extroverted, less socially isolated, and not socially ill at ease are more likely to attend AA meetings (Janowsky, Boone, Morter, & Howe, 1999). This serves as a reminder that treatment professionals can help clients to overcome social isolation by addressing issues of relationships and encouraging the development of social skills (Caldwell & Cutter, 1998).

A recent study examined the relationship between anger and affiliation with AA (Kelly et al., 2010). The sample of alcoholic individuals had substantially higher rates of anger compared with the general population. Although anger decreased over a 15-month period of AA involvement, it was still considered high. Interestingly, people with higher levels of anger were more likely to attend a greater number of meetings. The authors concluded, "AA attendance itself does not in fact lead directly to reductions in anger. However, it may be that, although the levels of anger remain quite high, AA helps attendees improve their ability to successfully *tolerate* anger" (Kelly et al., 2010, p. 442; italics in the original). Depression was noted to be higher among people in AA compared with the general population; greater attendance of AA decreased depression and alcohol use, and less depression could be a result of decreased drinking. Moderate to severe depression can put a client in the dual diagnosis or co-occurring disorders situation. Double Trouble in Recovery, a self-help group, was developed for people with both mental health and substance abuse problems and is discussed in Chapter 9.

In their meta-analysis of 74 studies of AA and outcomes, Tonigan et al. (1996b) reported that AA participation had a positive correlation with reducing drinking yet concluded that experiences in AA are so heterogeneous that it is not useful to "to seek omnibus profiles of AA affiliates or outcomes" (p. 65). Overall, there is no definitive picture of the personal characteristics that predict whether someone will do well in AA.

The tendency toward a spiritual orientation in some self-help groups is an additional factor in addressing personality traits and is one that can attract or repel individuals in self-help groups. Perhaps the areas of strongest concern about affiliation with self-help groups involve attitudes toward spirituality (Laudet, 2003; Magura, 2007). AA has often been described as a "spiritual recovery movement" (Galanter, 2007, p. 265) that cultivates greater meaning in the lives of people in recovery.

Spirituality is a more comprehensive term than *religiosity,* which implies engaging in rituals in some organized practice of a specific religion (Brown, Whitney, Schneider, & Vega, 2006). AA and other self-help groups can attend to the spiritual and emotional concerns of members that others, including physicians, do not address (Galanter, 2007). A more religious orientation than the spiritual orientation of AA is Celebrate Recovery, a Christian-centered recovery program that holds that Jesus Christ is the only higher power (Brown et al., 2006).

Laudet (2003) reported that 60% of clients in treatment considered the spiritual or religious part of 12-step groups an obstacle to their participation. Kelly et al. (2009) noted in their review of the research that atheists or agnostics do not derive less benefit from AA than people who have an orientation that is spiritual, religious, or both; however, they are less likely to affiliate with AA. Kelly et al. (2009) concluded that current research is not adequate to ascertain the role of spirituality in recovery and that more research is needed. Other secular self-help groups, as discussed later, have developed to address the discomfort of a spiritual or religious orientation. Although the issue of spirituality is important, research shows that the social support provided by AA is stronger and more important than its spiritual aspects (Kelly et al., 2009).

A well-known substance abuse researcher, Keith Humphreys, in an editorial titled "The Trials of Alcoholics Anonymous" in the journal *Addiction* (2006b), concluded:

> Strong views about AA one way or the other will always survive, no matter what evidence accumulates, but the studies of the past 15 years have established beyond any reasonable doubt that high-quality trials are possible, and that such studies usually reinforce rather than undermine the excellent reputation the fellowship enjoys around the world. (p. 618)

NARCOTICS ANONYMOUS

Compared with AA, considerably less is known about the dynamics of NA meetings and their effect on people who attend. NA was founded in 1953 in California (White, Budnick, & Pickard, 2011). Although only 18 years younger than AA, NA has yet to garner the research attention it deserves. This lack of research is perhaps correlated with the harsher societal judgments of people addicted to narcotics than those addicted to alcohol. NA is more often included with rather than distinguished from studies of 12-step programs, and the few studies that exist tend to lack the strong methodology of studies of AA (Moos & Timko, 2008; White et al., 2011).

Two important research assumptions are that NA is like AA and other 12-step programs and that conclusions from studies of AA should apply to NA (White et al., 2011). For example, some researchers are comfortable applying research results from AA to NA because they share the characteristics of speaker and 12-step meetings, sponsors, and similar literature (Moos & Timko, 2008). Surely there are differences between members of NA and other self-help groups that have yet to be studied, especially considering that members of NA are likely to be addicted to illegal substances. See Box 7.3 for a first meeting attended by a drug addict.

A membership survey of NA is completed at every world convention, the last one in San Diego, California, in 2011 (NA World Services, 2012). There were 17,492 responses. NA holds more than 61,800 meetings per week in 129 countries. Members averaged 3.2 meetings per week. In the 2011 survey, 74% of respondents were Caucasian, 11% were African American, 8% were Hispanic, 2% were Asian, 1% were indigenous, 3% identified as multiracial, and 1% identified as "other."

One study of a sample of 91 new members of NA in Australia reported correlations among self-help participation, decreased substance use, and improved social support (Toumbourou, Hamilton, U'Ren, Steven-Jones, & Storey, 2002). People who attended at least a weekly meeting of NA over 1 year had lower levels of marijuana and alcohol use than those who attended sporadically (Toumbourou et al., 2002). Another study reported that people who participated in only AA, only NA, or both had the same abstinence rates after 1 year and that rates were higher for those who did not participate in either program (Crape, Latkin, Laris, & Knowlton, 2002).

> ### BOX 7.3 The Experience of Michael D. at a Self-Help Meeting
>
> I met a guy named Leon, who knew the moment he looked at me that this was my first meeting. He gave me his number and a meeting list, and told me to call him the next day. I went to a diner and sat in the window, amazed to feel hopeful. I found another meeting to go to, late night, far on the West Side.
>
> There was a deranged man in headphones dancing obliviously in the middle of the room; somebody shooed him away. Homeless guys slept in the back. There were two glamorous women, dazzlingly made up, in dresses and heels. Two men spoke: the first talked about how he had spent his life fantasizing about having a farm to grow his own weed and mushrooms, but then, bafflingly to him, had become a crack addict. The second guy had recently been homeless and had worked as a gravedigger before his life went haywire. His story went like this: "I went back to the shed and had a couple of belts. Then I went back to digging the grave. Then I went back to the shed, and had a couple of belts. Then I went back to digging the grave. Then I went back to the shed."
>
> *Source:* Doughty (2012, p. 181). Reprinted with permission.

Although there has been greater research interest in NA over the last 10 years, there is not yet a clear research agenda for evaluating NA (White et al., 2011). More remains to be known about the efficacy and effectiveness of NA, including comparisons of characteristics of members of AA with those of members of NA.

A variety of other self-help programs have developed through the years. The best known of these is Rational Recovery, which was started by social worker Jack Trimpey in 1986 as an alternative to AA and is based on the rational emotive therapy of Albert Ellis. This orientation avoids the potential spiritual quagmire and supports rational thinking and good decision making. Although far less available than AA and NA, Rational Recovery is a strong alternative for substance abusers who are uncomfortable with a spiritual orientation in recovery. The Rational Recovery approach does not consider alcoholism a disease and does not require spiritual beliefs to work on recovery. In an early review of Rational Recovery, Galanter, Egelko, and Edwards (1993) reported that 75% had attended AA in the past and 82% had higher ratings of Rational Recovery principles than of 12-step principles in helping them with their recovery.

In 1994 the board of Rational Recovery Self-Help voted to end its agreement with Rational Recovery and become Self-Management and Recovery Training (SMART) Recovery (Allwood & White, 2012). Differences of opinion were likely responsible for the split, yet no clear picture has emerged in the literature for what happened to bring about the changes. At the end of 2011 there were 667 SMART Recovery meetings being held weekly around the globe (Allwood & White, 2012).

Far less research attention has been paid to SMART Recovery and two other large self-help groups, Women for Sobriety (started by Jean Kirkpatrick in 1975) and LifeRing (Kaskutas & Subbaraman, 2011), than to AA or NA. LifeRing is an abstinence-based organization founded by Marty Nicolaus in 1999 in California (LifeRing, 2012). It was developed into a national organization in 2001.

AL-ANON AND NAR-ANON

A number of support groups are available to family members of alcoholics and addicts; however, little research is available on self-help groups for family members (Timko et al., 2013). Al-Anon was started by the wife of AA cofounder Bill W., Lois, in 1951. The Al-Anon international membership survey of fall 2012 found 86% of members were female and 14% were male (Al-Anon Family Groups Headquarters, 2012). On average, members had almost 12 years of participation. For almost 36% of members, the husband was alcoholic. For people with alcohol problems associated with an Al-Anon member, 41% were still actively drinking and 47% were AA members in 2012.

In their review of the literature, Timko, Young, and Moos (2012) found support for Al-Anon participants reporting less stress and greater coping abilities. In a recent study comparing newcomers and regular members of Al-Anon, regular members had less stress and better quality of life than people new to Al-Anon (Timko et al., 2013). There were no differences between the groups on physical and psychological health, although newcomers were more likely to have used alcohol recently and to have substance problems. This points to overall better functioning by people who participate in Al-Anon over time.

Modeled after Al-Anon, Nar-Anon is specifically for family members and friends of addicts. Less is known about Nar-Anon. After one failed attempt, Nar-Anon was officially launched in 1968 in California, and in 1986 the Nar-Anon World Service Office was established.

Research is needed on Al-Anon outcomes for Al-Anon participants, the therapeutic process of attending Al-Anon, and the relationship between Al-Anon participation and partner or family member alcoholism (Timko, Young, & Moos, 2012). This important information is also needed for participants in Nar-Anon, as well as Alateen and Narateen (for teenage children of alcoholics and addicts).

SELF-HELP AND TREATMENT PROGRAMS WORKING TOGETHER

How do self-help groups and professional treatment work together? The interaction between self-help and professional treatment is common, and "the two sources of help appear to strengthen or bolster each other" (Moos & Timko, 2008, p. 513). Treatment professionals often refer clients to AA during treatment, as well as part of an aftercare program for clients showing good results (Gossop, Stewart, & Marsden, 2008; Humphreys et al., 1998; Kaskutas & Subbaraman, 2011; Magura, 2007). Counselors and others can do much to encourage and support self-help group participation during professional treatment (Laudet, 2003; Moos & Moos, 2004a, 2004b; Timko & DeBenedetti, 2007). Concurrent participation in treatment and in 12-step programs can help achieve higher rates of abstinence than participation solely in treatment or self-help groups (Fiorentine & Hillhouse, 2000).

One study of 927 clients in inpatient and outpatient treatment programs reported that 83% had some previous involvement with AA (Humphreys et al., 1998). In a study of early recovery from alcoholism, of 55 men and women in inpatient or outpatient treatment, 78% had previously been involved with AA (Caldwell & Cutter, 1998). It can be difficult to understand these findings in this context—they can be interpreted positively to show how well-known and available self-help programs can be; alternatively, they can be seen as ineffective because so many participants later required professional treatment.

Although some health care professionals choose to solely recommend a self-help group, they should be cautious about referring patients to AA without some kind of professional assessment; clients who receive professional intervention and 12-step support tend to have more positive outcomes (Laudet, 2003). Emrick (1994) stated, "Referring alcohol-troubled individuals to AA only without careful consideration of the particular needs of the patient and without close monitoring of the patient's response to the organization is simply inadequate" (p. 355; italics in the original).

In a study of attitudes toward 12-step groups, Laudet (2003) reported that clinicians gave higher ratings and had greater interest in 12-step groups than did clients. Clients and clinicians were asked about their beliefs about 12-step groups, and the most frequent answers regarding the benefits were "the opportunity to help improve yourself and your life, help with sobriety and recovery, and fellowship with recovering peers" (Laudet, 2003, p. 2023). Clients and clinicians need to discuss prior experience in 12-step groups and beliefs about the program to foster the likelihood of client participation in self-help groups.

Treatment professionals can encourage self-help involvement, such as participating in meetings, reading the 12-step literature, and cultivating the self-identity as a member of a self-help group (Timko & DeBenedetti, 2007). It is important to educate health professionals so that they can refer to self-help groups (Kelly & McCrady, 2009).

In a comparison between 12-step programs and cognitive behavioral models, 3,018 patients from a U.S. Department of Veterans Affairs program, people in cognitive behavioral therapy, those in 12-step programs, and those in both cognitive behavioral and 12-step were all equally effective in supporting abstinence at 1-year follow-up (Ouimette, Finney, & Moos, 1997). The same data showed that people who participate in 12-step programs and "more intensive outpatient care" have better outcomes after 1 year (Moos, Finney, Ouimette, & Suchinsky, 1999).

In a study of 90 alcoholic males and their partners assigned to behavioral couples therapy, behavioral couples therapy combined with relapse prevention therapy, or behavioral couples therapy combined with AA, no clear link was found between participation in AA and better treatment outcomes (McCrady et al., 2004). Overall, although all interventions resulted in client improvement, no one intervention could be considered more effective than another.

Moos and Moos (2004b) concluded from their study of professional treatment and AA that AA should not be considered a substitute for professional help. This is especially the case for clients with more severe problems who need greater support and care than can be provided by a self-help group. However, extended affiliation with AA is related to better outcomes and reduces the need for additional treatment (Moos & Moos, 2004a). Overall, clients followed over a period of 8 years participated in AA for longer than they participated in professional treatment, regardless of whether they entered AA or professional treatment first (Moos & Moos, 2004a). After 16 years, 34% of people who did not participate in AA in the first year of the study were abstinent from alcohol; 67% of individuals attending AA in the first year were abstinent after 16 years (Moos & Moos, 2006).

Self-help group participation also cultivates helping others through sponsoring new members and participating in community services (Subbaraman, Kaskutas, & Zemore, 2011). Interestingly, one study of injection drug users found that sponsorship benefited the sponsor by increased abstinence more than it helped the person being sponsored (Crape et al., 2002). Kurtz and Fisher (2003) reported that 12-step affiliation offered members a way to make amends or give back within their communities, provided training for community service involvement, and provided spiritual principles to support participation in community services.

Overall, self-help groups assist with long-term recovery by helping participants form new friends and social support, providing some behavioral monitoring through having a sponsor and others to bolster recovery, encouraging participation in rewarding activities such as helping others, and supporting membership in a group that fosters hope and inspiration (Moos & Timko, 2008). Attending both professional treatment and 12-step meetings at the beginning of the recovery process provides the client with the opportunity to talk about experiences at meetings and to optimize chances for success.

LIMITATIONS OF SELF-HELP PROGRAMS

There is evidence that fewer than 5% of alcoholics go to AA and many drop out so quickly that there are great limitations on the effect of AA (Emrick, 1994). In its own survey in 1990, AA acknowledged that 50% of participants drop out after 3 months and 75% drop out by 12 months. Laudet (2003), in a study of clients and clinicians, reported that the most significant limitation of 12-step groups is that they cannot help people who lack motivation and do not want 12-step involvement. Yet it hardly seems fair to criticize self-help programs for not getting sufficient numbers of alcoholics and addicts to attend.

Dodes (2002) described the "significant limitations" (p. 225) of 12-step programs as one-size-fits-all approaches that do not address individual emotional factors that underlie addiction. Furthermore, Dodes (2002) claimed that 12-step programs can shame addicts and alcoholics by giving them the message they have not worked hard enough on their recovery. Members focus on their success stories and tend to be "insular," fostering the view that others need to work harder and then will ultimately "get the program." Dodes's (2002) main criticism of 12-step programs is that no attention is paid to understanding the reasons for addictive behaviors:

> It does not aid in finding actions that would more directly address what is driving your own individual addictive act, or in understanding yourself so that you can take control of the addiction without relying on the twelve-step organization or its "higher power" concept. (p. 227)

The high dropout rates from self-help programs are a concern, as mentioned earlier in this chapter. Kelly and Moos (2003) reported that people more likely to dropout from self-help groups are young, single, and White; have a lower level of motivation; and have greater social isolation. The study found that 40% of men in U.S. Department of Veterans Affairs residential programs of 21 to 28 days had dropped out of self-help programs at a 1-year follow-up and had worse substance outcomes. People more likely to drop out had lower levels of motivation, less experience with self-help groups before residential treatment, and less involvement with religion. This knowledge can assist clinicians to address these factors in treatment. Still, more needs to be known about reasons for leaving self-help affiliation (Laudet, 2003).

According to Reznicek (2012), "Members of AA and NA understand that people can change only themselves. These programs do not work on addicts; rather, addicts work these programs. AA and NA are where addicts go after they have gone through the ringer, experienced deep personal pain, and decided to change their lives" (p. 93).

SUMMARY AND CONCLUSION

Efforts to evaluate the effectiveness and efficacy of self-help programs began in earnest in the 1990s, with by far the most research attention focusing on AA, the largest and most popular of the 12-step programs. Most evidence points to AA as a successful approach for people who resonate with the principles and are seeking social support. People who gravitate toward self-help programs are more likely to be outgoing, to be willing to share their feelings with others, and to appreciate the important social network that self-help programs provide. Professional treatment and self-help group participation can together provide a complete approach to recovery from addiction.

It is important to have realistic expectations of the role of self-help groups in recovery from alcohol and drug addiction. Self-help groups are one option available to people who seek recovery, and programs that are less spiritual than AA can resonate with people who are uncomfortable with spiritual or religious orientations. People walking the road of recovery need to find environments in which they feel safe and comfortable to do the hard work of recovery.

Considerably more research is needed to evaluate the types of self-help program and the mechanisms that attract and deter individuals from participating. This includes addressing the issues of families of alcoholics and addicts in programs such as Al-Anon and Nar-Anon.

TREATMENT OF DIVERSE POPULATIONS

Culture has a strong effect on the use of alcohol and other drugs, whether it is considered an ordinary part of the day to have a glass of wine with dinner or the acceptance of injecting illegal drugs. Patterns of use of alcohol and drugs develop out of the beliefs, attitudes, values, and expectations of behavior that a culture associates with specific drugs (Castro, Barrera, Mena, & Aguirre, 2014; Westermeyer, 1987). Although alcohol is the most widely used drug around the globe (Cagney, 2006), there is no single cultural meaning of alcohol use. In the United States alcohol use can be celebratory, can be ceremonial, or can occur in social isolation. These beliefs and attitudes have historical roots and are also shaped by social, economic, religious, and political forces such as social acceptance, customs and laws, as well as cost and availability of alcohol and other drugs.

Alcohol and drug use can be influenced by a variety of cultural factors, including personal beliefs about culture, migration patterns, levels of urbanization, and socioeconomic status (Ferguson, 2012; Schoeneberger, Leukefeld, Hiller, & Godlaski, 2006; Westermeyer, 1987). Although immigrants may become acculturated to the drinking patterns of the larger society, subcultures can strongly affect attitudes and behaviors toward alcohol and drugs as drinking patterns of the country of origin are brought to the United States (Cagney, 2006; Galvan & Caetano, 2003).

This chapter examines a number of issues related to the treatment of diverse populations. Rather than making an exhaustive review, the chapter highlights the major issues for these special populations. Each topic can be the subject of an entire chapter or an entire book. This chapter also explores what is known about responses to treatment; however, as shown, we cannot say that one kind of treatment is best based on culture, race, ethnicity, gender, or age.

Across cultures there may not be agreement as to what constitutes problem drinking and drugging. Far more research attention has been paid to alcohol, and little research exists on how culture and drug use affect each other. Definitions of race and ethnicity are complex and can be further complicated as substance abuse issues intertwine with cultural background, religion, social class, and minority status (Cagney, 2006). When examining the substance use problems of specific minority groups, one factor cannot account for how substance problems develop. Therefore, race and ethnicity by themselves cannot explain alcohol and drug use behaviors. As shown in this chapter, socioeconomic status has great influence on both substance abuse and access to treatment.

McAndrew and Edgerton's *Drunken Comportment: A Social Explanation* (1969) is a classic work that showed it is the cultural expectations of drunken behavior rather than the specific properties of alcohol that determine behavior. In some countries such as the United States, reckless and even dangerous behaviors can be explained away and excused by the statement "I was drunk." (This is less true today, because increasingly intoxicated individuals are held more accountable for their behavior, as seen in tougher drunk-driving laws in recent years.) In other cultures, intoxication results in passive behaviors, such as among the Yuruna Indians of the rainforests of South America, the Camba of Bolivia, and the rural Japanese fishing community of Takashima (McAndrew & Edgerton, 1969). Cagney (2006) reached the same conclusion: "The enormous cross-cultural variation in the way people drink and the way they behave when they drink cannot simply be attributed to different levels of consumption or genetic differences" (p. 117).

Today it is known that historical, cultural, social, and psychological factors are important and encourage us to look toward the development of theoretical explanations. The *cultural content model* explains patterns of alcohol use according to the values and norms (shared rules and guidelines for behavior) of specific cultural groups (Cagney, 2006). The *cultural conflict model* holds that issues that result from racism, alienation from the larger culture, acculturative stress, and a sense of powerlessness can influence individuals to use alcohol in problematic ways. Acculturation of immigrant groups supports adopting the cultural practices and traditions of the larger society, and this can include increased alcohol and drug use (Caetano, Vaeth, & Rodriguez, 2012; Karriker-Jaffe & Zemore, 2009). *Acculturative stress* refers to the challenges of adapting to the social patterns of the larger group that can affect immigrants, especially prejudice and discrimination (Castro, Stein, & Bentler, 2009). These general theories cannot account for all alcohol or drug use.

There exists a range of cultural attitudes from abstinence to acceptance of very heavy drinking. Although specific cultures and subcultures support different acceptable limits on alcohol and drug use, modern global society can also promote substance abuse as a way of coping with life's challenges. According to Westermeyer (1999): "It is a great leap from describing the use of psychoactive substances within a particular group at a certain period to hypothesizing specific etiologic (causal) factors for substance abuse in the sociocultural realm" (p. 253). Although drinking patterns remain within the realm of specific countries and cultures, increased globalization has affected alcohol use, leading Cagney (2006) to remark: "By the end of the twentieth century, faster communications, increasing physical and social mobility, the rise of multinational corporations, and greater international collaboration had created a global market for alcohol and seen the emergence of global drinking cultures in some contexts" (p. 9).

Today it is well accepted that culture has powerful effects on the psychological well-being and overall health of individuals (Eckersley, 2006). Although perhaps an overly simplistic explanation, modern Western cultural influences such as consumerism and materialism can reduce the quality and importance of interpersonal relationships and a sense of personal control that can encourage substance abuse.

RACE AND ETHNICITY

In this section we review substance abuse issues and their treatment for Native Americans, Latinos, African Americans, and Asian Americans. The complexity of race and ethnicity creates special challenges for the examination of substance abuse treatment. We have U.S. data from the 2012 National Survey on Drug Use and Health by the Substance Abuse and Mental Health Services Administration (SAMHSA, 2013b) that address the types and amount of substance abuse and the dependence among different races and ethnicities. It is important to contemplate whether it is appropriate to try to fit together types of treatment and racial and ethnic categories—so many factors are involved, including the meaning of culture and family to individuals with substance abuse problems.

Since the 1990s the treatment field has acknowledged the importance of providing culturally competent services to clients (SAMHSA, 1999). These include treatment staff members belonging to the same backgrounds as clients served, staff knowledge of the native language, sensitivity to cultural nuances, and incorporation of ethnic values and traditions into treatment. A deeper understanding of the substance abuse problems of racial and ethnic groups can assist with the development of national and local public health policy, the development of both treatment and prevention programs that can address the varying needs of the groups, and the documentation of "treatment need" that can help expand access to services (SAMHSA, 2010).

This chapter shows that access to treatment has less to do with race and ethnicity and more to do with socioeconomic status (Wells, Klap, Koike, & Sherbourne, 2001). As will be discussed in Chapter 10, the institutional racism and differential treatment by the criminal justice system has resulted in far longer prison sentences for African Americans than for Whites in cocaine sentencing (Hart, 2013; Heath, 2001).

Using U.S. data from 2012, the highest rates of substance abuse and dependence are found among Native Americans (21.8%; SAMHSA, 2013b). Among other groups, 8.8% of Hispanics, 8.7% of Whites, and 8.9% of African Americans have issues of substance abuse or dependence. Asian Americans have the lowest rates of substance abuse or dependence at 3.2%.

Native Americans

Native Americans have significantly higher rates of alcoholism than other groups that are associated with other health, social, and economic problems. Today Native Americans are more likely than other groups to live below the poverty line, have higher rates of diabetes, and lack health insurance (Mignon & Holmes, 2013). Native American history is replete with significant issues of oppression and alienation that bear on perceptions of alcohol use and alcoholism (Yellow Horse Brave Heart, 2003). Alcohol has been used as a "tool in the political, economic, and sexual exploitation of Native peoples" (Coyhis & White, 2006, p. 35). Native Americans with substance abuse problems vary in terms of their identification with their cultural identity—this often takes the form of choosing to live either on reservations or in urban areas. People who live on reservations are those more likely to have serious alcohol problems (Spillane & Smith, 2007).

In Native American families it is easy to see the ripple effects of alcohol and drug use through the generations. In a study of Native American grandparents raising their grandchildren, substance abuse and dependence directly led to the parenting role of the grandparents in 32% of cases (Mignon & Holmes, 2013).

In the 1980s greater attention began to be paid to incorporating traditional practices and infusing positive cultural identity into treatment programs (Beauvais, 1998; French, 2004). People who grow up off reservations are less likely to want treatment geared specifically for Native Americans and may be comfortable in programs that are not culturally specific. Others seek specialized treatment for Native Americans, especially if they had grandmothers, other Native elders, or both in their early lives who shared the importance of traditional healing.

Although there is little literature on Native American treatment outcomes, a study of Native American adolescents in residential treatment reported that there was greater treatment completion among older adolescents (age 16–18) and those under pressure from the criminal justice system (Fickenscher, Novins, & Beals, 2006). The Red Road approach to treatment is modeled on the 12 steps of Alcoholics Anonymous and incorporates self-discovery and Native American traditional healing practices into substance abuse treatment (White Bison, 2002). The Partridge House, of the St. Regis Mohawk Tribe in Hogansburg, New York, is a well-known program that offers inpatient alcohol and drug treatment for Native American men and women age 21 and older through a blend of self-empowerment approaches and traditional teachings (St. Regis Mohawk Tribe, 2013).

As shown later for other racial or ethnic groups, there is less emphasis on treating minorities in culturally specific treatment programs, yet for Native Americans there seems to be special interest in such programs. Although there has been acculturation over hundreds of years, the draw of traditional teachings is critically important and needs to be honored by treatment programs. See Box 8.1 for a Native American view of how culture can support sobriety.

BOX 8.1 The Solution Is in the Culture

The following illustrates the importance of culture in Native American substance abuse recovery:

> There are solutions for us as Indian people, and for some of us it is a return to the traditional ceremonies of our nations. For some of us, it is to seek out an Elder and have him or her help us find our path to the Good Road, or to the Red Road as we call it. For many of us it is participation in sobriety sweat lodges. It will require learning our ways of prayer. Many of us are now smudging with sage, cedar, sweetgrass or the other herbs of Mother Earth. We are forming our Circles of Recovery and we are praying with the Eagle Feather, passing it back and forth to talk to one another when subjects of importance are discussed. Some of us seek a vision in the traditional way, going on the hill with the guidance of our medicine people. And some are revitalizing the old warrior or clan societies after talking with Elders who still remember those ways.

Source: White Bison, Inc. (2002, p. 10).

Hispanics and Latinos

As the fastest growing ethnic group within the United States, a lot of research has been conducted on the alcohol and drug problems of Hispanics, especially in the early 2000s. Hispanics are from many countries and do not necessarily share the same culture, making it difficult to offer generalizations about substance abuse (Lundgren & Delgado, 2008; Trepper, Nelson, McCollum, & McAvoy, 1997). Mexican Americans, South or Central Americans, Cuban Americans, and Puerto Ricans are four large Hispanic groups in the United States (Caetano et al., 2012).

The study of the association between acculturation and alcohol problems among Hispanics has not yielded findings that are consistent (Caetano et al., 2012). Although issues of research methodology can be at play, inconsistent research results can also reflect birthplace, age at coming to the United States, gender, and characteristics of the specific Hispanic group. As with all racial and ethnic groups, there is variation in how closely Hispanic individuals identify with their cultures.

A history of substance abuse problems is associated with family problems for both Hispanic men and Hispanic women (Canino, Vega, Sribney, Warner, & Alegria, 2008). The 2010 National Survey on Drug Use and Health (SAMHSA, n.d.b) found that Hispanic adults born in the United States are more likely to use substances than those not born in the United States. For Latino middle school children, those with strong traditional family values and greater ethnic pride were less likely to use alcohol and cigarettes (Castro et al., 2009). Another study reported that Hispanic women age 19 to 21 born in the United States had a higher risk of drug addiction than immigrants (Turner, Lloyd, & Taylor, 2006). Turner et al. (2006) encourage more attention to "what it is about acculturation that increases danger for adverse outcomes" (p. 86).

Recent research found that Hispanic males with higher levels of acculturation to the United States were more likely to drink alcohol if they had higher incomes than their peers (Karriker-Jaffe & Zemore, 2009). Unemployment can be a risk factor for heavy drinking among Latinas, and protective factors include being older and having a strong religious affiliation (Galvan & Caetano, 2003). Latinas in need of drug treatment have a harder time and can face even more judgment because their culture emphasizes the role of women as mothers (Trepper et al., 1997).

Treatment programs specifically for Hispanics are "extremely rare" (Sparks, Tisch, & Gardner, 2013, p. 68). A recent study reported that a family-centered treatment model titled Celebrando Familias! was successful in Hispanic communities (Sparks et al., 2013). Hispanic participation in self-help programs has received little research attention (Alvarez, Jason, Olson, Ferrari, & Davis, 2007). Research also needs to look more closely at the effect of acculturation on the Hispanic population.

African Americans

Patterns of alcohol and drug use by African Americans vary according to age, gender, and social class. For people living in poor urban areas, alcohol is readily available, "with a liquor store on every block" (Mignon, Faiia, Myers, & Rubington, 2009, p. 120).

Crack cocaine, a cheaper form of cocaine, is used by all ethnic groups but is most common among poor African Americans living in inner cities (Wechsberg, Zule, Riehman, Luseno, & Lam, 2007). In a study of 443 African American crack abusers, respondents were given feedback about their drug use, were offered help in developing social support, and were given information about the treatment process. Respondents then were randomly assigned to either an intervention group or a control group (Wechsberg et al., 2007). The authors reported that there were no statistically significant differences between the intervention and the control groups—both groups experienced significant decreases in crack use. At a 3-month follow-up, only 7.6% of people in the intervention group said they had entered treatment, not much higher than the 5.5% of people in the control group who had done so. These low rates of entry into treatment can be associated with socioeconomics: 79% had no health insurance, 68% were unemployed, 75% needed financial assistance to pay for treatment, and 70% needed transportation. Overall, it is clear that this sample of African Americans was also of low socioeconomic status.

African American adolescents are more likely than other adolescents to be referred to programs to divert youth from the juvenile justice system or to correctional facilities, rather than to outpatient substance abuse treatment (Robbins et al., 2002). This is a clear acknowledgment of institutional racism leveled at African Americans.

The National Survey of Drug Use and Health, reporting 2010 data, found that only 14.2% of African Americans in need of alcohol treatment and only 24.2% of people in need of treatment for illegal drug use received treatment in a substance abuse facility (SAMHSA, n.d.a). One study of relapse prevention needs reported that African Americans have greater self-efficacy and stronger coping skills than Whites (Walton, Blow, & Booth, 2001). The Black church is also known as an important resource that can support substance abuse prevention and treatment (Brown, Lacey, Blount, Roman, & Brown, 2006). Yet African Americans can have more difficulties after treatment, including fewer resources, high stress, low income, and low support communities (Walton et al., 2001). Clearly, far more research on treatment is needed to reduce the barriers to treatment for African Americans.

Asian Americans

The cultural values and norms of self-restraint and the high priority placed on family both influence drinking patterns of Asian Americans (Naegle, Ng, Barron, & Lai, 2002). Like other multinational ethnic groups, Asian Americans represent a variety of countries, including China, Korea, India, Japan, and Vietnam, with some cultural variations. Overall, Asian Americans are concerned about "losing face"; therefore, individuals and family members may have a hard time acknowledging an alcohol or drug problem (Fong & Tsuang, 2007; Naegle et al., 2002).

Little research attention has been paid to the substance abuse problems of Asian Americans. This is typically justified by the comparatively low rates of alcohol and drug problems among this group. Data from 2003 to 2011 showed that 4.9% of Asian Americans were in need of treatment, lower than the 9.5% national average (SAMHSA, 2013). Yet only 5.3% of Asian Americans in need received specialized substance abuse treatment, compared with a national average of 10.4%.

Asian Americans are underrepresented in treatment because of cultural barriers, as well as specific barriers to treatment (Fong & Tsuang, 2007). Asian families may be insular and not recognize that addiction is the problem. Asian Americans do not usually accept 12-step programs, preferring approaches that are not confrontational and that do not require them to air their problems in public (Naegle et al., 2002). It may be more helpful for Asian Americans to address substance abuse within the context of concern about overall health—holistic approaches can be especially meaningful (Naegle et al., 2002). Not surprisingly, Asian Americans prefer outpatient treatment settings, including outpatient detoxification, to minimize the stigma and shame associated with substance abuse problems (Fong & Tsuang, 2007; Naegle et al., 2002). Lack of services provided by Asian American staff can also deter entry into treatment.

Group Comparisons

A number of studies compare racial and ethnic groups regarding substance abuse. In a study comparing national data regarding access to treatment, Whites were the group most likely to receive treatment for alcohol, drug, or mental health problems (Wells et al., 2001). African Americans were more likely to have no access to treatment (25.4% vs. 12.5%). Hispanics were reported to receive less care and have longer waiting times for care than Whites (22.7% vs. 10.7%). Overall, African Americans and Hispanics were consistently found to have greater unmet needs for treatment, reduced access to treatment, and poorer quality of treatment than Whites.

A recent study of alcohol and treatment completion reported the same disparities between treatment access for Whites versus African Americans and Hispanics (Saloner & Le Cook, 2013). Racial and ethnic minorities comprise about 40% of those receiving treatment in public substance abuse treatment programs, an acknowledgment of lower socioeconomic status and lack of private health insurance. Approximately 50% of African Americans and Hispanics in public alcohol treatment in the sample did not complete treatment compared with 62% of Whites. Saloner and Le Cook (2013) concluded that the differences are related to socioeconomic status, with more unemployment and homelessness among African Americans and Hispanics. Clearly more attention needs to be paid to enhanced Medicaid coverage for substance abuse treatment for minorities, an important issue to consider as the United States implements the Affordable Care Act.

Knowledge of the differences in racial and ethnic patterns of alcohol and drug use can be important in developing treatment programs, yet more needs to be done. The idea of culturally developed interventions for specific groups is "intuitively appealing" (Colby, Lee, Lewis-Esquerre, Esposito-Smythers, & Monti, 2004, p. 51), yet only more research will determine whether this works. Further research is needed to shed light on whether culturally specific programs lead to better treatment outcomes than generic treatment programs (Galvan & Caetano, 2003). It is possible that culturally specific programs may show better outcomes, not because they are more effective but because they are more attractive to, as well as better at retaining, ethnic minorities.

Treatment administrators and staff members need to create a comfortable environment for all clients in residential and outpatient treatment. An important part of the clinician's role is to address sociocultural issues that affect treatment attendance, retention, and outcomes (Abbott & Chase, 2008). This includes getting a sense of how strongly individual clients identify with their culture and whether this identification can enhance motivation for recovery.

In the field we often reflect on how the history of substance abuse treatment is the history of White men offering treatment to other White men (Mignon et al., 2009). This disparity has been reduced in recent years to include women and adolescents, as discussed next (McCrady, Owens, Borders, & Brovko, 2014).

ADOLESCENTS

Treatment of adolescents as a specialty began in the 1980s, and considerable research on adolescent substance abuse has been produced since that time (Zavala et al., 2005). Regarding alcohol, 2.2% of 12- to 13-year-olds, 11.1% of 14- to 15-year-olds, 24.8% of 16- to 17-year-olds, and 45.8% of 18- to 20-year-olds in the United States drank alcohol in 2012 (SAMHSA, 2013b). Among adolescents age 12 to 17, illicit drug use in 2012 was 9.5%. People age 18 to 25 had the highest percentage of illicit substance abuse at 21.3%.

As indicated in Chapter 1, the newly revised *Diagnostic and Statistical Manual of Mental Disorders* (*DSM-5;* American Psychiatric Association, 2013) has removed the distinction between substance abuse and substance dependence found in the *Diagnostic and Statistical Manual of Mental Disorders*, Fourth Edition, Text Revision. The diagnosis has been changed to substance use disorder and is likely to obscure rather than clarify differences in substance abuse severity for adolescents. That is, distinguishing between physical addiction (substance dependence) and experimentation or problem use (substance abuse) was a helpful dichotomy for assessing the severity of the alcohol or drug problem and determining the appropriate type of treatment. People who have physical dependence on substances are more likely to need inpatient treatment or an intensive outpatient program, whereas people with less severe problems can receive outpatient counseling and probably referral to a 12-step program. The one diagnostic category of substance use disorder may make it even more challenging to determine the best treatment practices for adolescents. See Box 8.2 for a client description of life before entering residential treatment.

The adolescent brain is still developing, and substance use and abuse can have long-term consequences, including changes in brain structure and functioning (Squeglia, Jacobus, & Tapert, 2009). A major concern is that "Exposure to alcohol and drugs during a period of critical neurological development may interrupt the natural course of brain maturation and key process of brain

---

BOX 8.2 *Description of Life Before Residential Treatment*

I started off when I was about ten…eleven, twelve, I started doing a lot. Cause there was nothing else. I was rarely going to school. And then I was always depressed, so I always needed something to get me up. Cause I have a lot of family problems, like my dad, he was always in and out of prison. My mom, she was getting high. My brothers were getting high. And I mean that's what I know, so that's all I know how to do. But I don't want—I don't want to know that. I don't want to know about it anymore. I want to know something else.

Source: Currie (2003, p. 843).

development" (Squeglia et al., 2009, p. 31). These changes in cognitive functioning can be apparent within 1 to 2 years of heavy alcohol use of 20 drinks per month. This is especially the case if the adolescent has 4 to 5 drinks at one sitting, known as binge drinking. Marijuana use among adolescents is also associated with decreased cognitive abilities. Potential consequences include memory problems that can affect academics, as well as social and occupational problems in adulthood. Thus, there is damage from the drug use and serious consequences can include reduced functional ability in adulthood. Although the risks are real, Clark (2004) suggested there may be a bias in favor of publishing studies that show the negative consequences of adolescent alcohol use—there can be an inherent bias toward discouraging alcohol and drug use in American society.

There is emerging evidence that adolescent attention deficit hyperactivity disorder and behavior problems known as conduct disorder are associated with adult alcohol dependence, a more severe form of substance problems than substance abuse (Edwards & Kendler, 2012). Research shows that alcohol and drug abuse can be a response to mental health issues for both adolescents and adults (Clark, 2004). Substance use can be a way of coping with mental health disorders, including depression. Sexual abuse and physical abuse are associated with serious substance abuse problems (Blood & Cornwall, 1996). Mental health problems can be linked with severe substance abuse problems, poor outcomes, and short periods of treatment (Shane, Jasiukaitis, & Green, 2003). Shane et al. (2003) concluded that "co-occurring problems appear to profoundly limit treatment effectiveness" (p. 393). Accurate assessment of mental health disorders is critical to developing effective treatments for adolescent substance abuse and addressing co-occurring disorders (Mark et al., 2006; Shane et al., 2003).

In a national survey of substance abuse treatment facilities, 29% of facilities in the United States offered services to adolescents (SAMHSA, 2011a). Yet there is a large unmet need for adolescent substance abuse treatment (Griswold, Aronoff, Kernan, & Kahn, 2008; SAMHSA, 2012c, 2013b). National data reveal that in 2012, 1.6 million U.S. adolescents age 12 to 17 (6.3%) were in need of treatment for alcohol or illegal drug problems (SAMHSA, 2013b). However, only 10% of all adolescents in need of substance abuse treatment received it from a substance abuse treatment program.

Like adults, adolescents with no health insurance coverage have fewer treatment options. In 2007 American adolescents with major depression but without insurance were less likely than those with private health insurance or Medicaid to receive treatment (SAMHSA, 2011b). Only 17.2% of adolescents received treatment, compared with 42.9% of those with Medicaid and 40.6% with private insurance.

A national study of 144 "highly regarded" (Brannigan, Schackman, Falco, & Millman, 2004, p. 904) adolescent programs revealed that these strong reputations might not be earned. The strongest element in the programs was the quality of staff. Programs performed poorly on assessment and treatment matching, engaging and retaining adolescent clients in treatment, cultural competence, gender issues in treatment, and treatment outcomes. However,

Brannigan et al. (2004) concluded that poor outcomes may not be surprising because these are relatively new areas for substance abuse research.

Because risk factors for adolescents include parental substance use, childhood abuse, sexual abuse, and neighborhood and family dysfunction, the community and schools can play an important role in prevention (Blood & Cornwall, 1996; Tobler, Livingston, & Komro, 2011). Adolescents whose parents divorce during their adolescent years have been found to have greater drug use than those with intact families or with families in which divorce occurred when the children were younger (Needle, Su, & Doherty, 1990).

Parents play a critical role in both prevention and treatment, and family therapy is important for the treatment of adolescent substance abuse (Griswold et al., 2008; Tanner-Smith, Wilson, & Lipsey, 2012). Group therapy has also been shown to be effective with adolescents (Burleson, Kaminer, & Dennis, 2006). Burleson et al. (2006) reported that marijuana-using adolescents with high levels of conduct disorder did better in group therapy if they were mixed with clients with lower levels of conduct disorder, a reminder that there can be benefits to mixing adolescents with mild, moderate, and severe problems within the same group. Group therapy has also been shown to be successful in keeping adolescents in treatment longer and reducing marijuana use, although one study reported that there was no reduction in drinking to intoxication or illegal behaviors (Battjes et al., 2004). Smith, Hall, Williams, An, and Gotman (2006) reported that both group and family therapy are efficacious treatments. In their meta-analyses of 45 studies, Tanner-Smith et al. (2012) reported that practically all types of treatment were associated with decreased substance abuse (especially marijuana) and that family therapy at this point in the development of research has the most positive findings. See Box 8.3 for a description of an adolescent in treatment who is looking to the future.

More research is needed to learn about the effect of drugs and alcohol on learning capabilities and the long-term consequences of adolescent substance abuse, including correlations with mood disorders and other mental health problems (Squeglia et al., 2009). Research priorities for adolescents should include improving treatment access, exploring harm-reduction strategies, developing a range of treatment types, developing randomized trials, and focusing on the issues of diverse adolescent samples (Colby et al., 2004). The

---

BOX 8.3 A Teen in Residential Treatment Looks to the Future

I'm turning 17 in October. And I'm not gonna be like the little teenager for all my life, sitting around smoking dope. I gotta do something with my life, you know? What happens if I have kids down the line? What am I gonna do? Sit there and get high with them? Or try to hide from them? I can't do that, you know.

Source: Duroy, Schmidt, and Perry (2003).

goal is not only to have a successful treatment experience but also to cultivate the development of healthy lifestyles (Compton & Pringle, 2004).

WOMEN

There has been a long-standing lack of sensitivity to the substance abuse treatment needs of women (Trepper et al., 1997). This includes research into the 1990s that focused on male samples and the assumption that women and men had the same treatment issues (Greenfield et al., 2007).

Rates of alcohol and illicit drug use are typically higher among men than women. In 2012, 56.5% of U.S. males age 12 and older drank alcohol compared with 47.9% of U.S. females (SAMHSA, 2013b). Also in 2012, 11.6% of men compared with 6.9% of women used illegal substances. Substance dependence (physical addiction) was 11.5% for men and 5.7% for women according to the data from 2012.

Yet women have special issues when it comes to substance use. Women are known to become intoxicated with smaller quantities of alcohol; are more likely to develop medical problems as a result of drinking, especially liver problems such as cirrhosis; and are more likely to have higher death rates from alcoholism compared with men (Walter et al., 2003). Walton et al. (2001) reported that women may have less peer pressure to use substances because they are less likely than men to go to bars and more likely to use substances alone or with a partner. However, it is likely in the years since the Walton et al. study was published, more women are going to bars alone—an Internet search found numerous sites that give advice for staying safe when going to bars solo. Women are less likely than men to seek help in a substance abuse treatment program and are more likely to go to their primary care physicians or to a mental health setting to avoid the stigma of substance abuse (Green, 2006).

Women account for approximately one-third of people who receive substance abuse treatment services (Brady & Ashley, 2005). In a U.S. survey of substance abuse treatment facilities, 32% offered services specifically for women (SAMHSA, 2011a).

Women face more obstacles to treatment than men, including economic barriers and stigma (United Nations Office on Drugs and Crime, 2004). Overall, women have less education than men and lower levels of social support that influence access to treatment (Greenfield et al., 2007). Women are more likely than men to have family responsibilities, including caring for children (Brady & Ashley, 2005; United Nations Office on Drugs and Crime, 2004). The federal Adoption and Safe Families Act (ASFA) of 1997 requires legal permanency hearings within 12 months of foster care placement for children who have been in care for 15 of the past 22 months (Green, Rockhill, & Furrer, 2006). With this time pressure, one outcome of ASFA has been a greater focus on timely substance abuse treatment for women (Green, 2006). ASFA was designed to avoid children languishing in a foster care system and gets mothers to enter substance abuse treatment more quickly after their child protection cases begin. One study showed that in addition to getting into treatment more quickly, mothers remained in treatment longer than they did before ASFA (Green et al., 2006). Although the ASFA legislation has been controversial, this can cultivate collaboration between child protection agencies and substance abuse treatment programs, as well as encourage women to enter treatment.

In a study of relapse prevention needs, women had stronger coping skills, fewer negative social influences, and less exposure to substances than did men (Walton et al., 2001). It is of critical importance that women may have to wait significantly longer periods to enter treatment than men (Downey, Rosengren, & Donovan, 2003).

Abuse History

A history of child abuse is associated with substance abuse and co-occurring disorders in a complex web that can be difficult to sort out and that can complicate recovery (Brems, Johnson, Neal, & Freemon, 2004; Gil-Rivas, Fiorentine, Anglin, & Taylor, 1997). Men and women with a physical or sexual abuse history typically begin their drinking at an earlier age than do people without an abuse history (Brems et al., 2004). Although men can also be victims of childhood abuse, women are more likely to have histories of childhood abuse and trauma, including physical, sexual, and emotional abuse, that affect their substance use. In a sample of men and women in a detox program, 20% of men and 50% of women reported childhood physical or sexual abuse (Brems et al., 2004).

In an older study of men and women in outpatient substance abuse treatment, men with a history of physical abuse were more likely to have anxiety, depression, suicidal thoughts, and posttraumatic stress disorder (Gil-Rivas et al., 1997). For women, physical abuse was associated with anxiety, depression, suicidal thoughts and attempts, and posttraumatic stress disorder. Importantly, people with histories of childhood abuse were as likely to complete treatment and remain abstinent for the 6-month follow-up as clients without an abuse history.

Women with a history of childhood sexual abuse and substance abuse are more likely to have attempted suicide (Jarvis & Copeland, 1997). In a study of 146 homeless women in residential substance abuse treatment, 69% reported a history of emotional, physical, or sexual abuse (Sacks, McKendrick, & Banks, 2008). Emotional abuse was reported by 51%, physical abuse was reported by 44%, and sexual abuse was reported by 39%. Most suffered multiple forms of abuse.

A history of trauma can be associated with poorer treatment outcomes. People with abuse and trauma histories were more likely to have psychological problems and severe substance abuse problems. Overall, people who suffered childhood abuse did not improve as much in treatment as women who had not suffered abuse (Sacks et al., 2008). As Brems et al. (2004) concluded, "Preventing child abuse may well be one of the most powerful means of preventing substance abuse" (p. 818).

Pregnant Women

Little attention was paid to the substance abuse problems of pregnant women until the 1990s, after years of concern in the 1980s about "crack babies." The stigma attached to drug-addicted pregnant women was severe and resulted in legislation in some states to charge women with child abuse crimes if they tested positive for drugs at delivery. In response, the National Institute of Drug Abuse, the Center for Substance Abuse Treatment, and other federal agencies provided significant funding, resulting in a 250% increase in funding for the treatment of pregnant women in Massachusetts alone (Daley, Shephard, & Bury-Maynard, 2005).

It later became clear that the concern over an epidemic of crack babies was overblown and sensationalized in the media. That does not mean that cocaine use during pregnancy is not without risk—cocaine use during pregnancy is associated with low birth weight (Daley et al., 2005). Babies born to opioid-dependent mothers can experience a type of withdrawal, known as neonatal abstinence syndrome, that includes greater risk of low birth weight, respiratory and feeding problems, and seizures (National Institute on Drug Abuse, 2012b). Women who drink during pregnancy can have children with fetal alcohol spectrum disorders who sustain lifelong cognitive problems, including low IQ.

On average, 5.9% of pregnant American women used illicit drugs in 2012; 8.5% drank alcohol, 2.7% were binge drinkers, and 0.3% were heavy drinkers (SAMHSA, 2013b). Research shows that women who received substance abuse treatment while pregnant are less likely to deliver prematurely and their babies are more likely to have a healthier birth weight (Daley et al., 2000). Although residential treatment is more expensive, it provides continuity for women who are homeless and come from abusive environments; it also provides the necessary stability for pregnant women (Daley et al., 2005). In a study comparing 739 women who delivered their babies while in residential treatment, there were lower rates of morbidity (illness) and mortality (death), even compared with women in the general U.S. population (Burgdorf, Dowell, Chen, Roberts, & Herrell, 2004). For pregnant women who are opioid dependent, methadone and buprenorphine can be safely used (Jones et al., 2008).

There is a long running debate about whether women should be in the same treatment programs as men or in women-only programs known as "gender-specific" treatment programs (Walton et al., 2001). One factor is that male dominance in society can be associated with male dominance in treatment (Greenfield et al., 2007). This can result in staff members and even female clients giving more attention to the needs of male clients.

No clear picture emerges for the best treatment types for women. In a review of the research, gender-specific treatment was not more effective than mixed-gender treatment groups (Green, 2006). Yet a personal history of trauma can make women more comfortable with gender-specific treatment than with mixed-group treatment (Greenfield et al., 2007). In a literature review of women's treatment options, Greenfield et al. (2007) concluded that for programs that are gender specific, "the effects of these changes on treatment outcomes remain unclear" (p. 13). Overall, they found that research shows mixed results and randomized controlled trials are needed to assess outcomes for women in both mixed-gender and gender-specific treatment programs.

LESBIAN, GAY, BISEXUAL, AND TRANSGENDER PEOPLE

The American lesbian, gay, bisexual, and transgender (LGBT) population has higher rates of substance abuse than the general population; some estimates are as high as 20% to 30% (Hunt, 2012). LGBT individuals endure discrimination in the workplace, in housing, in health care, and in recognition of their personal and family relationships. Therefore, higher rates of substance abuse may be explained by "increased stress associated with the societal stigma attached to being a sexual minority" (Cochran, Peavy, & Robohm, 2007, p. 162). The LGBT population can also experience stigma and discrimination in efforts to access substance abuse treatment and mental health services (Enders, 2009).

It is a problem to hire treatment staff members who have knowledge and understanding of LGBT issues, such as coping with homophobia and legal issues surrounding recognition of relationships, including marriage. Treatment of LGBT populations requires counselors to know the processes by which LGBT individuals learn to accept their sexual orientation, "come out," and develop self-acceptance (SAMHSA, 2001b). For some counselors this means addressing a personal feeling of ambivalence or negativity.

According to U.S. survey data from 2010, 6% of substance abuse treatment programs offered special programs for LGBT clients (SAMHSA, 2011a). However, it may not be clear whether treatment programs offer LGBT-specific services. For example, one study reported that 71% of the programs for LGBT clients were no different from services offered to all clients (Cochran et al., 2007). Only 7.4% of programs identified any service that was developed to meet the needs of LGBT clients. Cochran et al. (2007) reported that there is "extremely limited access to LGBT-specific treatment services for substance misuse" (p. 168). The most important concerns are that client needs are addressed in treatment—feelings of safety and of being understood—and that services are provided with sensitivity to LGBT health needs, including mental health needs. See Box 8.4 for a description of the Pride Institute for LGBT substance abuse treatment.

More research is needed on the experiences of LGBT clients receiving substance abuse treatment, because there is "comparatively little known about the most effective way to treat this population" (Cochran et al., 2007, p. 162). It remains to be determined whether LGBT clients feel the need for specific services and, if they do, what those specific services should be.

HIV/AIDS

Drug addiction and HIV/AIDS have been closely linked since the beginning of the epidemic in the early 1980s—this includes both contracting HIV and

> ### BOX 8.4 Pride Institute for LGBT Substance Abuse Treatment
>
> The Pride Institute in Minnesota addresses substance abuse, mental health, and sexual health problems through a variety of programs. In 1986 the Pride Institute was the first inpatient treatment center dedicated to exclusively serving the needs for the LGBT community. In 1991 outpatient programs were added. Today the Pride Institute offers a 42-bed residential program, intensive outpatient adult programs, and a unique program for clients with sexual health concerns.
>
> *Source:* Pride Institute (n.d.).

transmitting it to others (National Institute on Drug Abuse, 2012a). Intravenous drug use and sharing of needles are high-risk behaviors associated with the transmission of HIV/AIDS, as discussed in Chapter 2. Being under the influence of drugs is associated with risky sexual behavior, and sexual relations are the most common way that HIV is transmitted—this includes trading sex for money or drugs. Drug addicts with HIV can have greater cognitive impairment and more complex medical needs.

According to 2010 data, in a U.S. survey of substance abuse treatment programs, only 9% offered services specifically for clients with HIV or AIDS (SAMHSA, 2011a). It is fair to say that almost any kind of substance abuse treatment can be helpful in stemming the spread of HIV. Substance abuse treatment can open the door to addressing HIV status and can support adherence to antiretroviral therapy (Palepu, Horton, Tibbetts, Meli, & Samet, 2004). Substance abuse treatment is also associated with lower rates of hospital emergency room utilization by people with HIV (Palepu et al., 2003).

In addressing prevention of HIV/AIDS, the World Health Organization (2004) commissioned a study of the effectiveness of substance abuse treatment that resulted in a review of more than 100 studies of different types of treatment using various methodologies. All types of treatment and harm-reduction efforts were found to be able to reduce the risk of HIV for injection drug users. This includes reduction in drug use, reduction in use of injection drugs, and reduction in levels of risky behaviors. One exception to this is the finding from a sample of 349 HIV-infected individuals with alcohol problems that treatment was not associated with a decline in risky sexual behavior (Palepu et al., 2005). Overall, the World Health Organization (2004) concluded that "substitution maintenance treatment such as methadone is the most effective treatment for reducing the spread of HIV/AIDS" (p. 3).

The World Health Organization remains active in the global fight against HIV/AIDS. Its new global health sector strategy for 2011 to 2015 has established the following four goals: (a) optimize HIV prevention, diagnosis, treatment, and care; (b) integrate HIV and health service delivery to make the best use of resources; (c) build strong and sustainable health systems;

and (d) reduce vulnerability and remove structural barriers to accessing services (World Health Organization, 2011). While there has been considerable success in treatment and prevention of HIV/AIDS, more needs to be done to integrate HIV/AIDS treatment and substance abuse treatment (Volkow & Montaner, 2011).

OLDER ADULTS

The aging baby boom generation is responsible for a burgeoning older population, and because baby boomers were known for their substance use, the future elderly American population will include more older people who use substances (Colliver, Compton, Grfroerer, & Condon, 2006). Yet, drinking and drug use by older people has received little research attention and is not considered a significant social problem (Benshoff & Harrawood, 2003). More research is available on alcohol use because illegal drug use is still "relatively rare" (Simoni-Wastila & Yang, 2006, p. 383) among older people.

The people most at risk of drug abuse are older women, people who are socially isolated, those who have a history of substance abuse or mental health problems, people with overall poor health, and those who have prescriptions for medications with abuse potential (Simoni-Wastila & Yang, 2006). Approximately 25% of older American adults use prescribed medication with abuse potential.

There is little information on the screening, assessment, and treatment of substance abuse among older people (Colliver et al., 2006). Barriers to identification include ageism, lack of knowledge of substance abuse by family members and health care professionals, and the complex interaction of general health and mental health with alcohol and drug problems (Crome & Crome, 2005). It is not a surprise that older people with alcohol problems have more medical issues and longer hospital stays than people who do not have alcohol issues (Saleh & Szebenyi, 2005). One study of residential treatment compared older patients with younger and middle-age patients and showed better outcomes for the older patients with the same levels of aftercare and participation in 12-step groups as the comparison groups (Lemke & Moos, 2003). In another study of residential treatment, older patients had more physical health problems but lower severity of alcohol dependence and fewer psychiatric problems than middle-age patients (Oslin, Slaymaker, Blow, Owen, & Colleran, 2005). The older and middle-age patients had the same levels of treatment completion, and at 1-month follow-up, older patients had the same outcomes as middle-age patients. However, the older patients were less likely to participate in aftercare services than were middle-age patients. Reasons remained unclear but could be attributed to health issues, finances, transportation problems, or no offer of aftercare services.

The Center for Substance Abuse Treatment (2005a) recommends group therapy for relapse prevention using cognitive behavioral approaches. Motivational interviewing models that have shown success with younger populations need to be tested with older adults (Hansen & Gutheil, 2004).

The same controversy over whether women should be mixed with men in treatment groups or have gender-specific treatment also applies to older people with substance abuse problems. As before, there are no clear outcome patterns and recommendations for how best to treat older people. A U.S. survey of substance abuse treatment programs found only 7% offer specialty programs for older people (SAMHSA, 2011a). An argument for specialized treatment approaches for older people is that they have more accompanying medical problems (Colliver et al., 2006).

One reason there is little research on the efficacy (controlled studies) of treatment for older people is that few seek treatment and it is hard to enroll a sufficient number of older people in research studies (Colliver et al., 2006). Greater efforts to develop and evaluate substance abuse treatment for older women in particular are needed because they are more likely to outlive men (Greenfield et al., 2007). Also, more research on the type of drug use is needed, especially because misuse of prescribed medications can be an issue (Colliver et al., 2006). More attention from physicians, nurses, and other health professionals can go a long way to diagnosing and referring older people for substance abuse problems. Finally, prevention research focuses on children, adolescent, and young adults, and "there is little or no research base on how best to prevent drug abuse among older adults" (Colliver et al., 2006, p. 263).

SUMMARY AND CONCLUSION

Across the life course, race and ethnicity, socioeconomic status, and gender all affect the use of alcohol and drugs. The cultural impacts are seen when immigrants coming to the United States use alcohol and drugs in the same way they were used in the country of origin. It is also the case that immigrants acculturate and take on the alcohol and drug use patterns of larger American society. Race and ethnicity, socioeconomic status, gender, and age also affect access to treatment and the type of treatment provided. Socioeconomic status is a huge issue that gets at the heart of access to treatment, as well as the type and quality of treatment provided. People who must rely on publicly funded programs are likely to get less treatment and poorer quality treatment.

A lot of research is needed to fill out the picture of the substance abuse problems of specific races and ethnicities. Staff members in treatment programs need to reflect the races and ethnicities of clients and bring the values and traditions of clients' backgrounds into treatment settings. This includes seeking answers to questions about whether generic treatment versus culturally specific treatment is preferable, as it seems to be for Native Americans.

The substance abuse problems of adolescents have received considerable research attention in recent years, and more is known about appropriate treatment of adolescents than is known about treatment of women and older people. More research is needed on the LGBT population and their treatment needs.

Great inroads have been made in addressing HIV/AIDS, and substance abuse treatment is known to reduce the transmission of HIV/AIDS. The debate over whether gender-specific and age-specific programs are preferable and have better outcomes than mixed-gender and mixed-age groups, respectively, is likely to continue.

TREATMENT OF CO-OCCURRING DISORDERS (DUAL DIAGNOSIS)

*T*he relationship between substance abuse and mental illness is a complex and tangled one in clinical practice and in research (Aase, Jason, & Robinson, 2008; Flynn & Brown, 2008). Substance abuse and mental health problems are closely associated—intertwined even—and one can cause the other. Trying to determine which came first can be a chicken-and-egg dilemma. People with mental health problems are at an increased risk of developing substance use disorders (Laudet, Magura, Vogel, & Knight, 2004; Zimmerman et al., 2003). Adolescents and adults with the more severe form of substance use disorder, substance dependence, are also more likely to have mental health problems than are people who abuse alcohol or drugs (Chan, Dennis, & Funk, 2008).

This chapter reviews co-occurring disorders and the special challenges of trying to treat people with both mental and substance use disorders. *Dual diagnosis* was the term originally used to describe clients with both substance abuse and mental health disorders, but over time this has changed to *co-occurring disorders*. These terms are used interchangeably in this chapter to acknowledge that the literature uses both, even though individual researchers and clinicians may have a preference for one term or the other. *Comorbidity* is a more general term, coined by Feinstein in 1970, that refers to clients or patients who have distinct additional illnesses or diseases (Merikangas & Swanson, 2010). For example, comorbidity may refer to a patient with substance use disorder who also has a mental health disorder or any other kind of medical problem.

The field has known since the 1980s and 1990s that 50% to 70% of clients receiving substance abuse treatment also have a mental health disorder (Center for Substance Abuse Treatment, 2005c). A review of people receiving mental health services found 20% to 50% with substance abuse problems. In a survey of 453 substance abuse treatment providers, including clinicians, supervisors, and agency directors, estimates of co-occurring mood disorders such as depression and bipolar disorder were the highest at 40% to 42% of clients receiving services (McGovern, Xie, Segal, Siembab, & Drake, 2006). McGovern et al. (2006) found that agency professionals estimated that 24% to 27% of their clients had anxiety disorders or posttraumatic stress disorder (PTSD), 16% to 21% of clients had severe mental illness, 18% to 20% had antisocial personality disorder, and 17% to 18% had borderline personality disorder (defined later in this chapter).

In a study using national data, people with substance use disorders were more likely to seek treatment from mental health programs than from substance abuse services (Mojtabai, 2005). One possible explanation is that mental health services can be more readily available than substance abuse treatment services. Another explanation is that clients perceive their problems to be mental illness rather than substance abuse. In addition, some individuals may self-medicate for their mental disorders by using alcohol and drugs. For others, a mental health diagnosis helps them to qualify for disability benefits. It is not a surprise that people with more severe substance abuse problems tend to use substance abuse treatment services and those with more severe mental health problems tend to use mental health programs.

Clinicians and researchers are left to tease out the relationships among complex individual and environmental factors (Aase et al., 2008). Compared with people who have less severe disorders, people with severe mental illness and substance use disorders are more vulnerable to relapse and rehospitalization, have more depression and suicidality, and have greater noncompliance with medical care, including medications (Laudet, Magura, Cleland, Vogel, & Knight, 2004). They are also at higher risk of HIV infection, more legal troubles, greater utilization of medical services, and greater medical costs. Within this population, there are poorer outcomes in general and greater vulnerability to relapse (Aase et al., 2008; Burns, Teesson, & O'Neill, 2005; Warren, Stein, & Grella, 2007).

Invariably, the presence of a mental health problem with a substance abuse problem makes it more difficult to treat a client. People with co-occurring disorders are more likely than either population alone to have economic issues such as low level of education and difficulty in holding a job (Laudet, Magura, Vogel, & Knight, 2000). Another complication is that it can be difficult to assess and support intrinsic motivation for change for people with substance abuse or dependence and severe mental health disorders (DiClemente, Nidecker, & Bellack, 2008; Drake et al., 2001). There is also a relationship between co-occurring disorders and a greater risk of involvement in the criminal justice system, as discussed in the next chapter.

Treatment compliance on the part of clients with dual diagnosis is a challenge. One study reported that 40.5% of people with co-occurring disorders had treatment compliance problems (Herbeck et al., 2005). This can include missing appointments and stopping medications because of side effects or other reasons, such as lack of insurance and lack of access to medications. Herbeck et al. (2005) concluded that people with severe impairment and lower socioeconomic status were more likely to have difficulty in maintaining the treatment regimen.

A further complication occurs when a client has a mental health problem and is abusing a number of substances. Research has shown that people with co-occurring disorders and polysubstance abuse, not just one drug of abuse, are likely to have the most severe problems (Warren et al., 2007). There is also the issue of the severity of mental health problems (Flynn & Brown, 2008). For example, depression can be mild, moderate, or severe. Thus, co-occurring disorders can refer to a multitude of problems and diagnoses of varying severity. Flynn and Brown (2008) describe it this way: "The term co-occurring disorder includes a multiplicity of diagnostic categories, a broad range of severities of disorder, and a potential for confounding between severity in one area and diagnosis in another" (p. 38).

For people in substance abuse treatment, a diagnosis of a mental health problem can be made early or can take some time. In an 18-month follow-up study of a sample of 107 patients with co-occurring disorders in methadone maintenance treatment in Spain, there were 19 new mental health problems diagnosed during treatment (Astals et al., 2009). The most common new diagnosis was depression, followed by antisocial personality disorder and borderline personality disorder. This speaks to the difficulty of accurate assessment on treatment admission, whether to inpatient or to outpatient programs. It also speaks to the need to have patients stabilized before accurate diagnoses can be made.

Clients can be confused about acknowledging and defining their problems. For people who have been substance abusers or addicts for many years, it can be especially difficult to recall which came first. Some clients are unaware of having two problems. See Box 9.1 for a description of an alcoholic woman who was in her 30s before learning that she also had bipolar disorder.

BOX 9.1 Alcoholism and Bipolar Disorder

A woman said she had only been treated for alcoholism and had relapsed a number of times because her mental illness was not addressed until late in treatment:

> When you're not working on your mental illness along with it [alcoholism], it is almost nil. . . . You can't do it. . . . Most time, my chemical use is like self-medication. I was dealing with those feelings, putting them away. . . . If you are bipolar, you are manic, you use booze to bring yourself down. I didn't really have a chance to make it until I knew I was dual diagnosis. Then I started working on that, I go to behavioral centers and psychiatric units, to work on that . . . then I was not working on alcohol. So, I was working on one or the other. . . . That was all messed up, too! I was finally going to a center that works on both. That's what I'm doing here.

Source: Sun (2007, p. 10).

In a study of 310 respondents with co-occurring disorders who were attending Double Trouble in Recovery self-help groups (described later in this chapter), 50% said they experienced substance problems before they developed mental health problems, 38% said they experienced mental health problems before they used drugs or alcohol, and 12% stated they developed both problems at the same age (Laudet et al., 2000). Importantly, 69% said their mental health problems got worse when using substances. Within this sample, the most difficult recovery challenges were, according to respondents: (a) coping with their feelings, including shame, anger, and guilt; (b) employment issues, such as finding work and holding on to a job; and (c) the fear of "picking up"—returning to alcohol or drug use.

In a randomized clinical trial of 126 adolescents with major depression and substance use disorder, 77% experienced depression before substance abuse, whereas 30% developed depression after or at the same time as the substance abuse (Libby, Orton, Stover, & Riggs, 2005). Men and women between 18 and 25 years old may comprise the age group most vulnerable to dual diagnosis (Chan et al., 2008).

In a subsequent journal article, Laudet, Magura, Cleland, et al. (2004) inquired of clients how they first began their substance use. Fifty-seven percent responded it was a "desire to fit in," "to belong," and "to be accepted," factors especially important to adolescents. Sixty-eight percent of individuals with bipolar disorder, 61% of respondents with schizophrenia, and 51% of people with depression gave these responses.

SOCIAL NETWORKS AND FAMILY SUPPORT

Healthy relationships and a strong support network can be challenging for clients with dual diagnosis, especially people with severe mental illness. People with severe mental illness can have a harder time cultivating positive relationships, can find it more difficult to remain engaged in activities and work, and are more susceptible to boredom (Laudet, Magura, Cleland, et al., 2004). In a sample of formerly homeless clients with dual diagnosis, social networks were found to be small (Hawkins & Abrams, 2007). Reasons for the few supportive resources included the death of people who were supportive, respondents who withdrew or pushed away family and friends, and family members who had problems that were so significant they were unable to provide support. The neediness and constant demands of some clients with dual diagnosis can also "burn out" family and friends. See Box 9.2 for a description of family problems.

In a study of clients with dual diagnosis in residential treatment programs, people with the strongest social support had the best treatment outcomes (Warren et al., 2007). Strong social support was also associated with better psychological functioning, as well as less heroin and cocaine use. In a time when treatment resources are less available (Flynn & Brown, 2008), cultivating family and friendship support networks is essential (Townsend, Biegel, Ishler, Wieder,

> ### BOX 9.2 *Severe Stress on an Individual With Dual Diagnosis and on Family*
>
> I used to walk out. And I'd go over to the corner store. . . and we used to sit there and drink beer and stuff. . . . So I'd get back home and hear it again, and again, and again. . . . It was just the same thing every day. Or I'd get into a fight with [my wife] . . . the whole family. I'm fightin' the whole family. I mean, fightin'—not just arguments. It was fightin'. They're like, " . . . you gotta get out. You have to leave."
>
> Source: Hawkins and Abrams (2007, p. 2037).

& Rini, 2006). Research on social networks of clients with dual diagnosis needs to focus on the dynamics of relationships with family and friends. A deeper understanding of these relationships, and of how the clients understand them, can be helpful in building wider, stronger, and healthier networks (Hawkins & Abrams, 2007). Clinicians, as a part of treatment, need to support family involvement (Drake et al., 2001). In addition to clinicians, family and friends can bolster self-confidence by encouraging individuals with dual diagnosis to believe they can change their lives in positive ways (Laudet, Magura, Cleland, Vogel, & Knight, 2003).

TREATMENT ISSUES

Although the presence of co-occurring disorders was known in the late 1970s, it was not until the late 1980s that the separation of treatment systems was acknowledged as a large part of the problem in caring adequately for people with co-occurring disorders (Center for Substance Abuse Treatment, 2005c; Laudet, Magura, Vogel, et al., 2004). Previously, professional help had consisted of medical treatment, including medications with a focus on stabilization, while giving little attention to the psychosocial factors that left individuals with dual diagnosis at greater risk of substance abuse, such as social isolation and lack of activity and purpose (Laudet, Magura, Vogel, et al., 2004). It had been either substance abuse or mental health treatment, and discussions of integration initially focused on having both services available at the same agency. Today we recognize the importance of integrated services provided, for example, by clinicians trained in both substance use disorders and mental health issues (Flynn & Brown, 2008). A literature review noted that integration of services for co-occurring disorders provided to clients in residential treatment is clearly preferable (Brunette, Mueser, & Drake, 2004). Ideally, clients experience a consistent philosophy and approach to treatment recommendations and to treatment (Drake et al., 2001).

The Quadrants of Care Model can be effective in determining the appropriate assessment of clients and matching them with the appropriate treatment (Center for Substance Abuse Treatment, 2005c). The model was developed by the National Association of State Alcohol and Drug Abuse Directors (NASADAD) and the National Association of State Mental Health Program Directors (NASMHPD) as a way to classify the severity of dual diagnosis. The four-quadrant framework provides a strategy to understand the varying severities of co-occurring disorders, and it fosters integration between mental health and substance abuse treatment resources. The four categories within the Quadrant of Care Model are as follows (Center for Substance Abuse Treatment, 2005c; Mauer, 2006):

- Quadrant I: Low severity of substance disorder and low severity of mental disorder (treatment provided in primary care medical practices)
- Quadrant II: Low severity of substance use disorder and severe mental disorder (treatment provided in mental health systems by professionals who are competent in substance abuse treatment)
- Quadrant III: Severe substance disorder and low severity of mental disorder (treatment provided in substance abuse systems by professionals who are competent in mental health treatment)
- Quadrant IV: Severe substance disorder and severe mental disorder (treatment provided by a program that fully integrates mental health and substance abuse treatment)

The Quadrants of Care is a well-used model for conceptualizing the mental and addiction problems of people with both problems, and it offers a logical approach to classifying and understanding these complex disorders (McGovern et al., 2006). In their self-report survey of 453 clinicians, administrators, and supervisors in substance abuse treatment programs, McGovern et al. (2005) found that the highest prevalence rates were in quadrant III, people with severe substance use disorder and low severity of mental illness, followed by quadrant IV, people with severe substance use and severe mental disorder. This is not a surprise considering these are the views of professionals working in substance abuse treatment programs. Although the model is useful in conceptualizing the relationship between substance abuse and mental health disorders, it does not determine specific services clients should receive. For all that is written about the value of the model, "there is no empirical validation for the quadrant model" (McGovern et al., 2006, p. 270).

Barriers to effective treatment of clients with dual diagnosis, according to a survey of substance abuse professionals, included lack of physicians and psychiatrists, lack of staff members qualified to provide mental health services, and insurance or billing problems (McGovern et al., 2006). It is hard to get counselors with dual qualifications. Still, further education and training can be successful. One small study reported that training for substance abuse clinicians can increase their knowledge of co-occurring disorders, improve attitudes toward working with these clients, and even improve overall job satisfaction (Hunter et al., 2005). A strong therapeutic relationship between client and therapist may be especially important to people with the complexities of dual diagnosis and may help to retain these clients in treatment longer.

For individuals with co-occurring disorders, the issues are so complex and the needs are so great that one type of treatment is not likely to meet the needs of all clients with dual diagnosis (Carroll, 2004). The behavioral therapies most likely to be used with people with depression or bipolar disorder are cognitive behavioral therapy, motivational interviewing, and contingency management. Cognitive behavioral therapies are "moderately effective" (Carroll, 2004, p. 781) in reducing both substance abuse and depression. Motivational interviewing is useful in engaging and retaining clients in treatment and supporting follow-up care. Contingency management has "robust effects" (Carroll, 2004, p. 781) in reducing alcohol and drug use with people who have co-occurring disorders, as well as those without a dual diagnosis.

One study of outpatient treatment for individuals with dual diagnosis reported that additional features found in therapeutic communities showed "modest" support for effectiveness over the control group (Sacks, McKendrick, Sacks, Banks, & Harle, 2008). These helpful services included case management, psychoeducational classes, trauma-informed substance abuse treatment, and encouragement of personal responsibility and self-help.

Behavioral therapies for people with co-occurring disorders are uncommon, and even less common are these therapies for adolescents with dual diagnosis (Cornelius et al., 2011). Clients who received outpatient cognitive behavioral therapy and motivational enhancement therapy for an alcohol use disorder and a mental health disorder had better outcomes than clients in a comparison group. Larger studies in a number of sites are needed to determine the efficacy of these therapies for adolescents and young adult populations. See Box 9.3 for a description of a mother whose son was helped by an inpatient facility for people with dual diagnosis.

Homelessness

There is a strong relationship between co-occurring disorders and homelessness (Aase et al., 2008). One study that focused on the relationship between homelessness and substance abuse reported that one-third of people in an Australian sample had substance abuse problems before they became homeless and two thirds were initially homeless and then developed substance abuse problems (Johnson & Chamberlain, 2008). Clearly homelessness is a serious obstacle to recovery from co-occurring disorders (Herman, Galanter, & Lifshutz, 1991). Approximately 10% to 20% of the U.S. homeless population has "severe" dual diagnosis (Drake, Osher, & Wallach, 1991, p. 1149). It is estimated that 15% of the homeless population in the United States are veterans, yet there are few studies to address co-occurring disorders among homeless veterans (Balshem, Christensen, Tuepker, & Kansagara, 2011).

In a study of homeless veterans with psychiatric disorders, of all potential medical problems, by far the most common were addictive disorders,

BOX 9.3 WestBridge Treatment Facility Testimonial

WestBridge is a group of facilities specifically intended for the treatment of men and women with dual diagnosis. Developed in the early 2000s, its facilities are located in Massachusetts and Florida. Inpatient and outpatient treatment are integrated using the model of the Dartmouth Center for Evidence-Based Practices. The following is the testimonial of a mother whose son experienced success after completing the WestBridge inpatient program:

I'm so grateful to WestBridge. Without their help my son would have died by now. We had been to multiple treatment centers, but none was the right fit. They either addressed his substance abuse and ignored or minimized coexisting mental health issues or addressed the mental health issues and left out the substance abuse focus. This and the lack of long-term support resigned him and our family to continually arrive where we started.

When I called WestBridge I was desperate for someone to help me as a single mother. Kevin Keefe came to our house and talked my son into trying WestBridge. My son wanted to get better but didn't know how to go about it, and I didn't know how to support him any longer. I knew I needed to step away but also knew he was not ready or capable of doing things on his own.

WestBridge developed a plan that engaged and challenged him but also supported him. We have had big ups and downs that WestBridge has ridden out with us. For me, WestBridge is part of our family. They have allowed not only my son to move along with his development as a man, but also have allowed me to "get a life" outside my family. Their sustained compassion and commitment to wellness and health at my son's pace have been a miracle for our family.

My son has been sober for a year, is going to school and is enjoying his life. If someone told me three years ago this was possible, I wouldn't have believed it. I am truly grateful to all of these dedicated people. They are a treasure to this community and the world at large.

Sources: WestBridge Community Services (2012a, 2012b).

often accompanied by mood disorders (Goldstein, Luther, Haas, Gordon, & Appelt, 2009). In a sample of people with severe and persistent mental illness, those who also had substance abuse problems were more likely to lose their homes because of behavioral issues (Schutt & Goldfinger, 2009).

Peer support for recovery is as important to the homeless population as it is to the nonhomeless population with dual diagnosis (Aase et al., 2008).

Herman et al. (1991) reported that people who are homeless may use 12-step programs more frequently than others—this could be attributed to their few resources and to other kinds of treatment being unavailable to them. It can also be related to the warmth of the building and the free coffee available at self-help meetings.

There have been considerable improvements and expansion of services to people who are homeless with the goal of placing them in low-cost housing; however, these services remain inadequate. More than 20 years ago Drake et al. (1991) wrote about the same barriers that still exist today: lack of funding, lack of coordination among federal agencies, and inadequate availability of low-cost housing.

Ethnicity

There are few studies of the effect of ethnicity on clients with dual diagnosis (Aase et al., 2008). One study compared White and non-White clients with dual diagnosis who were referred to 12-step programs and cognitive behavioral treatment after discharge from residential treatment (Jerrell & Wilson, 1997). Non-Whites (mostly Hispanics) were more likely to have less supportive environments, have lower psychological functioning, endure greater stigma, and be underserved by interventions. Although focused exclusively on adolescent mental health issues and not dual diagnosis, one study reported that there were almost no differences among African Americans, Latinos, and Whites in having their problems identified by teachers and other adults and in receiving encouragement to seek treatment (Alegria et al., 2012). This finding suggests that referrals for treatment are becoming as available for racial and ethnic minorities as they are for Whites.

TYPES OF MENTAL HEALTH PROBLEMS

A considerable number of mental health problems are associated with substance abuse, far too many to examine in detail in relation to alcohol and drug use disorders within this chapter. In particular, anxiety disorders, major depression, PTSD, bipolar disorder, borderline personality disorder, antisocial personality disorder, and attention deficit hyperactivity disorder are associated with alcoholism and drug addiction (Mueser et al., 2012; Ohlmeier et al., 2007; Spanagel, 2009).

Through the years there has been a shift from treating substance abuse first to treating substance abuse and mental health issues together (Watkins, Hunter, Burnam, Pincus, & Nicholson, 2005). This was not easy because the public mental health systems and substance abuse treatment systems were independent of each other into the 1990s (Drake et al., 2001). The rationale was that it is harder to diagnose mental health problems for people with substance abuse problems and that abstinence was necessary to accurately assess a client and determine whether substance abuse was the primary problem or was secondary to the mental health problem. Experts disagree on whether and how long abstinence is needed before prescribing medication (Watkins et al., 2005). Some experts recommend 1 month or longer of abstinence before assessing for mental disorders (Center for Substance Abuse Treatment, 2005c; Flynn & Brown, 2008). Although 1 month may be the average, clients withdrawing from methadone or benzodiazepines (drugs that relieve anxiety) are likely to require longer periods (Nace & Tinsley, 2007).

Anxiety Disorders

Anxiety disorders are closely associated with substance use disorders (Merikangas & Swanson, 2010). In the 1950s Conger (1956) developed the *tension reduction hypothesis*, which held that some people drink alcohol to excess to reduce their anxiety levels. This can cultivate further drinking and become a pattern—anxiety, drinking to relieve anxiety, further anxiety, more drinking, and so on. As Spanagel (2009) noted, "Because of the mutual interaction between anxiety and alcohol, it is possible that anxiety disorders promote the development of alcoholism and, vice versa, that alcoholism promotes the development of anxiety disorders" (p. 679). Spanagel (2009) also noted that research that addresses which problem may occur first has "yielded inconsistent results" (p. 679).

The anxiety disorders associated with substance use disorders include social phobia, generalized anxiety disorder, panic disorder, and agoraphobia (fear of wide open spaces; Marmorstein, 2012). In a national sample of adults, Marmorstein (2012) found that social phobia typically preceded substance use disorder, as did panic disorder and agoraphobia to a lesser degree. Generalized anxiety disorder typically occurred after the development of the substance abuse problem.

Spanagel (2009) noted that panic disorders and social phobia predict alcohol problems for adolescents and young adults but do not typically occur after the person becomes alcoholic, another acknowledgment that alcohol or other unprescribed drugs can be used to self-treat anxiety disorders. Overall, because this association between anxiety and substance abuse, especially alcohol, is well known, appropriate assessment of clients includes gathering information on anxiety.

Depression

Depression is common among people with alcoholism and drug addiction, and as with anxiety, it can be difficult to determine which came first—the depression or the substance use disorder. Some people try to stave off depression by using alcohol or other drugs, and over time this leads to a downward spiral in which both the depression and the drinking grow worse. The *self-medication hypothesis* is that substance abuse develops as a response to and serves as a coping mechanism for dealing with depression (Libby et al., 2005). Alternatively, in some cases substance abuse begins first and "generates neurobiological changes that increase the risk of depression" (Libby et al., 2005, p. 1650). Libby et al.'s 2005 review of the adolescent literature found more support for depression resulting from substance abuse. More recent research addresses the importance of working to distinguish between major depression that is linked to intense alcohol use and major depression that occurs independently of drinking (Schuckit, Smith, & Kalmijn, 2013). Spanagel's (2009) review of the literature found no agreement on whether depression causes alcoholism or alcoholism causes depression: "No consensus has been reached regarding the specific mechanisms underlying the association disorders, and it remains unclear whether one of the disorders causes or predisposes to the other" (p. 680).

Although it is interesting to try to tease out which comes first, the emphasis in treatment is on recovering from both problems. As with other co-occurring disorders, there are generally poorer treatment outcomes for people with depression and substance use disorders than for people with one disorder (Nunes & Levin, 2008). For some clients the depression clears up with abstinence; for others the depression continues. As discussed previously, it can be difficult to determine whether or when to prescribe antidepressants—although we typically think abstinence will help depression, appropriate use of antidepressant medication may help clients become abstinent. In their meta-analysis, Nunes and Levin (2008) reported that substance abuse treatment can result in significant lessening of depression. This may be associated with abstaining from substances that are depressants or a decrease in depression could happen because of a positive response to treatment. Nunes and Levin (2008) concluded that antidepressants should be prescribed when evidence of depression is independent of the substance abuse problem or when depression is sufficiently severe that medication is clinically warranted.

Depression in people with opiate dependence is relatively common. Research has found that antidepressant medications have mixed results in opiate-dependent patients; this research tends to be more heavily weighted toward negative outcomes for reasons that remain unclear (Nunes, Sullivan, & Levin, 2004). However, methadone maintenance and buprenorphine treatments for people with opioid dependence have both been shown to bring about significant improvements in depression.

Anxiety, depression, and substance abuse can also be a mix. In a study of anxiety, depression, and alcoholism, both anxiety and depression decreased after several weeks of abstinence (Driessen et al., 2001). Not surprisingly, people with persistent anxiety and depression had the greatest risk of relapse.

Bipolar Disorder

Bipolar disorder, formerly known as manic depression, is a recurrent disorder characterized by periods of depression that alternate with periods of hypomanic behaviors. It is typically attributed to a chemical imbalance in the brain and can be hereditary. Bipolar disorder I is considered the more severe form of manic and depressive episodes, and bipolar disorder II is considered the milder form, with less intense manic episodes that alternate with depression (American Psychiatric Association, 2013). It is estimated that between 14% and 65% of people with bipolar disorder have a substance abuse problem (Brown, Suppes, Adinoff, & Thomas, 2001; Levin & Hennessey, 2004). The development of bipolar disorder in adolescence is highly associated with substance abuse (Lenin & Hennessey, 2004). The diagnosis of bipolar disorder and substance abuse can be especially challenging, because some bipolar symptoms could result from the substance use. Bipolar disorder with substance use disorder can be associated with an earlier onset of symptoms, more frequent hospitalizations, and noncompliance with medications (Brown et al., 2001).

There is little information on effective treatments for the combination of bipolar disorder and substance dependence (Weiss et al., 2007). Weiss et al. (2007) reported that people receiving specialized integrated group therapy (a combination of treatment for each problem) for both bipolar and substance abuse had better outcomes than clients who received regular group counseling for substance dependence. People receiving integrated group therapy had fewer days of using substances, especially alcohol, and had better treatment attendance than those receiving the regular drug group counseling.

Borderline Personality Disorder

Borderline personality disorder is characterized by intense and unstable relationships, crisis orientation, fear of abandonment, unstable self-image, impulsive behavior, attention seeking, and chronic feelings of emptiness (American Psychiatric Association, 2013). Estimates indicate that of people with substance use disorder, as many as 65% may also have borderline personality disorder (Pennay et al., 2011). People with both diagnoses are at higher risk of noncompliance with treatment, poorer outcomes, and higher rates of relapse. Although there are various treatments for substance use disorders and borderline personality disorder, there are few treatment options for both (Gianoli, Jane, O'Brien, & Ralevski, 2012). There is little research at this point on the use of medications for borderline personality disorder and substance abuse.

Dynamic deconstructive psychotherapy has been studied as a treatment for alcoholism and borderline personality disorder (Gianoli et al., 2012). *Dynamic deconstructive psychotherapy* seeks to help clients establish a more positive self-image and to better respond to emotional experiences in their lives. One small randomized controlled trial of 30 clients found greater improvement in limiting alcohol use, less depression, and less institutional care than for people who received regular outpatient care, known as "treatment as usual" (Gregory et al., 2008, p. 35). The authors concluded that this treatment was effective and efficacious. Further research supported that after 30 months, people receiving dynamic deconstructive psychotherapy showed significant improvement in the symptoms of borderline personality disorder and depression and a reduction in drug use (Gregory, DeLucia-Deranja, & Mogle, 2010).

Dialectical behavior therapy is an approach that assists clients in gaining control over their emotions and in practicing healthier interactions with others. It can be used with clients who have the sole diagnosis of borderline personality disorder, as well as with those who also have substance abuse problems (van den Bosch, Verheul, Schippers, & van den Brink, 2002). Dialectical behavior therapy uses cognitive behavioral techniques to help regulate emotions and cope with distress, and it incorporates meditative practices. Four treatment modules are used over 1 year: weekly individual psychotherapy with a primary therapist, weekly groups focused on skills development, weekly supervision and consultation for the therapists, and the availability of telephone contact between client and therapist to receive coaching as the client practices new skills. In a comparison of women with borderline personality and people who had both borderline and substance abuse problems, van den Bosch et al. (2002) found that dialectical behavior therapy was successful in reducing the symptoms of borderline personality disorder but did not show an effect on the substance abuse problems.

A third type of treatment, *dual focus schema therapy*, incorporates cognitive behavioral skills with interventions aimed at correcting early negative ideas about the self-image of clients and their perceptions of others (Ball, Maccarelli, LaPaglia, & Ostrowski, 2011). In one study comparing individual drug counseling (focused specifically on addiction) and dual focus schema therapy, Ball et al. (2011) reported that individual drug counseling showed reduced symptoms for a variety of personality disorders, including borderline and antisocial personality disorders. In their review of six studies comparing dynamic deconstructive psychotherapy, dialectical behavior therapy, and dual focus schema therapy, Pennay et al. (2011) concluded that all studies showed client improvement but there was insufficient evidence to show that one was better than the others.

Antisocial Personality Disorder

Substance abuse and antisocial personality disorder are also highly correlated (Ruiz, Pincus, & Schinka, 2008). Antisocial personality disorder is characterized by a pattern of disregard for the rights and feelings of others and of violations of social norms, including legal problems (American Psychiatric Association, 2013). Individuals with this disorder have no concern for their safety or that of others, are manipulative, and engage in impulsive and perhaps even dangerous behaviors. Perhaps the most troubling characteristic is the lack of remorse for aggressive and negative behaviors.

Antisocial personality disorder is known to be a difficult problem to treat, and clients with both this disorder and substance use disorders are "particularly disadvantaged" (Mueser et al., 2012, p. 52) with more severe illness, greater impairments in functioning, and troubled family relationships. In a review of the literature, antisocial personality disorder was found to be, in some studies, a negative factor making recovery more difficult and, in other studies, a positive factor in treatment retention in therapeutic communities (Ohlin, Hesse, Fridell, & Tatting, 2011). Among 123 patients receiving buprenorphine treatment for opioid dependence, people with antisocial personality disorder, especially younger patients, had an increased risk of not completing the treatment program.

Attention Deficit Hyperactivity Disorder

Research has shown approximately 15% to 45% of adults with attention deficit hyperactivity disorder (ADHD) also have alcohol or drug use disorders (Ohlmeier et al., 2007). One study of a Turkish sample in residential treatment reported that people diagnosed with ADHD began their alcohol use, abuse, and addiction at significantly younger ages than did residents who did not have ADHD (Ercan, Coskunol, Varan, & Toksoz, 2003). No significant differences were found in the severity of alcohol dependence. At 1-year follow-up, 55.6% of residents without ADHD relapsed, whereas 80% of those with ADHD relapsed. Ercan et al. (2003) concluded that "childhood ADHD history seems to accelerate the development of alcohol dependence, but does not necessarily lead the person to a more severe this is a quote alcohol dependence, contrary to existing findings" (p. 354). The authors suggest this may be because the sample had been diagnosed with chronic and sufficiently severe alcohol problems that warranted inpatient treatment.

SELF-HELP GROUPS

Aase et al. (2008) reviewed 59 articles on 12-step programs and self-groups to conclude they can be helpful for people with dual diagnosis. A different literature review on 12-step programs for people with dual diagnosis found that this population attends at the same rate as people who have only substance abuse problems (Bogenschutz, Geppert, & George, 2006). In a subsample of 104 clients with dual diagnosis in outpatient or day treatment programs, after 1 year these clients attended more 12-step meetings than those without dual diagnosis and had comparable rates of abstinence to those with mental health problems (Chi, Satre, & Wesner, 2006).

Several 12-step programs address mental health and substance abuse, including Dual Recovery Anonymous and Double Trouble in Recovery. Dual Recovery Anonymous started in 1989. Members are encouraged "to share their stories of dual recovery, practicing the Steps on both chemical dependency and emotional or psychiatric illness, and sponsorship" (Dual Recovery Anonymous, 2009). Double Trouble in Recovery (Hazelden Foundation, 2013) is for people dually diagnosed with substance abuse and psychiatric disorders. It started in 1989 in New York State. Most research focuses on this self-help program (Laudet et al., 2003; Laudet, Magura, Cleland, et al., 2004; Laudet, Magura, Vogel, et al., 2004; Vogel, Knight, Laudet, & Magura, 1998). Double Trouble in Recovery can reflect a more comprehensive approach of mutual support and understanding than can other 12-step types of programs that focus only on abstinence (Aase et al., 2008). In one study of people in Double Trouble in Recovery, 75% also attended the more traditional 12-step meetings of Alcoholics Anonymous or Narcotics Anonymous (Laudet et al., 2000). Of people who did not attend other self-help groups, 17% expressed concern "because they feel uncomfortable, judged, or not accepted because of mental health issues or medications" (Laudet et al., 2000, p. 324). Attendance at Double Trouble in Recovery was associated with a greater likelihood of abstinence and was found to be most helpful when participation is active and consistent (Laudet, Magura, Cleland, et al., 2004).

People most likely to remain in Double Trouble in Recovery for 1 year were clients who were older and had more severe consequences as a result of their drug use, including arrests (Laudet et al., 2003). They also had more psychiatric symptoms, but they were not taking medications and were abstinent from drugs and alcohol. People with dual diagnosis who lived in supportive housing environments, participated in outpatient treatment, and believed they were capable of achieving their goals were more likely to stay in treatment (Laudet et al., 2003). Overall, clinicians should refer their clients with dual diagnosis to Double Trouble in Recovery (and other support groups for people with dual diagnosis) to encourage hope, elicit support, and develop a network of people doing well in their double recovery (Laudet, Magura, Vogel, et al., 2004).

RESEARCH CHALLENGES

The challenges of research on co-occurring populations are significant—it is difficult, if not impossible, to generalize regarding the various mental health diagnoses, varieties of drugs of abuse, types of treatment, different levels of care, and types of 12-step fellowships, as well as to consider demographic variables, including age, gender, race, and ethnicity (Bogenschutz et al., 2006). This makes it extremely difficult to collect data on all potential combinations of problems (Flynn & Brown, 2008; Watkins et al., 2005).

Regarding recommendations for the treatment of clients with dual diagnosis, federal policy recommendations, clinical guidelines, and research findings have yet to bring together a clear picture of best practices for individuals with dual diagnosis (Kushner, 2014; McGovern et al., 2006). McGovern et al. (2006) state, "Addiction treatment providers may find themselves lost between the vague and the overly particular" (p. 267).

Tools for screening and assessing mental health problems among substance abuse clients are critical for determining appropriate client care (Chan et al., 2008). Screening and assessment instruments preferably should be brief, simple to use and interpret, and helpful in developing a treatment plan (Carey, 2002). Standardization of screening and assessment tools can also go a long way toward developing stronger research protocols (Broome, Flynn, & Simpson, 1999; Chan et al., 2008).

The lack of experimental designs in research has made it unclear how helpful 12-step groups are for people with dual diagnosis (Aase et al., 2008; Bogenschutz et al., 2006). Yet it appears that self-efficacy and strong social support are related to positive outcomes (Aase et al., 2008).

As discussed in previous chapters, best practices do not always find their way into clinical practice. Important work remains to be done on the implementation of best practices into services for co-occurring disorders (Ouimette et al., 2007). See Box 9.4 for recommendations for improving services for people with co-occurring disorders.

> ### BOX 9.4 Recommendations for Improving Services for Clients With Co-Occurring Disorders
>
> 1. Develop a strategic plan for service integration that includes the input of directors of mental health and substance abuse treatment programs.
> 2. Develop a single source of funding, rather than distinguishing financial resources by mental health and substance abuse, or pool funds from several sources; seek joint grant–funded projects.
> 3. Improve data collection systems to make better research studies possible.
> 4. Provide education to mental health and substance abuse treatment professionals to develop a strong appreciation for the other; cultivate dual diagnosis specialists in treatment programs.
> 5. Develop a common language and definitions of terms that apply to individuals with dual diagnosis; develop screening and assessment tools that are applicable to people with co-occurring disorders in an effort to establish universal treatment policies and procedures.
> 6. Create a co-occurring administrative role to oversee treatment services and institute program-monitoring procedures.
>
> ---
>
> *Sources:* Drake et al. (2001) and Ouimette et al. (2007).

SUMMARY AND CONCLUSION

Substance abuse disorders are associated with various mental health disorders, including anxiety disorders, depression, borderline personality disorder, bipolar disorder, and antisocial personality disorder. Overall, people with co-occurring disorders have fewer individual resources, fewer family and social support resources, poorer treatment outcomes, and greater risk of relapse.

The treatment of dual diagnosis disorders can be especially challenging because of the variety of mental health problems and the levels of severity of the substance abuse and mental health problems. An important barrier to treatment has been the lack of professionals with dual qualifications.

The treatments provided to people with dual diagnosis include dialectical behavior therapy, dynamic deconstructive psychotherapy, and dual focus schema therapy. They show some effectiveness. However, more research is needed to determine whether one therapy is preferable to others and which therapies are best for the specific types of mental health problems that occur with substance use disorders.

Today the substance abuse treatment field recognizes the importance of integrating treatment for both mental health and substance abuse problems, preferably by professionals trained in both areas. Education and training of treatment staff members can be successful in fostering more positive attitudes toward people with co-occurring disorders and can increase the comfort of professionals in treating individuals with dual diagnosis.

SUBSTANCE ABUSE AND CRIMINAL JUSTICE POPULATIONS

*T*he relationship between drug use and crime is complex. Drug users and addicts often engage in criminal activity to support their drug use. For other offenders, criminal activity leads them into drug use. Researchers have been especially interested in whether the drug use or the criminal activity came first (Colman & Vander Laenen, 2012). The focus should be on the balance between ensuring public safety and meeting the needs of offenders and their families, yet criminal offenders and their needs are not high priorities in American society. In reality, the criminal justice system is "a primary service delivery system" for juveniles and adults with substance abuse, mental health, and other problems (Henderson, Taxman, & Young, 2008, p. 163). This speaks to the importance of offering a range of high-quality services to offenders; however, substance abuse treatment within correctional programs is limited (Grella et al., 2007). This chapter examines what is known about treatment options and the effectiveness of substance abuse treatment provided to correctional populations.

Criminal justice research often focuses on recidivism and program outcomes (Lemieux, 2002; Center for Substance Abuse Treatment, 2005). However, there is no agreed-upon definition of recidivism. *Recidivism* typically means the offender is rearrested or returned to prison. Regardless of the definition, a considerable amount of research over years attests to the very high rates of recidivism among all offenders, regardless of whether they have substance abuse problems or not. In Massachusetts, approximately half of all released inmates are reincarcerated within 3 years (Massachusetts Bar Association Drug Policy Task Force, 2009b). Predictors of recidivism include a prior criminal record, prior residential placement, and whether the offender has significant mental health problems (Broner, Mayrl, & Landsberg, 2005; Sullivan, Veysey, Hamilton, & Grillo, 2007).

Although much attention has been placed on the association between illegal drugs and crime, there is a stronger association between alcohol use and violent crime, which has received less attention in the literature (Martin, Maxwell, White, & Zhang, 2004). For illicit drugs, the concern is that individuals are committing crimes to get money to buy drugs; for alcohol, the concern is its association with violence (McMurran, 2007). This violence extends beyond interpersonal violence to include the violence perpetrated by international drug cartels.

The very high arrest rates typically focus on the individual drug users. The most frequent drug arrests are for drug possession, followed by drug sales. Drug importers, manufacturers, and major and minor drug dealers—those involved in the business of drugs—are arrested infrequently (Human Rights Watch, 2009). Drug offenders tend to see themselves as users of drugs rather than as criminals. In a qualitative study of 40 drug-using offenders, respondents "were convinced that recovery from drug use would lead them to a stop in their offending" (Colman & Vander Laenen, 2012, p. 3), but "None of the respondents labeled themselves as former offenders" (p. 5).

Some of the worst effects of the war on drugs have included increasing the number of drug arrests—even though this does not reduce illegal drug use and more severely punishes minority offenders (Massachusetts Bar Association Drug Policy Task Force, 2009b). The harsh economic effects negatively affect individual offenders and their families by significantly reducing their opportunities for employment if they have a criminal record. This has negative economic effects as well on states and on the federal government. By spending scarce resources on incarceration, funds are less available for rehabilitative social programs for offenders, as well as for other groups in need.

The history of the intersection of drugs and criminal activity came to the forefront in the 1980s with the passage of harsh drug laws in the United States. Tougher drug laws mandated in the 1970s and 1980s led to an explosion in the prison population in the 1990s, especially with regard to tough sentencing for crack cocaine users (Forman & Larivee, 2013; Wexler, 2003). By illustration, in Massachusetts alone, between 1980 and 2006, the state prison population increased by 368% and the jail and county house of correction (sentences less than 2.5 years) populations increased 522% (Massachusetts Bar Association Drug Policy Task Force, 2009a). Between 1980 and 2006 new house of correction and state prison commitments increased from 6.5% to 23%. Overall, on the federal level, 48% of inmates in federal prison were incarcerated for drug offenses by 2011 (Carson & Sabol, 2012). As we see in the following sections, the high rates of incarceration disproportionately affect racial and ethnic minority groups.

RACISM IN THE CRIMINAL JUSTICE SYSTEM

The association between race and length of prison sentence has long been noted in the criminal justice literature. The criminal justice system is the place where racism can be seen clearly, especially in drug crime sentencing. However, although African Americans and Whites engage in drug use, possession, and sales at approximately the same rates (Alexander, 2010), African Americans are the "principal targets" of the war on drugs (Human Rights Watch, 2009, p. 1).

Alexander (2010) traces the history of the crack cocaine media campaign in the mid-1980s to the strategic efforts of the Reagan administration to build support for the war on drugs, stating: "The media campaign was an extraordinary success" (p. 5). At the time, some people thought the war on drugs was designed to rid poor minority communities of drugs, yet these minorities, especially African Americans, paid the price of the war on drugs in lengthy prison sentences. As mentioned in Chapter 8, the concern in the 1980s over an epidemic of "crack babies" was largely overblown, and although these infants experienced withdrawal from drugs, they did not face the lifelong problems of people born with fetal alcohol spectrum disorder (Mignon, Faiia, Myers, & Rubington, 2009).

Crack cocaine, a cheaper form of regular white powder cocaine, was typically used by poor minorities, whereas white powder cocaine was more typically used by Whites. Until recently, federal offenders found in possession of 1 gram of crack cocaine received the same prison sentences as offenders found with 100 grams of powder cocaine, known as the 100:1 crack–powder cocaine sentencing disparity. The clear result was far more incarcerated minority offenders. Simply put: "To punish crack users more harshly than powder users is analogous to punishing people who are caught smoking marijuana more harshly than those caught eating marijuana-laced brownies" (Hart, 2013, p. 292).

In its analysis of the Uniform Crime Reports of the Federal Bureau of Investigation (FBI) and U.S. Census data, Human Rights Watch (2009) found that 1981 was the year of lowest disparity between African Americans and Whites, when African Americans were arrested at 2.8 times the rate of Whites. The years of greatest disparity were 1988 through 1993, when African Americans were arrested at five times the rate of Whites.

In Massachusetts, racial disparities have been shown to increase with the severity of the drug crime, especially for people serving mandatory minimum state prison or county house of correction sentences (Massachusetts Bar Association Drug Policy Task Force, 2009a; Massachusetts Sentencing Commission, 2010). In Massachusetts in 2006, 80% of state residents were White, 7.9% were Hispanic, 6.9% were African American, and other races accounted for 5.2% of state residents (Massachusetts Bar Association Drug Policy Task Force, 2009a). However, in the same year, for offenders convicted on drug possession charges in the state, 56.9% were White, 20.7% were Hispanic, 19.7% were African American, and other races or unknown race were 0.8%. Overall, the greatest racial disparities were seen in mandatory minimum sentences, with minorities accounting for an astonishing 74.5% of mandatory drug crimes (Massachusetts Bar Association Drug Policy Task Force, 2009a; Massachusetts Sentencing Commission, 2010).

These racial disparities that were so acute in the 1980s and 1990s continue to have an extraordinary effect on minorities and their families. Among inmates age 18 and 19 in 2011, African American males were incarcerated at greater than nine times the rate of White males (Carson & Sabol, 2012).

New York has made significant changes in its drug laws in recent years. In the 1970s and 1980s New York had among the harshest punishments for drug crimes, known as the Rockefeller Drug Laws, which required lengthy mandatory minimum prison sentences (Sayegh, 2013). After considerable advocacy, in 2009 New York instituted the Rockefeller Drug Law reforms that both eliminated mandatory minimum sentences and offered the alternative of diversion to treatment for drug offenders (Pearson, 2012). By sending drug offenders to drug courts, a study of the New York system found a savings of $5,144 per offender. If the costs of crime victimization are included, the savings increased to $13,284 per offender. The New York State cost for the fiscal year 2011 to 2012 was $45,516.37 for each prison inmate.

In Massachusetts it is estimated that $90 million could be saved each year if the number of inmates with drug convictions was reduced to the 1985 level (Forman & Larivee, 2013). Although the tide is turning—drug sentences are no longer as harsh and the use of crack cocaine has been reduced—the policies developed to respond to crack continue to have a severe effect on inmates' sentences. For example, in Massachusetts 70% of current inmates in state prison received their sentences under the mandatory minimum laws.

SUBSTANCE ABUSE TREATMENT FOR CRIMINAL OFFENDERS

Substance abuse treatment is needed in all correctional settings. It is needed for prison inmates and for people living in the community who are under the supervision of the courts, such as probationers and parolees. In 2012, among U.S. adults on probation, 37% had substance abuse or dependence problems (Substance Abuse and Mental Health Services Administration, 2013b). This is significantly higher than the 8.2% of adults with substance problems who were not on probation.

Former prison inmates face myriad problems and are likely to return to drug-using environments that put them at high risk of relapse (Binswanger et al., 2012). Regarding financial obstacles, one former inmate stated, "Most people relapse in the first six months because it's so stressful because they have no help. There's no financial help to even get housing or to . . . buy clothes for work or a bus pass to even try to look for a job" (Binswanger et al., 2012, p. 3). This speaks to the need to offer a variety of programs to assist with reentry, including housing, vocational training, substance abuse treatment, and other services. See Box 10.1 for an example of the difficulties in community reentry.

Substance abuse treatment is known to significantly reduce arrests and reincarceration (Garnick et al., 2007; Wexler, 2003). In a meta-analysis of 28 research studies of drug treatment programs, it was found that criminal activity can be reduced by as much as 29% to 36% (Halloway, Bennett, & Farrington, 2006).

BOX 10.1 Return to the Community After Incarceration

One participant in a study of people released from prison addressed the challenges of returning to his community:

[The biggest problem is] not going back to the same lifestyle that got me in prison, 'cause I have seen some of the old people that I used to hang out with, and some of them are clean and sober and doing good and some of them are still up to the same, but you know . . ., it was hard for me to like say "I need to go," you know, cause I had spent so much time with them over the years that now that some of them are still getting high and still doing the things they do, it was hard for me to just say, "Hey, I can't not be your friend, but I just can't be around you at this time, because that's just too much of a trigger for me cause it's just one little slip up and I go back." . . . [T]he hardest thing is not going back into the lifestyle that got me put in prison and finding a job.

Source: Binswanger et al. (2012, p. 5).

Legal coercion is brought to bear when clients do not voluntarily seek treatment (Perron & Bright, 2008). Results of studies that compare outcomes for coerced and noncoerced clients have mixed results (Burke & Gregoire, 2007). In Burke and Gregoire's (2007) study comparing coerced and noncoerced clients, people who were coerced stated they had less drug use 6 months after treatment ended. In a national survey of public treatment programs, both short- and long-term residential treatment and outpatient treatment were shown to have lower dropout rates when clients were under some form of legal coercion, with short-term residential treatment showing the greatest effect (Perron & Bright, 2008). Yet a meta-analysis of 129 studies on coercion of offenders into treatment from 1970 to 2005 reported that overall "mandated treatment was ineffective, particularly when the treatment was located in custodial settings, whereas voluntary treatment produced significant treatment effect sizes regardless of setting" (Parhar, Wormith, Derkzen, & Beauregard, 2008, p. 1128). One key factor here can be client motivation, as discussed later in this chapter.

Although in some studies clients under legal pressure to participate in treatment have the same characteristics as people who come voluntarily, other research indicates that mandated clients may be less prepared to participate in treatment and therefore more resistant to treatment; in addition, they may have a greater number of problems than voluntary clients (Perron & Bright, 2008). Another factor is that in cases of legal coercion, clients do not have choices related to the services they receive. Potentially, these services could be of lower quality than those provided otherwise—clients who seek treatment on their own are likely to have more choices about treatment and may have stronger self-advocacy skills than legally coerced clients. The literature does not yet answer the questions associated with comparing quality of services offered to voluntary and coerced clients.

Diversion Programs

Diversion programs seek to take youth and adults out of the juvenile justice and criminal justice systems and provide them with the opportunity for treatment. They have been increased, in part, in response to research showing that interventions such as residential boot camps and outpatient group counseling have not been found to be effective for substance abusers in correctional settings (McMurran, 2007; Pearson & Lipton, 1999).

Although some diversion programs rely on court judges to determine appropriate candidates for diversion, other programs accept candidates for treatment at earlier points in the criminal justice process (McMurran, 2007). These are especially good alternatives for nonviolent offenders. Decision points for diverting offenders from the criminal justice system can occur after arrest but before court arraignment or a bail hearing, after arraignment or a bail hearing, after a preliminary court hearing, after a plea of guilty or determination of guilt, or after conviction with a suspended sentence that depends on treatment completion (Center for Substance Abuse Treatment, 2005).

Coercion and Motivation for Treatment

Client motivation for treatment and recovery is important in any type of treatment setting, whether treatment is voluntary or coerced. Research shows that clients who are coerced into treatment can have positive outcomes (Cosden et al., 2006; Parhar et al., 2008). Yet there is a mixed picture regarding whether people legally mandated into substance abuse treatment stay longer than those who are not legally required to go to treatment (Parhar et al., 2008). There is also a mixed picture of whether coerced clients are able to make the best use of treatment under these conditions: "Although coercion is a strong impetus for many offenders to enter treatment, it is not clear that the external motivation created by a desire to avoid incarceration is sufficient for offenders to effectively utilize treatment" (Cosden et al., 2006, pp. 604–605). Clients have different levels of motivation, and programs may have different admission criteria—they may focus only on accepting the most highly motivated clients and thereby may appear to be more successful than other types of programs.

As discussed in previous chapters, the picture of motivation is complex and can be even more so with criminal justice clients (Cosden et al., 2006). A big issue with criminal justice populations is motivation for a change in lifestyle and facing the challenges of becoming law abiding. The criminal justice system may be successful in giving offenders the opportunity for treatment, but something must happen to cultivate intrinsic (internal) motivation: "Although legal coercion may be sufficient extrinsic motivation to accept treatment, continued engagement in recovery must be reinforced by getting the client to recognize and acknowledge the emotional and physical harms to themselves and others caused by drug abuse" (Sung, Belenko, Feng, & Tabachnick, 2004, p. 24).

In a study of 712 youthful offenders in Australia, the respondents had poor motivation for treatment, with only 10% willing to access substance abuse treatment (Lennings, Kenny, & Nelson, 2006). Furthermore, although almost 40% of the sample had significant substance abuse problems, fewer than half (18%) were offered substance abuse treatment and fewer than half who entered treatment completed it. Here, we see low motivation by prospective clients, as well as lack of motivation on the part of professionals to offer treatment to these young offenders.

A study of 661 men in prison in Kentucky reported that overall levels of motivation for substance abuse treatment were low (Hiller et al., 2009). However, greater age was associated with increased motivation as older inmates "mature out" and experience fewer behavioral and other problems in their incarceration. Interestingly, inmates who had more significant family issues, mental and physical health issues, and employment issues had greater motivation for treatment. This could be explained by the idea of "hitting bottom" and feeling so down that the inmates will try anything to improve the quality of prison life, especially those serving long sentences.

In a study of 578 offenders, intrinsic motivation correlated with completion of the drug court program; however, "it played only a small role in predicting outcomes" (Cosden et al., 2006, p. 614). Cosden et al. (2006) concluded, "Although the presence of offender motivation . . . was not a strong predictor of positive outcomes, neither was the lack of motivation a deterrent to success" (p. 614). The authors suggest that this may be related to having the skills needed to function without alcohol and drugs and that these skills can be more important than motivation. Overall, in the best circumstances, offenders need independent living skills, motivation, and job skills to position themselves to be successful.

One study of 116 inmates who used drugs reported that almost half of those involved with drugs had low intellectual abilities (Vandevelde, Broekaert, Schuyten, & Van Hove, 2005). Staff can misunderstand and consider these clients to have lower motivation rather than lower intellectual abilities. Interestingly, the inmates with higher intellectual abilities were less motivated for substance abuse treatment than were those with low or average abilities.

Studies of coerced clients may not necessarily take client motivation into account when examining effectiveness (Center for Substance Abuse Treatment, 2005). It is also the case that while individuals are in treatment, motivation can improve. Overall, more remains to be learned about motivation for treatment among substance-abusing offenders and about how motivation affects treatment.

Drug Courts

Today drug courts are considered a critical part of the U.S. criminal justice response to drug offenses and offenders. Drug courts have been responsible for considerable changes in criminal justice responses to drug offenders.

These issues are not only related to criminal justice but are public health issues as well (Center for Substance Abuse Treatment, 2005). The first drug court opened in 1989 in Miami–Dade County, Florida. The amount of research on the effects of drug court is greater than research on all types of other criminal justice programs combined (National Association of Drug Court Professionals, 2013). The National Association of Drug Court Professionals boasts more than 27,000 members, which is a testament to the commitment to drug courts as an important criminal justice alternative in the United States.

A central premise of drug courts is that intervention and treatment must be coordinated by courts, substance abuse treatment agencies, and some form of community supervision—probation, for example—all of which are monitored by the court. Rather than the typical adversarial relationship seen in most courts, drug courts emphasize recovery within a professional support network. Typically drug courts provide an initial period of orientation and drug education, followed by treatment. Clients are also typically tested for drug use through urine specimens; are given educational, vocational, or both types of services; and receive help with the transition to aftercare programs (Center for Substance Abuse Treatment, 2005).

Drug courts are effective, but their effectiveness may depend on the screening procedures used. That is, people accepted into drug court programs can be given screening and assessment tools to ensure they have some motivation for recovery, and prospective clients can be subjected to processes that determine who is most likely to succeed in the program. In some programs this means that only people determined to be the most likely clients to succeed in the drug court program are given the opportunity to participate.

A considerable literature attests to the effectiveness of drug courts (Cosden et al., 2006; National Association of Drug Court Professionals, 2013). Drug courts are useful in keeping clients in treatment longer and reducing both alcohol and drug use and criminal behavior (Burdon, Roll, Prendergast, & Rawson, 2001). In a review of 16 studies of drug courts, it was found that, considering the variety of study designs, almost all studies showed a reduction in substance use (Wittouck, Dekkers, De Ruyver, Vanderplasschen, & Vander Laenen, 2013). Wittouck et al. (2013) concluded that "moderately positive results" (p. 2) were found across the studies for positive effects while participating in the program. Not surprisingly, the effect of drug courts is reduced once clients have graduated from the programs. At this point little research evidence addresses the long-term effects of drug courts on future behavior.

Drug courts are not without criticism. There are ethical considerations regarding exerting legal pressure on defendants and convicted offenders to accept something they would prefer to reject. Drug courts place emphasis on punishment through differential sanctions and may make limited use of positive reinforcement to support recovery (Burdon et al., 2001). One study of interviews with 55 drug court graduates reported that they were concerned about the professionals' lack of respect for their time and subjecting them to long waiting times for services, an especially important concern of people who had jobs (Wolfer, 2006). Concern was also expressed that staff members did not treat clients equitably: "Some graduates clearly chafed under what they considered to be favoritism in handling of different cases, where some people in the program received lenient sanctions for the same offenses for which others received more serious sanctions" (Wolfer, 2006, pp. 318–319).

Therapeutic Communities

Therapeutic communities are residential programs in which clients remain for a number of months to receive substance abuse treatment, and they can help ease the transition back into society. In the late 1980s a federal project called Project REFORM, funded by the Bureau of Justice Assistance, and another program called Project RECOVERY, funded by the Center for Substance Abuse Treatment, began to address the substance abuse problems of prison inmates (Wexler, 2003). In 1994 funding was provided to states to develop therapeutic communities for substance abusers in the criminal justice system in the form of the U.S. Department of Justice Residential Substance Abuse Treatment for State Prisoners Formula Grant program.

In the mid-1990s therapeutic communities were considered a "major innovation in American correctional institutions" (Wexler, 1995, p. 57). Today therapeutic communities within American prisons are the most frequently used treatment approach and have garnered considerable research attention (Butzin, Martin, & Inciardi, 2005; Grella et al., 2007). They are considered successful treatment programs for substance-abusing inmates, with program standards tested by the Therapeutic Communities of America and the Office of National Drug Control Policy (Center for Substance Abuse Treatment, 2005). In a literature review, evaluations of therapeutic communities in corrections showed positive outcomes 1 to 3 years after return to the community (Butzin et al., 2005).

Therapeutic communities can be used before incarceration or after incarceration. Research on therapeutic communities for prison inmates shows they can improve behavior within correctional environments, reduce recidivism, and reduce substance abuse (McMurran, 2007; Smiley-McDonald & Leukefeld, 2005). Overall, men and women who participate in correctional therapeutic communities have better outcomes in reducing substance abuse and lower rates of recidivism (Hall, Prendergast, Wellisch, Patten, & Cao, 2004). See Box 10.2 for an example of a therapeutic community within a prison environment.

In a study comparing people coming out of prison in Delaware who received standard community supervision with those who were in therapeutic communities for substance abuse, only 10% of people were abstinent among the no-treatment group, whereas 32% of those in a therapeutic community were abstinent (Butzin et al., 2005). People who participated in work release in their transition from prison back to the community had a higher

---

BOX 10.2 Amity Prison Therapeutic Community

The Amity Prison Therapeutic Community is housed within the R. J. Donovan Correctional Facility in San Diego, California. Inmates with drug problems can volunteer for the program if they have only 9 to 12 months left on their sentences.

Approximately 200 inmates participate in the Amity program at any time. They receive counseling from staff members who are recovering alcoholics and addicts and have criminal histories themselves. After completion of the program, participants are offered the opportunity to enter Vista, a smaller therapeutic community within the Amity program.

In a randomized controlled trial of 715 incarcerated men, participants were assigned to Amity or to a control group. On average these men had been incarcerated for 6 years and had been arrested 27 times. The Amity group experienced a 9% lower rate of recidivism than the control group. However, the treatment did not affect levels of self-reports of substance use or the graduates' chances of getting a job.

Sources: Prendergast, Hall, Wexler, Melnick, and Cao (2004).

---

rate of employment (54.6%) than did the comparison group that received no treatment (45.4%). Butzin et al. (2005) concluded, "The evidence of the effectiveness of a transitional TC [therapeutic community] is thus particularly impressive" (p. 357).

Peer support and positive rapport with a counselor are important in the therapeutic community experience (Welsh & McGrain, 2008). Although it is challenging to develop a sense of community within a prison environment that is often hostile, it is possible and can foster investment in mentoring others and in developing community-oriented values (Smiley-McDonald & Leukefeld, 2005). Therapeutic communities can also offer education and support to family members (Lemieux, 2002).

Not all research on therapeutic communities reflects positive changes in residents. In a study of 150 residents in mandated diversion therapeutic communities, those who were young, had less social support, and had lower levels of intrinsic motivation were more likely to be noncompliant with program rules (Sung et al., 2004).

A study of 4,165 men and women paroled from prison therapeutic community programs in California reported that they benefited equally from continued residential care and from outpatient care (Burdon, Dang, Prendergast, Messina, & Farabee, 2007). That is, people with the more severe problem, substance dependence, did as well in either residential or outpatient follow-up as did those with low-severity substance abuse problems.

> ### BOX 10.3 *The Thinking for a Change Correctional Program*
>
> Thinking for a Change is an integrated, cognitive behavioral change pro-gram for criminal offenders. It can be used to address the cognitive, emo-tional, and social needs of correctional clients. It is designed for use in various correctional settings, including probation and parole, community corrections, prisons, and jails. Clients in the program are taught cognitive restructuring and how to develop social and problem-solving skills. The Thinking for a Change curriculum provides 25 specific lessons that can be offered to men and women, as well as to juvenile offenders.
>
> *Source:* National Institute of Corrections (n.d.).

An array of innovative programs exist today that address substance abuse treatment within correctional settings. See Box 10.3 for an example of an inno-vative program that can be implemented in a variety of residential and outpa-tient programs for criminal offenders.

Court Commitment to Treatment

There are circumstances under which people with substance dependence are so deep in their addiction that they are not able to consent to treatment voluntarily. In Massachusetts such a circumstance is addressed in the legal statute of Massachusetts General Laws, Chapter 123, Section 35, and is commonly known as "Section 35." The guiding principle is that a person's alcohol or drug use puts the user or others at risk of harm because of addiction (Massachusetts Department of Public Health, 2013). A family member, guard-ian, police officer, or physician may petition the district court for an order for commitment to a licensed treatment facility for up to 30 days. This can include a period of detoxification and then a rehabilitation program. A Section 35 is typically reserved for the most severe drug and alcohol problems and is applied to a small but important proportion of people who receive treatment.

Drunk Driving

Substance abuse and the criminal justice system also intersect in cases of driving under the influence (DUI), also known as driving while intoxicated (DWI). According to national data, in 2012 among people age 12 and older, 11.2% drove under the influence of alcohol at least once in the preceding year (Substance Abuse and Mental Health Services Administration, 2013b). The rates were highest among people age 21 through 25: 21.9% drove under the influence of alcohol. Men are more likely to drive under the influence than women: 14.6% versus 7.9% in 2012. Drunk driving has decreased through the years because of advocacy programs and harsher legal sanctions. In 2012, driving under the influence decreased for 18- to 25-year-olds to 18.4%, down from 26.6% in 2002.

Mothers Against Drunk Driving (MADD) was started by Candace Lightner in 1980 after her 13-year-old daughter was killed by a drunk driver. MADD is a highly successful grassroots movement that has had great effect on changing drunk-driving laws in the United States. Under pressure from the federal government, all states have laws that set the legal limit for blood alcohol level at 0.08%, but specific laws and penalties are determined for each state (Governors Highway Safety Association, 2013). Importantly, a blood alcohol level of 0.08% does not necessarily mean that the driver is drunk or feels intoxicated; it means the driver has exceeded the limit allowed by law.

Although all states have drunk-driving laws, far fewer states have laws to address drug impairment while driving. Only 18 states forbid any presence of a prohibited substance or drug such as marijuana or cocaine in the driver's body while driving (Governors Highway Safety Association, 2013).

States typically have clear laws for drunk driving in terms of the sanctions that are graduated according to the number of drunk-driving arrests. In Massachusetts, Melanie's Law, named for a young girl killed by a drunk driver, was passed in October 2005 to strengthen the penalties and administrative sanctions for drunk driving. For example, first-time drunk drivers in Massachusetts can lose their license for 1 year, can face fines of $500 to $5,000, are required to attend driver alcohol education programs, and can face the potential term in a house of correction of up to 2.5 years (Governors Highway Safety Association, 2013). First-time drunk drivers may have been foolish and made a mistake; however, people facing a second drunk-driving charge are seen as those most likely to have serious alcohol problems. Drunk drivers in Massachusetts with five offenses lose their driver's license for life, can face up to 5 years in prison, and can face fines up to $50,000.

JUVENILE OFFENDERS

Overall, juvenile offenders have multiple problems, including poverty associated with living in violent areas, negative life events, poor education, involvement with child protection agencies, emotional problems, and early-life introduction to drugs (Sullivan et al., 2007). Juvenile offenders are more likely to have substance abuse problems compared with those who have had no contact with the juvenile justice system (Watson, 2004). The hope is that by offering substance abuse treatment services to juveniles, their involvement in delinquent activities will be reduced. Yet the juvenile justice system suffers considerable problems, including high rates of both substance abuse and mental health problems among offenders, lack of screening and assessment, and lack of collaboration among juvenile justice and community agencies.

It would seem likely that substance abuse treatment would affect and show a decrease in delinquent behaviors. Sullivan et al. (2007) state that this prediction "is based on the assumption that the drug or alcohol use or mental health symptoms in some accompany, cause, or exacerbate delinquent behavior and that by addressing symptoms of substance use through treatment, youth will not offend or not offend as frequently" (p. 571). This assumption is not necessarily the case. In a study of diversion for dually diagnosed juvenile offenders, this was not true—treatment did not have an effect on any future illegal behavior: "Delinquent behaviors seem to operate independently of symptoms, substance use, or whether services were received. Youth who received services were as likely to be rearrested as those who did not" (Sullivan et al., 2007, p. 571]). Another study of serious juvenile offenders reported that substance abuse treatment was successful in reducing substance abuse after 6- and 12-month follow-up, yet it did not affect juvenile offending outside of drug use offenses (Chassin, Knight, Vargas-Chanes, Losoya, & Naranjo, 2009). The intervention associated with a reduction in juvenile offending was family involvement in treatment, yet only one-quarter of the sample received family-oriented treatment.

In their study of youth who received treatment, young people reoffended at the same rates as those who did not receive treatment, including those with significant substance problems. Prior history and type of offense were better predictors of rearrest than was involvement with treatment (Sullivan et al., 2007).

Another important issue is whether children and adolescents are receiving treatment in correctional facilities and programs. In a national survey of substance abuse treatment for juveniles in the justice system, treatment was more likely to be found in large state-funded institutional facilities (66%) than in local jail and detention centers (20%; Young, Dembo, & Henderson, 2007). This is not surprising, because detention facilities are designed for short-term care for a transient group, whereas long-term institutional facilities are more likely to provide services to offenders who are with them longer. The survey found that approximately half of substance-abusing offenders received referrals on release to community agencies for follow-up treatment. More needs to be done to ensure that young offenders receive the aftercare services they and their families need.

In a study of substance abuse treatment for juvenile offenders in correctional programs, differences were found in services depending on whether the juveniles were institutionalized or they were living at home in the community (Henderson et al., 2007). Juveniles in institutional programs were more likely to receive comprehensive services, whereas those in outpatient community programs were more likely to receive services from qualified substance abuse professionals and were more likely to have family involvement in treatment.

There is a lack of information on the substance abuse treatment needs of youth in the juvenile justice system (Young et al., 2007). There is also inadequate use of screening and assessment tools, as well as insufficient treatment services to meet the needs of juvenile offenders (Nissen, 2007). The good news is that increasingly judges are sentencing juveniles to institutional care less frequently and that treatment programs are on the rise (Sullivan et al., 2007). Nissen (2007) concludes, "Creating seamless and integrated systems of care for youth with simultaneous substance abuse and delinquency problems is a daunting but achievable goal" (p. 57).

WOMEN'S SUBSTANCE ABUSE TREATMENT ISSUES

Substance abuse is a significant national problem for female prison inmates (Kates, Mignon, & Ransford, 2008; Phillips, Nixon, Phillips, Pfefferbaum, & Briody, 2000). Incarcerated women are typically not the recipients of the same types and levels of services as incarcerated men (Forman & Larivee, 2013). Because far fewer women offenders are in the correctional system, this has inappropriately provided justification for offering fewer resources. Fewer facilities for women make it likely that family members need to travel longer distances to visit the inmates (Kates et al., 2008). Women who have children have even greater difficulty in maintaining contact during their period of incarceration (Mignon & Ransford, 2012).

One study reported that although 36% of female defendants were identified in case records as having substance abuse problems, court personnel estimated that 66% to 90% of all women arraigned in courts had substance abuse problems (Hardy-Fanta & Mignon, 2000). Clearly, little effort was made to screen, assess, and diagnose women with substance abuse issues. In addition, a formal identification as a substance abuser increased the likelihood of court conviction.

In a meta-analysis of 24 studies addressing the effects of correctional programs for incarcerated women, those who participated in treatment programs for substance abuse were 45% less likely to reoffend after prison discharge (Tripodi, Bledsoe, Kim, & Bender, 2011). Among cocaine-dependent women with criminal involvement, the most important factors that determined whether women entered treatment were retaining custody of children, having a job and health insurance, and knowing of a community substance abuse treatment program to contact for assistance (Saum, Hiller, Leigey, Inciardi, & Surratt, 2007).

An evaluation of the Forever Free program, a therapeutic community based on a cognitive behavioral model for incarcerated women in California, found that participating in treatment and greater age reduced the risk of drug use and increased opportunities for employment on release (Hall et al., 2004). The Forever Free program has a cognitive behavioral curriculum that emphasizes relapse prevention, anger management, assertiveness training codependency, and parenting issues. At a 1-year follow-up, 44% of the comparison group returned to prison, compared with 33% of Forever Free participants.

Few controlled studies assess the effectiveness of substance abuse treatment for female offenders (Hall et al., 2004). Gender-specific treatment programs for women are critical for incarcerated offenders—planned, developed, and implemented especially for women and not relying on male models of programming (Kates et al., 2008).

RESEARCH ISSUES

All levels of research in criminal justice are needed. *Implementation research* identifies problems and successes in developing programs. This type of research can include interviews with correctional administrators, officers, and inmates to gather information on their early levels of satisfaction with a program and their perceptions of challenges and problems (Center for Substance Abuse Treatment, 2005). *Process evaluation* in the criminal justice system seeks to assess the effects on the clients within the program and assess the types and amounts of services, as well as the clients' attendance and participation. *Outcome evaluation*, as mentioned in earlier chapters, seeks quantitative data on the assessment of the effect of programs on client treatment outcomes. Typically, outcome evaluations are more detailed and expensive than the other types of research and include complicated statistical analyses that compare a treatment group with a control (no-treatment) group. For example, an outcome evaluation can include follow-up of criminal justice clients regarding recidivism, substance abuse relapse, and employment. Many of the studies reviewed in this chapter are examples of outcome evaluation.

Conceptual problems and issues of methodology contribute to agreement that is less than clear about what constitutes effectiveness in programs that use legal coercion (Perron & Bright, 2008). Efforts to assess the effectiveness in comparison of legally mandated treatment and voluntary treatment are complicated by the role of the intrinsic motivation of the offender. Yet most studies of mandated treatment do not assess client motivation (Parhar et al., 2008).

The lack of clear and consistent treatment findings makes it hard to determine the types and content of substance abuse aftercare services needed by criminal offenders (Grella et al., 2007; Pelissier, Jones, & Cadigan, 2007). Community-based and prison-based programs for substance-abusing offenders may need to expand the types of services they offer and are likely to need outcomes measures to meet performance objectives (Grella et al., 2007).

Research on how to improve responses to correctional populations with substance use disorders needs to consider the types and intensity of treatment, as well as whether programs need to be devised according to the offenders' specific alcohol- or drug-related offenses (McMurran, 2007). Although research has emphasized recidivism and treatment outcomes, family and other support networks are important (Lemieux, 2002). There is little in the literature on how to provide family-oriented treatment within correctional programs.

Future reforms in the provision of substance abuse treatment services need to include evidence-based criminal justice practices and the use of risk assessment instruments at pretrial, sentencing, probation, and parole. Individual states need to arrange to conduct periodic evaluations of new or existing criminal justice policies and require progress reports on the implementation and success of programs (American Civil Liberties Union, 2011). See Box 10.4 for recommendations for meeting the needs of criminal offenders with substance abuse problems.

> ### BOX 10.4 Recommendations for Meeting the Needs of Substance-Abusing Offenders
>
> 1. Risk–needs assessments need to be used to determine the severity of the substance abuse problem and its relationship to criminal activity.
> 2. Intervention needs to be focused on reducing the risks to people most likely to continue criminal offending and substance abuse.
> 3. Supervision of offenders on release from correctional facilities needs to be tailored to the risks of offenders, particularly the highest risk offenders, as well as ensuring that people in need of continued treatment receive it.
> 4. Intermediate sanctions need to be available for people who relapse; however, those who are not compliant with probation or parole requirements do not necessarily need to be reincarcerated but should receive increased community supervision and services.
> 5. Community integration needs to focus on removing barriers to housing and employment, supporting healthy family relationships, and ensuring that substance abuse and mental health problems continue to be addressed.
> 6. Data collection and outcomes measures are critical to evaluating the effectiveness of substance abuse treatment for criminal offenders; partnerships between criminal justice professionals and researchers can contribute to the growing body of research on what works.
>
> *Source:* Massachusetts Bar Association Drug Policy Task Force (2009b).

A collaboration among the Council of State Governments Justice Center in New York, the National Institute of Corrections, and the Bureau of Justice Assistance holds promise in the development of a treatment framework for addressing the needs of people with substance abuse and mental health problems in correctional populations to both reduce recidivism and support recovery (Osher, D'Amora, Plotkin, Jarrett, & Eggleston, 2012). The framework emphasizes the need to determine ways to allocate most appropriately the scarce resources available today. It recommends categorizing offenders and their treatment needs, and it arranges them into eight categories according to problem severity:

- Group 1: Low criminogenic risk, low severity of substance abuse, and low mental illness
- Group 2: Low criminogenic risk, low severity of substance abuse, and medium or high mental illness
- Group 3: Low criminogenic risk, medium or high substance abuse, and low severity of mental illness
- Group 4: Low criminogenic risk, medium or high substance abuse, and medium or high mental illness

- Group 5: Medium or high criminogenic risk, low substance abuse, and low mental illness
- Group 6: Medium or high criminogenic risk, low substance abuse, and medium or high mental illness
- Group 7: Medium or high criminogenic risk, medium or high substance abuse, and low mental illness
- Group 8: Medium or high criminogenic risk, medium or high substance abuse, and medium or high mental illness

The adoption of this framework, as well as the implementation of new policies and treatment, can go a long way toward improving treatment, supporting agency collaboration, and providing the basis for research results that can be compared (Osher et al., 2012).

SUMMARY AND CONCLUSION

There is a strong association between crime and substance abuse. Racism permeates the criminal justice system and has resulted in long mandatory minimum sentences for drug offenses, especially for African Americans. Overall, there is evidence that treatment for alcohol and drug problems by criminal offenders can reduce crime. A variety of options exist to assist criminal offenders with substance abuse problems, including drug courts, outpatient treatment, inpatient treatment, incarceration, and therapeutic communities. Drug courts and therapeutic communities both show strong treatment effectiveness.

Early screening, assessment, and diagnosis are critical to determining the appropriate sanctions and matching offenders to the appropriate available treatment. Screening and assessment of people arrested for drunk driving can help to determine appropriate sanctions. Early interventions in the problems of juvenile offenders can result in less harsh sanctions, can support healthier functioning of the family, and hold the potential of reducing substance abuse as juveniles grow into adults. Research can help develop greater understanding of the treatment needs of women in the criminal justice system.

The recently developed treatment framework for addressing the substance abuse and mental health needs of correctional populations can foster improvement in treatment, support collaboration among human service agencies, and encourage research protocols that allow comparisons of data.

SUBSTANCE ABUSE PREVENTION

The topic of prevention is among the most important in the substance abuse field. Although we know much about the ravages of substance abuse and addiction, we seem to know far less about how to help people avoid these pitfalls. Can we find the right type and amount of education and prevention activities to deter substance use and abuse? What is too little drug education? What is too much drug education—a level that turns off youth and adults alike?

Repeatedly, over many years, we have asked how we can stop substance abuse and addiction. Thankfully, we have moved beyond former First Lady Nancy Reagan's "Just Say No" campaign of the 1980s to more genuine efforts to understand risk and protective factors for substance abuse. One main question is, How do we know whether prevention efforts are successful? That is, How can we know that we have prevented individual children and adolescents from developing addiction problems? This chapter explores what is known about substance abuse prevention and what is not yet known. It covers school-based programs, including Drug Abuse Resistance Education (DARE), the importance of community partnerships in prevention efforts, and the need for culturally sensitive programming.

A number of models of prevention have been developed through the years. The public health approach is an alternative to the disease model, which claims alcoholics and addicts have a disease, and an alternative to the moral model, which blames individuals for their addiction. The *public health model* is a comprehensive effort to enhance public health and safety through education, prevention, and treatment. The public health model focuses on the effects of substance use on the physical health of individuals while remaining free of judgment about substance abuse (Jonas, 1997). Prevention models can also provide information, bolster self-esteem so that individuals can feel confident in refusing substances, and reduce the influence of other people who encourage substance-using or substance-abusing behavior. Substance abuse prevention efforts and studies of their effectiveness are aimed mostly at children and adolescents, although public health efforts include adult prevention as well.

Prevention activities in the 1960s and 1970s emphasized programs within schools to provide information on drugs. The belief at the time was that if accurate information were disseminated, youth would gain knowledge, cultivate negative attitudes toward drug use, and not begin to use or stop using substances (Stevens & Smith, 2005). These programs often employed scare tactics designed more to cultivate fear than to impart scientific knowledge.

The 1980s were an especially important time for substance abuse prevention. Since the early 1980s there has been a "rapid development" (Springer et al., 2004, p. 171) of prevention programs aimed at substance abuse. This attention to prevention activities was fostered by new federal laws. The Drug-Free Schools and Communities Act of 1986, followed by the Drug-Free Schools and Communities Act amendments of 1989, required education and prevention activities in schools and colleges. Failure to comply can result in loss of funding. The Safe and Drug-Free School and Communities Act of 1994 provided state funding for drug and violence prevention as essential components that promote school safety and reduce the demand for drugs (Center for Effective Collaboration and Practice, 1994). Among the findings of Congress at the time was that the "seventh National Education Goal provides that by 2000, all schools in America will be free of drugs and violence and the unauthorized presence of firearms and alcohol, and offer a disciplined environment that is conducive to learning" (Center for Effective Collaboration and Practice, 1994, p. 1). This was a hopeful time in prevention that had goals far beyond today's reality.

Most research has sought to evaluate individual programs; the research that has evaluated several substance abuse prevention programs at the same time typically has been school based (Springer et al., 2004). In the 1980s and earlier, substance abuse prevention for adolescents used a "simplistic approach" to teach adolescents in school-based programs to resist peer pressure related to substance use (Lee & Goddard, 1989, p. 301). Today's programs are far more comprehensive and have the benefit of research to show effectiveness and efficacy (positive results in randomized controlled research trials).

Overall, there is evidence that drug abuse prevention works well (Valente, Chou, & Pentz, 2007). Programs that are simple in design and implementation are more likely to be effective than more complex programs that require coordination involving lots of people and that require special skills sets (Dusenbury, Brannigan, Falco, & Hansen, 2003).

BASIC TYPES OF PREVENTION

Initial prevention efforts focused around three basic types of prevention: primary, secondary, and tertiary. *Primary prevention* refers to efforts to keep people from starting to use alcohol, drugs, or both in an attempt to avoid future addiction. It can include preventing drug use or avoiding problem use. For example, primary prevention programs impart knowledge on the consequences of substance abuse but can also help evaluate the level of risk for children of substance abusers (Merikangas, Dierker, & Fenton, 1998). *Secondary prevention* refers to reducing the effects of substance abuse by providing early intervention. Needle exchange programs are examples of secondary prevention. Another example is school-based prevention programs for children and adolescents who have already started to use alcohol, drugs, or both. *Tertiary prevention* refers to addiction treatment, although most people would not consider this a form of prevention. It is defined as a type of prevention because it aims to reduce the effects of substance abuse on the addict or alcoholic, as well as on family members and the community. Examples of tertiary prevention include inpatient treatment programs and outpatient counseling for substance abusers.

The substance abuse field has moved beyond these three basic categories of prevention and refined efforts to develop and expand types of prevention. *Universal prevention*, a form of primary prevention, refers to prevention activities developed to reach large segments of the population without regard to risk factors for substance abuse (Borsari, 2014). School-based programs for all children and adolescents are an example of universal prevention (Adelman & Taylor, 2003; National Institute on Drug Abuse, 1997; Texas Department of State Health Services, 2010). *Selective prevention*, also a form of primary prevention, refers to activities developed to reach specific groups known to be at higher risk of substance abuse. For example, these programs can target children from substance-abusing families or people from poor communities with high crime rates. *Indicated prevention*, a form of secondary prevention, refers to efforts to intervene early with individuals who show early symptoms of developing substance abuse problems. Even individuals who may not have developed a substance abuse problem may be considered high risk because of psychological or behavioral problems, school failure, or lack of social support (National Institute on Drug Abuse, 1997; Texas Department of State Health Services, 2010).

Timing of the delivery of prevention services is an important topic in prevention research. One argument is that because risk factors for substance abuse can been seen at very early ages, this is the optimal time to engage the individual in prevention activities. However, early adolescence is a typical time at which prevention activities begin (Gottfredson & Wilson, 2003). Today most prevention efforts are targeted at middle school students. At the other end of the spectrum, we ask how long prevention activities can serve as protective factors against substance abuse. Not surprisingly, prevention effects diminish over time (Brown, Guo, Singer, Downes, & Brinales, 2007; Ennett, Tobler, Ringwalt, & Flewelling, 1994).

School-Based Prevention Programs

School-based prevention programs have garnered the most research attention. School-based programs are known mostly as primary prevention or universal prevention programs. There is general support for both social skills training and cognitive behavioral approaches with youth. An early study of prevention programs reported that social skills training rather than information-focused sessions were more effective (Botvin, 1990). In their meta-analysis, Wilson, Gottfredson, and Najaka (2001) reported cognitive behavioral and behavioral interventions to be the most effective prevention programs. Mentoring, tutoring, work–study, and recreational programs and counseling that did not have a cognitive behavioral or behavioral orientation were found to be ineffective.

The Substance Abuse and Mental Health Services Administration (SAMHSA) committed to school-based prevention activities by developing the Safe Schools/Healthy Students initiative in 1999. This initiative promotes positive mental health and safe schools by cultivating working relationships among parents, schools, and community agencies (Hyde, 2013).

It has long been known that the earlier children use substances, the more likely they are to develop substance abuse and addiction problems (Beets et al., 2009). This is an important reason that research findings have tried to tease out the optimal time for prevention activities in the lives of youth. Yet there is mixed research on whether it is preferable to begin prevention activities in elementary school or wait until middle school, and these uncertain results are a compelling reason to continue to research this topic (Marsiglia, Kulis, Yabiku, Nieri, & Coleman, 2011). One reason to continue with universal prevention in elementary school is not only to reduce the drug use behaviors but to also address the attitudes that precede risky behaviors.

A study in the early years of prevention research reported that school prevention programs can teach basic information on alcohol and drugs, foster positive self-esteem, teach good decision-making and simple refusal skills, and successfully involve parents (Hahn & Papazian, 1987). In support of prevention activities for the youngest children, Hahn and Papazian (1987) declared: "The preschool children of today are the potential substance abusers of tomorrow" (p. 169). Elementary school students may be easier to engage because they may not have had the opportunities to try alcohol and drugs that middle school students have tried. The effectiveness of elementary school prevention activities is also likely to rest on follow-up prevention activities in middle school (Marsiglia et al., 2011).

In a study of 1,670 children of Mexican heritage, the prevention curriculum had no effect on substance use in middle school when it was provided only to fifth-grade children (Marsiglia et al., 2011). Yet offering the prevention curriculum titled Keepin' It REAL—for refuse, explain, avoid, and leave—that was provided in the seventh grade saw a reduction in alcohol, tobacco, marijuana, and inhalants. Overall, starting early in elementary school did not bring the desired results; middle school interventions were more effective.

A 5-year study of the Positive Action program was implemented in 20 public schools from kindergarten to fifth or sixth grade on three Hawaiian islands (Beets et al., 2009). Positive Action is a holistic and interactive social and character development program employing multiple components to improve behavior and academic performance. The program reduced the chances of using drugs and alcohol by approximately 58%, a huge success.

Today most school-based substance abuse prevention programs are aimed at middle school students (Stigler, Neusel, & Perry, 2011). In addition, most school programs are delivered by teachers (Gottfredson & Wilson, 2003). DARE is an important exception; in this program, uniformed police officers serve as the trained instructors, as discussed later in this chapter.

Overall, interactive programs that involve students and support the development of interpersonal skills show greater effectiveness than lecture-type noninteractive programs (Tobler & Stratton, 1997; Tobler et al., 2000). Interactive programs can include small-group activities and role-playing (Stigler et al., 2011).

In a study of 12- to 15-year-olds in Spain, students were assigned to a full prevention program group offering a variety of activities, a social skills group, a problem-solving group, or a control group (Espada, Griffin, Pereira, Orgiles, & Garcia-Fernandez, 2012). Students were surveyed before the prevention program, after completing the program, and again at 1 year. Although the three groups that received prevention services reduced alcohol use, the most significant positive finding in reducing use was for the students who participated in the full program with all components. This serves as a reminder that multiple prevention strategies offered within a comprehensive framework may be the best approach in substance abuse prevention.

Studies have made comparisons between teacher-provided prevention programs and student-provided prevention programs. One study compared four options in prevention programming: teacher-provided prevention, teacher-provided prevention with "booster" sessions, peer-provided prevention, and peer-provided prevention with booster sessions (Botvin, Baker, Filazzola, & Botvin, 1990). It found that the peer-led session in the seventh grade with follow-up booster sessions in the eighth grade reduced tobacco, marijuana, and alcohol use. In a meta-analysis, the most effective form of instruction was peer-alone delivery of prevention; this form was more effective than no-peer involvement and more effective than combined peer- and teacher-provided prevention programs (Gottfredson & Wilson, 2003).

Most studies of school-based prevention have been completed in urban school systems. A meta-analysis of 22 studies in rural student samples reported "a modest but consistent beneficial impact of drug prevention programs on later use as well as level of use" (Brown et al., 2007, p. 29).

An important challenge to effective prevention programs is to provide accurate information while not making drug use seem appealing. Failures of early prevention activities were attributed to the scare tactics thought to prevent drug use. Some research suggests that opposition to drug use can backfire because some youth have more knowledge about drugs and their effects and can reject the program as naive or even untruthful (Botvin et al., 1990; Brown & Kreft, 1998; Gottfredson & Wilson, 2003). The fact that drugs are illegal or forbidden can make them more appealing to some youth (Adelman & Taylor, 2003).

High-Risk Youth

Today, with universal prevention activities so popular, all students tend to receive the same types of prevention programs. However, there is concern that students at high risk of developing substance abuse problems may need more intensive services for prevention, intervention, or both. It is estimated that 5% to 15% of the student population is at high risk for substance abuse (Carboni, 2007).

In the 1960s and 1970s there was little research on risk factors for drug abuse prevention, and over time far more attention has been paid to youth who are at risk of developing substance abuse problems. Risk factors typically include living in poverty, family problems such as abuse and neglect, early aggressive behaviors, academic failure, and ready availability of drugs and alcohol. Parental substance abuse has an especially strong association with youth being at high risk (Merikangas et al., 1998). Some researchers have categorized the risk factors for substance abuse as falling within three major categories: the social environment, the family, and the individual risk factors. Research in the 1980s emphasized two risk factors over others: the social influences on substance use and the norms that favor substance use (Hawkins, Catalano, & Miller, 1992).

Research that focuses on youth deficits that correlate with substance abuse is the flip side of the coin that focuses on protective factors that place some children and adolescents at low risk for substance abuse (Lee & Goddard, 1989). Protective factors include a strong family and community that have sufficient emotional and financial resources to care for children. The deficit perspective focuses on families "needing help from experts who do for the family what it is incapable of doing for itself" (Lee & Goddard, 1989, p. 302). In contrast, the family strengths perspective supports empowerment by building on existing strengths and supports motivation while reducing resistance to change. By cultivating and strengthening family responsibility and control, family members can see that they can overcome a family history of substance abuse and are better able to prevent substance abuse in their children.

In 1995, SAMHSA and the Center for Substance Abuse Prevention funded a national 5-year evaluation of 46 prevention programs aimed at high-risk youth (Springer et al., 2004). Positive results in terms of reduced substance use emphasized strong behavioral life skills, focused on self-reflection, and engaged youth for significant periods. Although the reviews are mixed, targeting high-risk populations can be more successful than focusing on low-risk groups (Gottfredson & Wilson, 2003).

Schools on their own should not be expected to prevent substance abuse among children and adolescents (Carboni, 2007). Parental and community involvement are important as well. Some school-based prevention programs include parental involvement. An early study of parents of sixth graders aimed at substance abuse prevention reported strongly positive results (Grady, Gersick, & Boratynski, 1985). The curriculum, consisting of six sessions, found significant gains in parental decision-making facilitation and listening skills and concluded that "the parent program was highly successful in achieving its short-term objectives" (Grady et al., 1985, p. 548). This can speak to the importance of early intervention in elementary school, when the family has greater influence over children, than in middle school, when peer influence becomes stronger (Marsiglia et al., 2011).

There is also a distinction between having effective curriculum content and having effective delivery of the curriculum. In a national sample of both public and private schools, Ennett et al. (2003) reported that most providers of school-based prevention programs had effective content (62.25%) but that far fewer (17.44%) had effective delivery. Only 14.23% had both an effective curriculum and an effective delivery. Effective delivery is correlated with fidelity, which refers to the degree to which the people who implement the prevention program adhere to the curriculum "*as intended by the program developers*" (Dusenbury et al., 2003, p. 240; italics in original). Botvin et al. (1990) reported that there was a "low degree of fidelity by many teachers" (p. 56). Low fidelity or poor implementation of the prevention curriculum can result in reduced effectiveness.

Some fidelity problems include not completing the entire curriculum. Another issue is that training of teachers may not be adequate to ensure adherence to the prescribed curriculum (Dusenbury et al., 2003). Little is known about how staff training affects the delivery of the curriculum. For example, training sessions on communication strategies for HIV intervention did not necessarily translate into the outreach efforts of participants in the training sessions (Hong et al., 2005). One concern is that many teachers may feel they are improving the program by adapting and changing it and are unaware that these changes can affect the research findings on the effectiveness of specific programs (Dusenbury et al., 2003).

Overall, the many developments since school-based prevention efforts began in the 1960s have been generally worthwhile and successful. Stigler et al. (2011) conclude, "Given the predominance of school in the lives of youth, using school as a central coordinating institution for primary prevention and linking it to families, worksites, media, and community policies is an efficient public health approach to alcohol use prevention that also can be efficacious" (p. 160). See Box 11.1 for a summary of factors associated with effective substance abuse prevention programs.

Drug Abuse Resistance Education

DARE, the best known of prevention programs for youth, operates from the social skills training model, that is, supporting students to learn the skills to refuse drugs. DARE was developed by the Los Angeles Police Department and the Los Angeles Unified School District in 1983 (Ennett et al., 1994). By 1994 it was being used in 60% of schools in the United States (Botvin & Botvin, 1994). Today it is used in about 75% of school districts nationally and in 43 countries (ProCon.org, 2013). Its success is in its name recognition, in its ability to be used in so many schools, and in its ability to bring attention to drug abuse.

BOX 11.1 Characteristics of Effective Substance Abuse Prevention Programs for Youth

- Have a theoretical basis
- Address social norms around the use of alcohol and drugs
- Engage the media to raise public awareness
- Build self-esteem
- Foster social skills that help resist peer pressure
- Use interactive teaching methods
- Use peer leaders in prevention programs
- Offer continuity of programming with sessions over several years
- Train facilitators and support them in their work
- Ensure that the program is aimed at the appropriate developmental age
- Provide booster sessions to maintain preventive effects over time
- Ensure that programming is culturally sensitive

Sources: Skiba, Monroe, and Wodarski (2004); Stigler, Neusel, and Perry (2011).

However, "the results of DARE have been disappointing" (Botvin & Botvin, 1994, p. 770). Ennett et al. (1994), in a meta-analysis of eight studies in 1994, reported that the effects of DARE were "smaller than those for interactive programs" (p. 1398) and noted that their results "suggest that DARE's core curriculum effect on drug use relative to whatever drug education was offered in the control schools is slight and, except for tobacco use, is not statistically significant" (p. 1398). They concluded that "DARE's limited influence on adolescent drug use behavior contrasts with the program's popularity and prevalence" (Ennett et al., 1994, p. 1399). DARE uses significant financial resources that could be put toward programs that show greater effectiveness.

DARE provides curricula for kindergarteners through high school seniors but over the years has changed its focus to middle school grades (Gottfredson & Wilson, 2003). More recently, a study of 420 parents of fifth and sixth graders reported that they did not see an effect on their child's academic performance or attendance but felt positively about their child's understanding of drug use and improved views of police officers (Lucas, 2008). Parents reported their own greater awareness of substance abuse and more conversations with their children about substance abuse stemming from the children's DARE experiences.

It is likely that DARE will continue to be controversial, especially considering the mixed research findings regarding its effectiveness. Another concern about DARE is that using uniformed police officers as teachers supports the message that substance abuse is a law enforcement issue rather than a public health and social policy issue (Zeese & Lewin, 1998). However, DARE is now a large industry and overall seems entrenched and undeterred, despite the lack of evidence of its effectiveness: DARE will hold its 27th annual international training conference in Texas in July 2014.

COMMUNITY PREVENTION EFFORTS

Various community partnerships with primary and secondary schools, social service agencies, and colleges and universities can go a long way to cultivating and strengthening prevention programs. Families that have both substance abuse and mental health issues can especially benefit from these professional collaborations (Council on School Health and Committee on Substance Abuse, 2007). Local colleges and universities can provide the research expertise needed to evaluate the quality and effectiveness of programming.

Coalitions are important in providing drug abuse prevention programs because they include a variety of perspectives, including education, parent groups, local politicians, law enforcement, health programs, and businesses (Valente et al., 2007). These coalitions can do much more to identify needs, plan prevention programs, and reach a wider audience than only one agency can. A coalition, through shared missions, values, and goals, can find a balance between building a cohesive group and seeking connections to organizations outside of the coalition.

An example of a national effort to combat underage alcohol use came from the federal SAMHSA when it began to coordinate Town Hall Meetings across the country in 2006 (SAMHSA, 2012a). The aim of these meetings is to offer communities an opportunity to learn about underage drinking and its associated consequences while simultaneously using evidence-based prevention activities. The Town Hall Meetings occurred in 2006 and, most recently, in 2010. The number of meetings has grown consistently to 2,021 meetings in the United States in 2010. These meetings ensure that participants have up-to-date research findings on underage alcohol use and abuse. Almost half of the community-based organizations that sponsored the Town Hall Meetings in 2010 indicated that they planned to offer more. Two-thirds of the community-based organizations planned to host future prevention events. This is evidence that public awareness campaigns can be effective and cultivate collaboration among community agencies. One participant commented about the benefits of the Town Hall Meeting: "Our THM [Town Hall Meeting] was a collaboration between various organizations, which ensured success as well as great attendance. Additionally, the THM served as a springboard for other community events related to underage drinking prevention" (SAMHSA, 2012a, p. 8).

SAMHSA also offers a National Registry of Evidence-Based Programs and Practices to assist in developing new programs and to offer collaboration with prevention professionals. This is a database of more than 300 interventions for substance abuse prevention, as well as mental health and substance abuse

BOX 11.2 The SAMHSA Registry

SAMHSA (2013d) offers a registry, called the National Registry of Evidence-Based Programs and Practices, of more than 300 interventions that have been evaluated for research quality and readiness for dissemination. The project connects the community to those who can assist in developing treatment and prevention interventions. For each program, a number of characteristics are placed in the registry, including an overview of the project, research outcomes, ratings for research quality and readiness for dissemination, and contact information. The registry can serve as an initial step to assess what kinds of interventions may meet the needs of groups wanting to use prevention activities and then put them in touch with program developers.

Source: Substance Abuse and Mental Health Services Administration (2013d).

treatment. The purpose is to provide access to the public on effective programs and practices to assist them in developing their own programs. Although registration within the system is voluntary, all listings in the registry have been evaluated regarding the quality of the research and its readiness for dissemination (SAMHSA, 2013d). See Box 11.2 for a more detailed description of the National Registry of Evidence-Based Programs and Practices offered by SAMHSA.

PREVENTION OF COLLEGE SUBSTANCE ABUSE

Prevention of substance abuse has been an important public health issue for many years. Substance abuse among college students can be associated with freshmen being away from home for the first time, with fraternities and hazing, or with a continuation of substance use from the high school years. College drinking is more likely among young men than among young women and among White students than among African Americans and Asians (Javier, Belgrave, Hill, & Richardson, 2013). However, there is good evidence that prevention strategies can be successful in reducing substance use among all college students (Saltz, Welker, Paschall, Feeney, & Fabiano, 2009). A study of a brief intervention with female college students was effective in reducing alcohol use during the first semester and kept some women from starting to use alcohol during the first year (LaBrie et al., 2009). Another study reported that including parents in prevention activities was associated with a reduction in freshman students in initiating alcohol use and, for women, with "slowing growth in drinking over the freshman year" (Ichiyama et al., 2009, p. 67).

In an analysis of data from the 2011 College Health Survey, it was found that minority students thought other students were using substances more frequently than they were (Javier et al., 2013). Because student use of substances is influenced by their perceptions of use by their peers, this may place minority students are risk of great substance use. Javier et al. (2013) recommend college health and prevention activities that are gender and racially or ethnically specific.

In an innovative approach to strengthening college prevention from the National Institute on Alcohol Abuse and Alcoholism, teams of researchers focused on college drinking were matched with colleges and universities interested in reducing alcohol use among students (DeJong, Larimer, Wood, & Hartman, 2009). This Rapid Response initiative was successful in fostering higher quality research using evidence-based strategies to address college drinking, "a daunting problem on many campuses" (DeJong et al., 2009, p. 5).

Today there are many national initiatives that are used to address college substance abuse, mostly drinking, but that need to focus on changing the campus climate related to alcohol and drugs. Colleges need to develop clear substance use and abuse policies and to enforce sanctions consistently (National Center on Addiction and Substance Abuse at Columbia University, 2007). Alcohol and tobacco ads should be banned on campus and at sporting events. There needs to be training of faculty, staff, and students to recognize signs and symptoms of substance abuse and how to appropriately respond. Campus health centers need to routinely screen and provide necessary intervention while ensuring that services are provided by qualified substance abuse professionals.

CULTURAL SENSITIVITY IN SUBSTANCE ABUSE PREVENTION

Cultural sensitivity in the prevention context refers to racial or ethnic and cultural characteristics, experiences, and values that are included within the planning, development, and execution of substance abuse prevention activities (Resnicow, Soler, & Braithwaite, 2000). In this book we have seen differences in racial and ethnic minorities' use and abuse of substances, and now our attention turns to differences in substance abuse prevention.

In reality, most research on school-based interventions focuses on White urban and suburban youth (Stigler et al., 2011). It is known that acculturation puts youth at higher risk for substance use—this could be because of American norms that can support drug use and because of the stress of participating in two cultures (Marsiglia et al., 2011). Yet little is known about the responses of racial or ethnic groups to drug prevention (Resnicow et al., 2000). *Surface structure* efforts refer to how prevention efforts fit within a specific group, such as locations, food, music, and clothing preferred by the specific groups. *Deep structure* refers to the larger social, cultural, environmental, and emotional factors that influence behavior in a specific population.

For example, engaging parents and other adults may be preferable for African American youth, while focusing on peer pressure may be more appropriate for White youth.

An example of an important prevention program for minority adolescents is a 5-year research prevention project funded by SAMHSA. This program examines the effects of primary prevention for substance abuse and HIV/AIDS through refusal skills training and family educational skills related to substance abuse prevention (Wodarski & MacMaster, 2012).

In building on the study described previously for Mexican children in the Keepin' It REAL program (Marsiglia et al., 2011), another program was devised for students considered by teachers to be at high risk of substance abuse (Marsiglia, Ayers, Gance-Cleveland, Mettler, & Booth, 2012). The REAL Groups for seventh graders, a secondary prevention program, supplements the Keepin' It REAL program. The authors reported that Mexican students who participated in the REAL Groups had reduced alcohol use over students who did not participate (Marsiglia et al., 2011).

The Rural African American Families Health Project evaluated the efficacy of the Strong African American Families–Teen (SAAF-T) program (Kogan et al., 2012). In the project, 502 rural African American families with a child in 10th grade were assigned to SAAF-T or a family-centered program with the same five sessions of programming for families in either group. Youth in the SAAF-T group had higher levels of protective family management skills. In a separate journal article based on the same research, substance abuse problems were reduced by more than 30% in the sample receiving the SAAF-T program, compared with the young people in the alternative family-centered program (Brody et al., 2012). Brody et al. (2012) concluded, "The availability of preventive interventions designed for black adolescents, particularly those in rural areas, is crucial because few, if any, mental health or substance use programs exist for this population" (p. 114).

African American churches have also participated in prevention efforts and hold the potential for more prevention activities. In one study, a local university provided training and technical assistance to 23 faith-based organizations (Brown et al., 2006). Fifty-eight percent implemented the prevention programs the university had proposed. Overall, the experience was perceived as positive by participants.

As discussed in Chapter 8, of all ethnicities in the United States, Native Americans have suffered the most from substance abuse problems, lending even more immediacy to the need for prevention services. Arizona has offered a number of innovative prevention approaches. For example, the Hopi Tribe organized a task force to combat methamphetamine abuse (Gerard, 2005). Suicide prevention and stress reduction activities have been adopted by the Zuni, the White Mountain Apache Tribe, and the Gila River Indian Community. On a national level, the Native American Center for Excellence's Prevention Technical Assistance Resource Center was established with support from SAMHSA in 2007. This is a national project to promote substance abuse prevention programs in Native American communities across the country. The 2013 Native American Service to Science Initiative, sponsored by SAMHSA's Center for Substance Abuse Prevention, offers technical services to support evaluation of the effectiveness of Native American substance abuse prevention programs (SAMHSA, 2013c).

Overall, culturally sensitive prevention programs need to respond to the patterns and prevalence of substance abuse, as well as to the predictors and risk factors for substance use (Resnicow et al., 2000).

COST ISSUES

Substance abuse prevention activities can be cost-effective. A widely quoted statistic is that for each dollar spent on substance abuse prevention, there is a savings of up to $10 (National Institute on Drug Abuse, 2011). In their study of prevention, Wells, Lemak, and D'Aunno (2006) looked at decisions to incorporate prevention activities into their substance abuse treatment programs and the factors that supported adding prevention services. Because there is usually not a financial incentive to provide prevention services, managed care contracts typically do not provide them. For programs that receive Medicare and Medicaid funding, there is likely a greater opportunity to support the addition of prevention activities. No hospital-based treatment programs in the study offered prevention programs, whereas mental health centers were the most likely to offer prevention services. The concern about finances in today's economy has a negative effect on offering prevention and outreach services when financial incentives for treatment agencies do not exist.

There is recent information that prevention activities in the United States have been cut back, perhaps as a result of challenging financial times since 2008. In 2012, students age 12 to 17 who had seen or heard substance abuse prevention messages within schools were at 75%, a decline from the 78.8% in 2002. Students who received prevention messages outside of school have also declined over time—from 83.2% in 2002 to 75.9% in 2012 (SAMHSA, 2013b). Although the prevention activities seem to be on the decline, importantly the percentage of 12- to 17-year-olds who have substance abuse problems or substance dependence is also on the decline. In 2012, 6.1% of 12- to 17-year-olds had substance abuse or dependence, down from 8.9% in 2002. The reasons for the decline in substance abuse and dependence among youth during this 10-year period remain unclear, but surely prevention programs are happy to share in taking the credit.

Overall, considering the effect of substance abuse on communities in the United States, there are ethical, moral, and economic reasons to make even greater commitments to prevention (Wells et al., 2006).

The National Institute on Drug Abuse (2011) offers some guidance gleaned from the literature on establishing quality prevention programs. See Box 11.3 for research-driven principles of effective prevention.

BOX 11.3 Principles Derived From Research on Elements of Effective Prevention Programs

1. Prevention programs need to reverse or reduce risk factors and bolster protective factors.
2. Prevention programs need to address all forms of drug abuse, including alcohol, illegal drugs, and the inappropriate use of over-the-counter and prescription drugs.
3. Prevention programs need to target the types of drug problems in specific local communities.
4. Prevention activities need to address the substance abuse problems of specific populations based on age, gender, and race/ethnicity.
5. Family-based prevention programs need to incorporate parent training and foster family cohesiveness.
6. Prevention programs need to provide appropriate material for very young children by addressing aggressive behavior and strengthening academic and social skills.
7. For elementary school children, prevention programs need to deter aggressive behaviors, encourage self-control and emotional awareness, and support academic improvement.
8. For middle and high school students, prevention programs need to develop drug-resistance skills, foster appropriate assertiveness, build positive peer relationships, and encourage strong academic performance.
9. Universal prevention programs need to target important transition points, such as when students move from elementary school to middle school and then to high school.
10. Community prevention programs need to integrate two or more programs that have been found to be effective in bolstering total effectiveness. This can include offering school-based programming along with family-based programs.
11. Groups targeting prevention activities should include consistent messages offered in a variety of settings, such as schools, religious organizations, clubs, and media outlets.
12. Prevention programs need to adapt to the needs of communities and maintain their core elements, such as how the program is organized, what content is included, and how the program is delivered.
13. Prevention programs need to be provided over a long period and to include "booster" sessions.
14. Prevention programs need to train teachers on substance use and abuse topics and on appropriate classroom management techniques.

15. Prevention programs need to incorporate interactive techniques that allow children and parents to participate through small-group discussions or role-playing.
16. Prevention programs that have shown effectiveness in research studies can be cost-effective.

Source: National Institute on Drug Abuse (2011).

GLOBAL PREVENTION EFFORTS

A number of worldwide prevention efforts are noteworthy, and the World Health Organization often takes the lead. The global initiative sponsored by the World Health Organization and the United Nations Office on Drugs and Crime implemented a primary prevention project between 1998 and 2003 to reduce substance use and abuse among youth (World Health Organization, n.d.). It focused on eight countries: Belarus, the Philippines, Tanzania, Thailand, South Africa, the Russian Federation, Vietnam, and Zambia. Overall, the United Nations Office on Drugs and Crime (2013) focuses on evidence-based family skills training programs, programs offered in schools by specially trained teachers, and workplace prevention activities.

RESEARCH CHALLENGES

Although research has been substantial and sheds light on effective strategies for prevention, more remains to be known. Research on school-based approaches is limited in generalizability to school populations (Botvin et al., 1990). Meta-analyses do not typically distinguish between programs for high-risk youth and those aimed at all youth, another important area for further research (Gottfredson & Wilson, 2003). A family history of substance abuse is a strong predictor of vulnerability to addiction; therefore, research needs to address the transmission process in terms of both genetic and environmental factors (Merikangas et al., 1998). Because program evaluation is a critical component for prevention activities to ensure effectiveness (Skiba, Monroe, & Wodarski, 2004), prevention programs that lack the ability to evaluate their activities can collaborate with researchers to assess program effectiveness and efficacy. See Box 11.4 for recommendations for future research on substance abuse prevention.

> ### BOX 11.4 Prevention Topics in Need of Research
>
> Future research on prevention topics should include the following:
>
> 1. Distinguishing between the effectiveness of universal prevention activities for all and the effectiveness of prevention within high-risk groups (Gottfredson & Wilson, 2003)
> 2. Comparisons of prevention programs aimed at different school levels: elementary school, middle school, and high school (Gottfredson & Wilson, 2003)
> 3. The cumulative effects of prevention activities starting in elementary school and moving to middle school and beyond (Gottfredson & Wilson, 2003)
> 4. Development of a consistent methodology to measure the fidelity in school-based prevention programs (Dusenbury et al., 2003)
>
> *Sources:* Dusenbury, Brannigan, Falco, and Hansen (2003); Gottfredson and Wilson (2003).

SUMMARY AND CONCLUSION

There have been considerable efforts to prevent substance abuse in children and adolescents. Prevention efforts initially focused on primary prevention, the ability to stop drug use or abuse before it becomes a problem; secondary prevention, the intervention in early-stage abuse problems, and tertiary prevention, the treatment provided to people with substance abuse problems to curb the spread to those around them. Newer terminology includes universal prevention, which has activities aimed at an entire population, typically children and adolescents; selective prevention, which focuses on people at high risk of developing substance abuse problems, and indicated prevention, a form of secondary prevention, which is designed to intervene early in the actions of people developing substance abuse problems.

Overall, programs that target middle school children and are provided by peers tend to be considered the most effective. Although the DARE program has mixed results, tending toward the negative in recent years, it continues to enjoy great popularity in schools across the United States. Programs that offer culturally sensitive prevention programming are needed, as are programs to address the needs of college students. It is important that the quest continues to find the most effective prevention strategies.

THE FUTURE OF SUBSTANCE ABUSE TREATMENT

*A*fter considering all the information provided in the preceding chapters, we are left to ponder what this all means for the future of substance abuse treatment. Do the answers lie within complex research findings published in scholarly journal articles, within the individual, within the family, or within the community? Some parts of the answers lie in each place. From complex research methodologies we learn about the patterns of substance abuse problems, as well as the patterns of recovery from comparisons between experimental and control groups. From work with clients, we learn about the power of the individual to make choices to work toward recovery. From the family, we learn about the importance of support and interventions to steer someone toward a path of recovery. From the community, we learn about the power of prevention activities and the importance of providing community support services to meet the needs of substance abusers and their families.

We see in this chapter the growing complexities in research methods, yet the field is still struggling to provide the basics such as a fast and courteous response to requests for help. Unfortunately, the field continues to need the research that shows clients have a hard time accessing care and that agencies providing services do not necessarily provide a smooth experience from first phone call through treatment completion. We review the quality-of-life issues for substance abusers and the research challenges that the field continues to face. We also examine workforce issues in the substance abuse treatment field.

In focusing on high-quality research methods in the study of substance abuse treatment, are we limiting the ways in which we view successful treatment? If we emphasize "proof," we may reduce opportunities to try new things in treatment. Do we make a mistake by emphasizing only evidence-based practices as determined by randomized controlled trials? Probably. Sometimes there is a divine intervention or a spiritual awakening, and sometimes alcoholics and addicts become "sick and tired of being sick and tired."

At its simplest, we ask what can be done to maximize the opportunities for success for clients and their families. More than arguing over counseling styles, we need to work on public awareness that help exists and ensure the ready availability of help to individuals. Although we seek to help others in their recovery, there can be misery and suffering in abstinence as well. Hope for the future in helping others is clearly demonstrated within self-help groups that continue to be strong and popular in the United States today.

TREATMENT THAT RESPONDS TO CLIENT NEEDS

Substance abuse treatment organizations are already challenged in serving clients, but in the future they will need to improve quality of care while keeping costs low (Hoffman et al., 2012). Changes will need to be made to the structure and funding of substance abuse treatment to meet the needs of substance abusers "on demand" (Carr et al., 2008).

As we have seen, access to treatment remains a huge problem, especially for people with few to no financial resources. There are differences between private and public substance abuse treatment programs in terms of patient characteristics, as well as staff characteristics, as determined by sources of funding (Roman, Ducharme, & Knudsen, 2006). Pharmacologic treatments are more likely to be offered in private programs, and contingency management is more likely to be provided by public programs. Because public programs are more likely to serve people with low incomes, it is not surprising that the opportunity to earn rewards is so appealing. According to Roman et al. (2006):

> Given these successes (of people in recovery), as well as the broad and unique value of this field's service to society in reducing and moderating wide-ranging damages, disruptions, and insanities, it is surprising to find it as a notably disorganized industry that lacks a strong voice for its own growth, survival, and generalized interests. (p. 236)

Wait for Treatment

Substance abusers understandably have a hard time waiting for treatment (Carr et al., 2008). Frankly, once they have made the decision to seek treatment, they should not have to wait. They have a greater risk of continuing to use drugs and therefore greater associated medical problems the longer they must wait to receive treatment. Reducing waiting time can avoid the consequences of delaying treatment. Research shows that 25% to 50% of people on waiting lists for treatment are not admitted to treatment programs (Quanbeck et al., 2013). Substance abusers are likely to continue their substance use. Some of those waiting for treatment may interpret this to mean they did not need treatment (Redko, Rapp, & Carlson, 2006). For people in need of detoxification—where treatment need is immediate, perhaps to stave off severe withdrawal symptoms—even waiting 2 days is an excessive amount of time. One study reported that 54% of clients experienced waiting for an appointment as a barrier to treatment (Redko et al., 2006).

As the substance abuse treatment field takes on more qualities of the business field, it has also begun to address "customer service." A focus on efficiency in the provision of services can reduce waiting times for treatment. One study reported that waiting time was reduced 37% for both inpatient and outpatient treatment—from 19.6 to 12.4 days (McCarty et al., 2007). Recommended changes can include a greater number of clients per clinician, yet such a ratio can lead to greater staff stress and staff turnover. Offering more appointment times that keep the agency open longer can also lead to increased costs for payroll, as well as infrastructure issues. Overall, an agency must pay attention to the needs of clients and the needs of staff members.

Initial phone contacts can be frustrating. In a study of researchers making phone calls to 192 substance abuse treatment clinics, the average waiting time for an appointment was 7.2 days (Quanbeck et al., 2013). As a result of this study, and working to improve responses to requests for an appointment, the time was reduced to an average of 5.8 days. In 47% of cases the first phone call to the clinic to request an appointment was met with a voicemail message or no answer to the ringing telephone. In one agency the researcher had the following experience:

> April: First attempt, phone line goes dead; second attempt, can't leave a message, voice mailbox full; third attempt is met with a recording, and I leave a message that is not returned. Two more attempts are made on different days, but the line goes dead after several rings. July: Each call attempt is met with a voicemail: however, I cannot leave a message because the "mailbox is full." I tried the operator by dialing "0" but was unable to reach anyone or leave a message. (Quanbeck et al., 2013, p. 347)

This is nothing short of appalling. It is hard to imagine that agency administrators, clinicians, and support staff members do not have an awareness of the psychological difficulty of making the first call and do not see that to then be repeatedly rebuffed is simply unacceptable. Although this kind of research is important to make these points, it is discouraging that research on agency responsiveness is needed today. The importance of that phone call to ask for help is clearly stated by Quanbeck et al. (2013): "The initial phone call a patient places to request help with addiction may be the most important call that person ever makes" (p. 348).

In a study of "walk-through exercises," volunteers played the roles of client and family members to simulate the experience of seeking treatment (Ford et al., 2007). This process of seeking treatment admission uncovered multiple problems, including lack of engagement with and conflicting information given by staff members, considerable bureaucracy, challenges in meeting the needs of clients, and agency infrastructure problems such as poor telephone and other technological systems.

It is also important to request feedback on the level of satisfaction with services received and to consider the recommendations of clients in evaluating programs and planning for system improvements (Ford et al., 2007). It serves as a reminder that in our quest to find what's effective in substance abuse treatment, we have overlooked the simple courtesies and responsiveness that can go a long way to helping people in need of treatment. Although all clinicians and administrators may be concerned about client waiting times, the onus falls to the agencies to fix the problems. See Box 12.1 for a review of important agency responses to client initiation of treatment.

Quality-of-Life Issues

Substance abuse treatment research has placed great emphasis on whether alcoholics and addicts have quit or reduced their substance use. Far less attention has been given to the subjective experiences of substance abusers and their reports of their quality of life, as well as their levels of satisfaction with treatment (De Maeyer, Vanderplasschen, & Broekaert, 2009). For substance abuse treatment, the "ultimate aim is to improve the patient's quality of life" (Laudet, 2011, p. 44). Quality-of-life research has been important in studies of mental health care, and a team from Belgium is taking the lead in bringing this research orientation into substance abuse treatment (Colpaert, De Maeyer, Broekaert, & Vanderplasschen, 2013; De Maeyer et al., 2009).

In one study of quality of life, interviews were held with clients in residential treatment. The type of substance abuse problem—alcohol or drug dependence—was not a major factor in determining the quality of life (Colpaert et al., 2013). Most important factors were the severity of the addiction problem and whether clients had a co-occurring mental health disorder, both of which were associated with lower quality of life.

BOX 12.1 Recommended Agency Responses to Client Initiation of Treatment

1. A live courteous and helpful person should answer the telephone—avoid recorded messages.
2. Reduce waiting time for an initial appointment.
3. Focus on the clinical concerns of the client at the initial assessment.
4. Reduce the need to request repetitive information from clients.
5. Identify needs during assessment, including needs for mental health services, transportation, day-care services, and financial assistance.
6. Inform clients about the agency and what the client can expect from treatment.

Source: Ford et al. (2007).

In a study of people on outpatient methadone treatment for at least 5 years, those with low quality of life reported experiencing psychological distress, taking medications for mental health problems, and being unable to move to preferred housing (De Maeyer et al., 2011). People with higher quality of life reported at least one good friend and structured daily activities. In focus groups with drug users, De Maeyer et al. (2009) reported that quality of life for respondents was primarily concerned not with physical health but with a supportive social network. This serves as an important reminder that treatment needs to include factors that promote well-being beyond addressing the substance abuse. See Box 12.2 for reflections of drug users on their hopes for the future.

RESEARCH AND ORGANIZATIONAL PRACTICE

The organizational structures of most substance abuse treatment agencies are weak and demand for treatment is great, leaving the system unable to meet additional demands for access and for better quality of care (Hoffman et al., 2012).

BOX 12.2 Reflections of Drug Users on Their Hopes for the Future

A 48-year-old man in methadone treatment:

> We all want the same; some happiness in our life. Living on the street is so hard, there is nobody who will say to you: "If I was you, I wouldn't do that." Sometimes that is the only thing that you need, that you feel that somebody cares for you. (p. 7)

A 33-year-old woman in a halfway house:

> Dependence I also find very important. That is something a lot of people, me included, have problems with. That is, I want to strive for, to be independent and to take my life in my own hands. In the past, I was always dependent on something or someone, and now it is very important to do things on my own. (p. 12)

A 26-year-old man in a halfway house:

> In the past, I was working in the construction industry. Now I am working with disabled people, and I like doing it. Those people are depending on you, they want to talk with you, and I can't imagine I would have done this before, even not for one million euros. Now, when I look at myself, I notice I have more abilities, and I want to discover what else I have to offer. (p. 12)

Source: De Maeyer, Vanderplasschen, and Broekaert (2009).

Overall, the field is fragmented and does not cultivate opportunities for clinicians and administrators from different agencies to know one another and to work together (Corredoira & Kimberly, 2006). Peers can have the strongest influence on implementing new practices, yet innovations spread slowly because of this system fragmentation, which results in lack of contact with peers (Johnson, Ford, & McCluskey, 2012).

Change comes hard in substance abuse treatment, as it generally does in health care systems and organizations. The development of evidence-based practices takes time, often long after effectiveness has been established (ATTC Network Technology Transfer Workgroup, 2011). To provide some perspective, a new medical treatment, from the time of showing its effectiveness in research demonstrations, typically takes 17 years to be generally adopted throughout the system (Balas & Boren, 2000; Green, Ottoson, Garcia, & Hiatt, 2009). It is important to remember that dissemination of information is not sufficient to create alterations and improvements in addiction treatment (Condon, Miner, Balmer, & Pintello, 2008). Beyond dissemination of research findings lies the critical development of strategies for implementation.

Delays in implementing evidence-based practices in addiction treatment can come from several directions. There is an overall tendency for people, as well as organizations, to resist change, as is seen within substance abuse treatment (Condon et al., 2008). In addition, the moral model of the past, which holds that alcoholics and addicts are "bad" people rather than "sick" people, is still alive and well. If substance abusers are seen as less deserving of help, a treatment system will not respond or is likely to offer a weak and inadequate response. Another problem in moving forward is that the substance abuse treatment field grew up outside of the medical field—it has not developed the practices and routines that can push forward new knowledge within medical specialties. New and innovative practices can also be held back by financial constraints that limit staffing and services, as well as limiting appropriate infrastructures for newer technology (Condon et al., 2008).

In these tough economic times there is evidence that substance abuse treatment programs, like all human service agencies, are looking to or may feel forced to consolidate. Although this consolidation may occur for financial reasons, on the positive side, it can offer the opportunity to improve efficiency and effectiveness of substance abuse treatment (Corredoira & Kimberly, 2006). An additional advantage is that consolidation and acquisition of smaller treatment agencies can address the history of treatment programs operating in isolation. That is, these corporations can work toward standardization of substance abuse treatment nationally to ensure quality and consistency of services (Corredoira & Kimberly, 2006; Knott, Corredoira, & Kimberly, 2008). Today, CRC Health Group, which was established in 1995, is the largest provider of behavioral health services in the United States (CRC Health Group, 2011). In addition to substance abuse treatment services, CRC Health Group provides treatment for eating disorders, learning problems, and other mental health issues within 145 facilities throughout the country. Its services are provided within a variety of settings, including outpatient and inpatient treatment programs, boarding schools, wilderness camps, and therapeutic communities.

The National Institute on Drug Abuse (NIDA), in collaboration with the Substance Abuse and Mental Health Services Administration (SAMHSA), began the Blending Initiative in 2001 to bring together researchers, clinicians, and policy makers to collaborate on developing and implementing evidence-based practices (Condon et al., 2008). This has brought about links between federal SAMHSA funding and the implementation of NIDA research activities to accelerate the transfer from research into practice. For example, the Blending Initiative has worked on accelerating the adoption of buprenorphine treatment, rapid testing for HIV in substance-abusing populations, and motivational interviewing.

As indicated earlier, the substance abuse treatment field is increasingly using concepts from business practices (Johnson et al., 2012; Knott et al., 2008). Process improvement strategies, borrowed from the business field, seek to improve quality and efficiency by providing faster service at a lower cost (Hoffman et al., 2012). The efforts to reduce waiting times for initial treatment appointments are an example of a process improvement strategy.

The Network for the Improvement of Addiction Treatment (NIATx) supports treatment agencies in using process improvement strategies to increase access to and improve retention in treatment (Hoffman et al., 2012). The NIATx website acknowledges the severity of the problem: "Between patients and caring help lies a canyon of paperwork and burdensome processes" (NIATx, 2013).

NIATx (2013) offers treatment providers ways to better respond to clients by (a) reducing the waiting period between initial contact and first appointment, (b) reducing the number of clients who do not show up for appointments (phone reminders to clients of their appointments can help), (c) increasing the number of admissions to substance abuse treatment programs, and (d) supporting clients to stay through treatment completion.

Principles developed by NIATx encourage substance abuse treatment organizations to (a) understand and involve the "customer" (note the nod to business); (b) address and fix key problems such as staff turnover and client dropout rates; (c) choose a powerful leader for change; (d) obtain ideas from outside the organization and even the field by considering business practices of corporations; and (e) use *rapid cycle testing*, which involves employing a process of identifying problems, finding solutions through planning, implementing the solutions, assessing outcomes, and then institutionalizing those changes (Hoffman et al., 2012).

The challenges of providing readily accessible, affordable, and high-quality substance abuse treatment services are likely to persist over time. Overall, the substance abuse treatment field does not seem well poised to take its place in health care reform measures, and it remains to be seen what effects the new Affordable Care Act will have on the provision of substance abuse treatment services. In a study using the Health Reform Readiness Index, substance abuse treatment agencies were poorly prepared and have much to do to develop information technology, develop a qualified workforce, and ensure continuity of care (Molfenter, Capoccia, Boyle, & Sherbeck, 2012).

THE ROLE OF MEDICATIONS

There has been much concern over the role of prescribed medications in our society today. Through the years there have been dramatic increases in the use of medications as treatments for attention deficit hyperactivity disorder, depression, and bipolar disorder, among others. There has also been considerable concern about patients who develop addiction problems as a result of having been prescribed medication for pain.

A recent study of prescribed opioid use in 286 hospitals, excluding surgical patients, reported that 51% of patients were prescribed opioids such as morphine, fentanyl, and oxycodone during hospitalization (Conaboy, 2013; Herzig, Rothberg, Cheung, Ngo, & Marcantonio, 2013). Dramatic differences were found in opioid use by region of the United States: the Northeast had the lowest rate at 40%, the Midwest rate was 51%, in the South the rate was 54%, and the highest rate was in the West at 56%. This indicates that differences in prescribing medications may have more to do with hospital culture than with needs of patients. These drugs can add to the risk of overdose, can cause confusion in older people that can be related to falls, and can set patients up for addiction problems (Conaboy, 2013; Herzig et al., 2013). Overall, even hospital patients who were not given surgery, where the use of painkillers is expected, received high doses of opioids. More research needs to be done to examine and improve the safety of opioid use in hospitals and to standardize their use (Herzig et al., 2013).

As we have seen, medications can be useful in blocking effects of illegal drugs and reducing cravings for drugs, and they have a place in substance abuse treatment. For example, antidepressant medications still predominate in substance abuse treatment programs but newer medications such as buprenorphine are gaining ground (Knudsen, Ducharme, & Roman, 2007). Buprenorphine reduces physical symptoms of withdrawal and blocks the effects of opiates. Because private treatment programs are more likely to be based in hospitals, they are more likely to have physicians available to prescribe medications such as buprenorphine, offering an explanation for why more private rather than publicly funded programs are offering these medications (Knudsen et al., 2007; Roman et al., 2006). When older treatment professionals age out of the workforce and younger clinicians, who have grown up professionally with the use of medications, take the reins in the treatment field, the use of medications, especially buprenorphine, is likely to increase in detox programs and for long-term opioid addiction.

RECOVERY COACHING

Recovery coaching, also known as peer mentoring, has developed in recent years as an additional alternative for substance abusers seeking assistance. The role of the recovery coach is to support and encourage recovery with a hands-on approach. Although it shares some characteristics with the sponsorship relationship in 12-step programs and with the supportive elements of the relationship with a therapist, this role helps the client to develop an action plan for recovery (Center for Substance Abuse Treatment, 2009b). The recovery coaching experience can occur before a client enters formal treatment or after formal treatment. It is a structured approach to assist clients in meeting their responsibilities and doing what needs to be done through active problem solving. A recovery plan is different from a treatment plan in that it is developed and implemented by the client rather than by substance abuse treatment professionals (White & Kurtz, 2006). It reminds us of the considerable importance of a safe physical and social environment for the client and that a return to an unsafe environment after treatment completion can have negative consequences.

Recovery coaching can be a volunteer experience or it can be a highly paid position. Recovery coaching can take place in personal meetings, by telephone, by e-mail, or through Internet-based voice and video contact, such as Skype services. A search of the Internet reveals some coaches are, as of this writing, charging $125 per hour for the service.

WORKFORCE ISSUES

The development of the substance abuse treatment workforce is one of the most compelling issues in the field (Schmidt, Villarivera, & Aguiar, 2005). The field has not been quick to develop practice standards for alcohol and drug counselors and has lagged behind the development of training for mental health counselors (Greer & Kuehn, 2009; Kerwin, Walker-Smith, & Kirby, 2006). Until the 1990s recovering alcoholics and drug addicts were providing treatment, when recovery was the most important credential. This early workforce was primarily male and often lacked academic degrees. As polysubstance abuse became the norm, the treatment became more complex and the importance of academic and training credentials grew. Voluntary certification and state licensure have supported the development of academic programs and degrees in addiction studies (Greer & Kuehn, 2009; NAADAC, 2009).

In focus groups with counselors, concerns were expressed about low salaries, including the need to take on a second job, desire to move to management positions for financial reasons, and frustration with managed care policies (Schmidt et al., 2005). Another important concern was that not all counselors felt they had adequate training to treat dually diagnosed clients.

Staff turnover is a big issue in the substance abuse treatment field. Many attribute turnover to poor working conditions, lack of opportunity to advance with the agency, poor compensation, and other factors that have yet to be determined by research (Roman et al., 2006). Turnover can be reduced by ensuring that staff members have autonomy over their work, support for creativity in providing services, and adequate financial compensation and other kinds of rewards for strong work performance. Staff turnover can also be reduced by a "collaborative work environment" in which staff members have a say in management and a stake in "organizational commitment" (McNulty, Oser, Johnson, Knudsen, & Roman, 2007, p. 186).

Lack of clinical supervision can also be a factor in staff turnover. It is easy to feel overwhelmed with a difficult caseload, especially when strong supervision is not available. Appropriate supervision includes feedback on the clinician's performance from a more experienced and skillful clinician (Miller, Sorensen, Selzer, & Brigham, 2006). Today clinical supervision is a specialty within treatment, bringing with it ethical and legal responsibilities beyond those of counselors (Durham, 2007). In a recent survey of the New England workforce, 70% of clinical supervisors had a caseload and spent only 20% of their time in clinical supervision tasks, primarily related to reviewing entries in client records (Gumbley, 2012). See Box 12.3 for strategies related to learning new counseling and treatment approaches that emphasize the importance of clinical supervision.

BOX 12.3 Strategies for Learning New Counseling and Treatment Approaches

Three major steps are needed to learn a new skill:

1. *Preparatory information* is information that is gathered as part of the groundwork for learning new treatment approaches. This includes reading about the topic, receiving instruction from others, and observing others in their practice. As Miller et al. (2006) state, there is a lot of information "overload with little help in sorting wheat from chaff" (p. 30). Research on and the increasing implementation of buprenorphine treatment is an example of providing information that led to use.
2. *Monitored practice with feedback* refers to practicing a new approach with feedback from someone else. A counselor or therapist needs to be able to get some experience and constructive criticism. This is the bedrock of graduate programs in clinical fields.
3. *Supervision and coaching* refers to the importance of having the guidance of an expert. This kind of supervision can improve performance and offer positive reinforcement. Lack of good supervision is a big problem throughout the field of human services and is clearly seen in the substance abuse treatment field, where staff turnover is high.

Source: Miller, Sorensen, Selzer, and Brigham (2006).

In their national study of the substance abuse treatment workforce, Mulvey, Hubbard, and Hayashi (2003) reported that most treatment professionals are White (84.5%), between 40 and 55 years old, and almost evenly split between male and female (50.5% women and 49.5% men). A more recent picture of the workforce in New England found that 90% of the workforce is White, women represent 73% of the workforce, and men make up 27% (Gumbley, 2012). Less than 10% of the workforce today is in recovery, although 24% of staff members providing services directly to clients in New England in 2012 were in recovery. It appears as though the field is losing ground when it comes to issues of diversity—the importance of having an agency workforce that reflects the racial and ethnic makeup of clients does not seem to be a priority today.

Revealing the move toward greater educational attainment, 48% of direct care staff members in New England in 2012 had a master's degree and 23% had a bachelor's degree (Gumbley, 2012). Of these direct care staff members, 53% were certified or licensed, and only 20% had never been licensed or certified. Overall, private programs are more likely to have counselors with master's degrees than are public sector programs (Roman et al., 2006).

National standards can go a long way toward professionalizing the substance abuse workforce. At the forefront of these efforts are several organizations. The International Coalition for Addiction Studies Education (INCASE), established in 1991, is committed to improving the quality of addiction training and education, disseminating addiction research, and developing academic standards and an accreditation process (INCASE, 2013). The National Association of Alcoholism and Drug Abuse Counselors (NAADAC), founded under a different name in 1974, is an international organization boasting more than 75,000 clinical and academic members throughout the world (NAADAC, 2013). NAADAC and INCASE have developed a national academic accreditation system for colleges and universities that also meets state standards for licensure. This includes a national registry of college and university substance abuse programs and the development of a national career ladder to replace the varying state requirements (NAADAC, 2009). Known as the National Addiction Studies Accreditation Commission (NASAC), it is a voluntary accreditation organization for college and university addiction studies programs representing a collaboration between NAADAC and INCASE. It is the only organization that represents addictions programs at the associate degree, bachelor's degree, master's degree, and doctoral levels. NASAC offers the opportunity for substance abuse programs to be evaluated and voluntarily approved for accreditation (NASAC, 2012).

The International Certification and Reciprocity Consortium (IC&RC), established in 1981, is a global addiction and prevention credentialing organization. Membership as of 2011 included 45,000 professionals from 25 countries and from 47 states and territories in the United States. It offers credentialing in specialized areas such as alcohol and drug counseling, advanced alcohol and drug counseling, clinical supervision, prevention, criminal justice, co-occurring disorders, and peer recovery (IC&RC, 2013).

In all human services in recent years, we have begun to value quality leadership skills that can be learned while on the job and within academic environments. Leadership roles in substance abuse treatment can be sought by individuals or dropped in their laps. Some may spend years cultivating leaderships skills, whereas others are put in leadership roles simply because no one else is willing to do it. White and Albright (2006) recommend a "personal leadership plan" to best prepare for taking on the important responsibilities for leading the addiction field into the future and to help develop the next generation of leaders.

FUTURE RESEARCH ISSUES

No one will argue against the need for more substance abuse treatment research, and invariably there must be a call for more research to ascertain the best treatments for specific groups. Ideally, research clarifies the reasons for which treatment is successful and the mechanisms that make it successful (Miller, 1992).

Yet we must be reminded of some basic issues with research. Research studies often rely on self-reporting by respondents in terms of types and amount of alcohol and drugs consumed. Treatment can affect how forthcoming respondents are about earlier use of drugs, alcohol, or both. For example, in a sample of court-referred respondents 16 to 21 years old, of those who initially stated they had not been drinking before treatment, after receiving motivational interviewing, 33.5% corrected their earlier statement to admit that they had been drinking before treatment (Nirenberg, Longabaugh, Baird, & Mello, 2013).

Randomized controlled trials, as we have discussed, have been considered the gold standard for determining effectiveness (how well treatment works) and efficacy (proof established by randomized controlled trials). Yet they do not necessarily provide the whole picture. There are also limitations of randomized controlled trials for substance abuse in evaluating the recovery process (Tucker & Roth, 2006). As stated by Tucker and Roth (2006), "Questions concerning what influences people with substance-related problems to seek and engage in treatment and how these self-selection processes and contextual influences contribute to the change process, are not investigated readily by studies that assign participants randomly to treatment and control groups" (p. 919). Randomized controlled trials also focus on short-term effects rather than taking the long view of substance abuse recovery. Tucker and Roth (2006) concluded that research in the substance abuse treatment field should not be limited to randomized controlled trials and that research that addresses both effectiveness and efficacy is preferred over research that address either one alone.

Research that cultivates relationships between practitioners and researchers is likely to continue to grow. For example, researchers from DePaul University in Chicago and Oxford House, a residential program for substance abusers, developed a university–community collaboration to assess the success of Oxford Houses (Davis, Jason, Ferrari, Olsen, & Alvarez, 2005). They were able to obtain federal grant funding and cultivate collaboration through open community meetings with Oxford House residents, researchers, and community members.

Green et al. (2009) recommend more "participatory approaches to research... that can help shape the research questions and methods for sampling design, analysis, and interpretation that will ensure greater relevance, credibility, and implementation" (p. 169). Research findings need to be more relevant to practitioners—those expected to implement findings.

The Addiction Technology Transfer Center (ATTC) Network Technology Transfer Workgroup (2011) has done considerable work to develop a model to clarify and streamline ways in which research findings can be placed into the practice of addiction treatment. Some of these constructs are used in ways that are confusing; therefore, there must first be an effort to define terms in ways that all can agree on. The ATTC Network Technology Transfer Workgroup (2011) explains *innovation* as the process that begins from the point at which effectiveness and efficacy have been established and adds that it can be a treatment, a method, a technology, or even an idea. *Translation* is next, whereby the critical elements of the innovation are chosen, explained, and "packaged" to be given to others. The innovation is shared with others in the process known as *dissemination* to encourage use of the innovation, often through activities and promotional materials to raise awareness. *Adoption* refers to the process of deciding to use the innovation, but it does not necessarily lead to implementation. *Implementation* refers to making the innovation part of regular and routine treatment practice, including agency policy changes. This completes the process of incorporating innovations into substance abuse treatment.

Other terms are also used in a variety of ways that can be confusing. The ATTC Network Technology Transfer Workgroup (2011) recommends that the term *technology transfer* refer to a "multidimensional process that intentionally promotes the use of an innovation" (p. 174). The purpose is to speed up the "planned or spontaneous spread of an innovation" (ATTC Network Technology Transfer Workgroup, 2011, p. 175) in the process known as *diffusion*. Key term definitions can aid in attaining consensus within the substance abuse treatment field, as well as with all disciplines that rely on scientific inquiry.

Although it is of critical importance, research should not be the exclusive way we explore what works in substance abuse treatment. There must always be the important role of clinical judgment. See Box 12.4 for important ingredients for innovation in treatment that combine clinical knowledge, clinical experience, and research insight and today include business practices.

As noted by Miller (1992), "To the extent that practitioners can keep abreast of such developments and adjust their clinical work accordingly, there is reason to believe that the effectiveness of substance abuse treatment can be greatly increased" (p. 93). In addition, clinicians can provide important input into the development of research protocols. Ideally, research findings and clinical judgment are melded together in ways that provide holistic treatments for people with substance abuse problems.

> ### BOX 12.4 *Important Ingredients for New and Creative Designs for Substance Abuse Treatment*
>
> 1. Readily available assessment, treatment, and continuing care
> 2. Consistency in the quality of assessment, treatment, and continuing care
> 3. Use of up-to-date technologies for health records and communication
> 4. "Global" services that integrate substance abuse treatment within primary care and address the needs of individuals and their families
> 5. "Soft and minimal handoffs" that ensure there is continuity of care through a smooth and personalized referral process
> 6. Use evidence-based practices within treatment systems, including medications
> 7. Support that is provided to patients and their families before treatment, during treatment, and after treatment
> 8. Continuing care that is provided over an extended period, which can dissipate crises and reduce relapse
> 9. Assistance for clients and families in functioning as effectively as possible within their environment and in seeking safe housing and occupational support
> 10. Development of practical measures of progress over time to help ensure recovery stays on track
> 11. "Pay for performance" that ties payment for treatment to service quality and thus can reward the provider
>
> *Source:* Gustafson (2012).

SUMMARY AND CONCLUSION

Treatment that responds to the specific needs of clients is critical. Research that shows that even initial contacts to obtain treatment are troubled by difficulty of access, is necessary, perhaps because the findings are so disturbing. Long waiting times for inpatient and outpatient treatment are simply unacceptable. Using business practices, some agencies have been better able to serve their clients (or "customers") by reducing waiting times and smoothing the flow of provision of services.

The workforce has changed through the years from counselors who were primarily recovering alcoholics and addicts to counselors who are highly educated and trained professionals, many of whom have master's degrees. This will increase the demand for certifications and licensure from states through the efforts of organizations such as NASAC, INCASE, NAADAC, and IC&RC. An increasingly professionalized staff will smooth the way for greater use of medications to treat addiction, especially buprenorphine. Recovery coaching is likely to continue to grow in these next years as well.

Confusion regarding new definitions of substance abuse by the American Psychiatric Association (2013) will be made more complex because the *Diagnostic and Statistical Manual of Mental Disorders*, Fifth Edition, has collapsed the categories of substance abuse and substance dependence into the one category of substance use disorder. Lack of agreement regarding diagnosis is likely to ripple through treatment programs and make it even more challenging to try to match clients to the most appropriate treatment options in the next few years.

Many efforts have been made through research findings and clinical interventions to figure out what works for whom and under what conditions. Client motivation has been and always will be key. We have also seen how families, substance abuse professionals, and forms of coerced treatment can be useful. Walter R. Miller, one of the foremost researchers in the field, offered an important reminder more than 20 years ago: "In difficult economic times, hope is also provided by evidence that even relatively brief treatment can be substantially more effective than none at all" (Miller, 1992, p. 93). It continues to be our job to open the doors to people who need help and to provide high-quality professional services as determined by researchers and clinicians.

REFERENCES

Aase, D. M., Jason, L. A., & Robinson, W. L. (2008). 12-step participation among dually-diagnosed individuals: A review of individual and contextual factors. *Clinical Psychology Review, 28*(7), 1235–1248.

Abbott, P., & Chase, D. M. (2008). Culture and substance abuse: Impact of culture affects approach to treatment. *Psychiatric Times, 25*(1), 43–46.

Abraham, A. J., & Roman, P. M. (2010). Early adoption of injectable naltrexone for alcohol-use disorders: Findings in the private-treatment sector. *Journal of Studies on Alcohol and Drugs, 71*, 460–466.

Ackerson, B. J., & Karoll, B. R. (2005). Evaluation of an assertive community treatment–harm reduction program: Implementation issues. *Best Practices in Mental Health, 1*(2), 34–49.

Adamson, S. J., & Sellman, J. D. (2001). Drinking goal selection and treatment outcome in out-patients with mild–moderate alcohol dependence. *Drug and Alcohol Review, 20*, 351–359.

Addiction Technology Transfer Center Network. (2004). *The change book: A blueprint for technology transfer*. Kansas City, MO: ATTC National Office.

Addiction Technology Transfer Center Network Technology Transfer Workgroup. (2011). Research to practice in addiction treatment: Key terms and a field-driven model of technology transfer. *Journal of Substance Abuse Treatment, 41*, 169–178.

Addis, M. E., Wade, W. A., & Hatgis, C. (1999). Barriers to dissemination of evidence-based practices: Addressing practitioners' concerns about manual-based psychotherapies. *Clinical Psychology: Science and Practice, 6*(4), 430–441.

Adelman, H. S., & Taylor, L. (2003). Creating school and community partnerships for substance abuse prevention programs. *Journal of Primary Prevention, 23*(3), 329–369.

Al-Anon Family Groups Headquarters. (2012). *Membership survey*. Virginia Beach, VA: Author. Retrieved on May 12, 2014, from http://www.al-anon.org/pdf/MembershipSurvey.pdf

Alcoholics Anonymous World Services. (1952). Twelve Steps and Twelve Traditions. New York, NY: Author.

Alcoholics Anonymous World Services. (2002). *Alcoholics Anonymous 2001 membership survey*. New York, NY: Author.

Alcoholics Anonymous World Services. (2012). *Alcoholics Anonymous 2011 membership survey*. Retrieved August 7, 2013, from http://www.aa.org

Alegria, M., Lin, J. Y., Green, J. G., Sampson, N. A., Gruber, M. J., & Kessler, R. C. (2012). Role of referrals in mental health service disparities for racial and ethnic minority youth. *Journal of the American Academy of Child and Adolescent Psychiatry,* *51*(7), 703–711. doi:10.1016/j.jaac.2012.05.005

Alexander, M. (2010). *The new Jim Crow: Mass incarceration in the age of colorblindness.* New York, NY: New Press.

Allwood, S., & White, W. (2012, revised May 9, 2013). *A chronology of SMART Recovery.* http://www.williamwhitepapers.com/pr/2012%20A%20Chronology%20of%20SMART%20Recovery.pdf

Alvarez, J., Jason, L. A., Olson, B. D., Ferrari, J. R., & Davis, M. I. (2007). Substance abuse prevalence and treatment among Latinos and Latinas. *Journal of Ethnicity in Substance Abuse, 6*(2), 115–141.

American Civil Liberties Union. (2011). *Smart reform is possible: States reducing incarceration rates and costs while protecting communities.* New York, NY: Author.

American Psychiatric Association. (2013). *Diagnostic and statistical manual of mental disorders* (5th ed.). Arlington, VA: American Psychiatric Publishing.

American Public Health Association and Education Development Center. (2008). *Alcohol screening and brief intervention: A guide for public health practitioners.* Washington, DC: National Highway Traffic Safety Administration, U.S. Department of Transportation.

Anderson, D. J., McGovern, J. P., & DuPont, R. L. (1999). The origins of the Minnesota model of addiction treatment: A first person account. *Journal of Addictive Diseases, 18*(1), 107–114.

Apodaca, T. R., & Miller, W. R. (2003). A meta-analysis of the effectiveness of bibliotherapy for alcohol problems. *Clinical Psychology, 59,* 289–304.

Armor, D. J., Polich, J. M., & Stambul, H. B. (1976). *Alcoholism and treatment.* Prepared for the National Institute on Alcohol Abuse and Alcoholism. Santa Monica, CA: Rand.

Associated Press. (2012, March 30). Harry Crews: Author drew on his wild life [Obituary]. *The Boston Globe,* B11.

Astals, M., Diaz, L., Domingo-Salvany, A., Martin-Santos, R., Bulbena, A., & Torrens, M. (2009). Impact of co-occurring psychiatric disorders on retention in a methadone maintenance program: An 18-month follow-up study. *International Journal of Environmental Research and Public Health, 6*(11), 2822–2832.

Baker, A., Lee, N. K., Claire, M., Lewin, T. J., Grant, T., Pohlman, S., Saunders, J. B., Kay-Lambkin, F., Constable, P., Jenner, L., & Carr, V. J. (2005). Brief cognitive behavioural interventions for regular amphetamine users: A step in the right direction. *Addiction, 100,* 367–378.

Balas, E. A., & Boren, S. A. (2000). Managing clinical knowledge for health care improvement. In J. Bemmel & A. T. McCray (Eds.), *Yearbook of medical informatics 2000: Patient-centered systems* (pp. 65–70). Stuttgart, Germany: Schattauer Verlagsgesellschaft.

Baldwin, S. A., Wampold, B. E., & Imel, Z. E. (2007). Untangling the alliance–outcome correlation: Exploring the relative importance of therapist and patient variability in the alliance. *Journal of Consulting and Clinical Psychology, 75*(6), 842–852.

Ball, S. A., Maccarelli, L. M., LaPaglia, D. M., & Ostrowski, M. J. (2011). Randomized trial of dual-focused versus single-focused individual therapy for personality disorders and substance dependence. *Journal of Nervous and Mental Disease, 199*(5), 319–328.

Balshem, H., Christensen, V., Tuepker, A., & Kansagara, D. (2011, April). *A critical review of the literature regarding homelessness among veterans* (VA-ESP Project No. 05-225). Retrieved on May 8, 2014, from http://www.hsrd.research.va.gov/publications/esp/homelessness.pdf

Barnett, P. G., & Swindle, R. W. (1997). Cost-effectiveness of inpatient substance abuse treatment. *Health Services Research, 32*(5), 615–629.

Battjes, R. J., Gordon, M. S., O'Grady, K. E., Kinlock, T. W., & Carswell, M. A. (2003). Factors that predict adolescent motivation for substance abuse treatment. *Journal of Substance Abuse Treatment, 24*(3), 221–232.

Battjes, R. J., Gordon, M. S., O'Grady, K. E., Kinlock, T. W., Katz, E. C., & Sears, E. A. (2004). Evaluation of a group-based substance abuse treatment program for adolescents. *Journal of Substance Abuse Treatment, 27*(2), 123–134.

Beauvais, F. (1998). American Indians and alcohol. *Alcohol Health and Research World, 22*(4), 253–259.

Beckman, L. J. (1980). An attributional analysis of Alcoholics Anonymous. *Journal of Studies on Alcohol, 41*(7), 714–726.

Beets, M. W., Flay, B. R., Vuchinich, S., Snyder, F. J., Acock, A., Li, K. K., Burns, K., Washburn, I. J., & Durlak, J. (2009). Use of a social and character development program to prevent substance use, violent behaviors, and sexual activity among elementary-school students in Hawaii. *American Journal of Public Health, 99*(8), 1438–1445.

Benshoff, J. J., & Harrawood, L. K. (2003). Substance abuse and the elderly: Unique issues and concerns. *Journal of Rehabilitation, 69*(2), 43–48.

Berglund, M. (2005). A better widget? Three lessons for improving addiction treatment from a meta-analytical study. *Addiction, 100*(6), 742–750.

Betty Ford Center. (2013). *Home page.* Retrieved May 11, 2014, from http://www.bettyfordcenter.org

Bewley-Taylor, D. R. (2004). Harm reduction and the global drug control regime: Contemporary problems and future prospects. *Drug and Alcohol Review, 23,* 483–489.

The Bill W.–Carl Jung letters (from the January 1963 *Grapevine*). (1994, June). *AA Grapevine,* pp. 48–53.

Binswanger, I. A., Nowels, C., Corsi, K. F., Glanz, J., Long, J., Booth, R. E., & Steiner, J. F. (2012). Return to drug use and overdose after release from prison: A qualitative study of risk and protective factors. *Addiction Science & Clinical Practice, 7*(3). Retrieved October 3, 2013, from http://www.ascpjournal.org/content/7/1/3

Blondell, R. D. (2005). Ambulatory detoxification of patients with alcohol dependence. *American Family Physician, 71*(3), 495–502.

Blondell, R. D., Smith, S. J., Servoss, T. J., DeVaul, S. K., & Simons, R. L. (2007). Buprenorphine and methadone: A comparison of patient completion rates during inpatient detoxification. *Journal of Addictive Diseases, 26*(2), 3–11.

Blood, L., & Cornwall, A. (1996). Childhood sexual victimization as a factor in the treatment of substance misusing adolescents. *Substance Use & Misuse, 31*(8), 1015–1039.

Bogenschutz, M. P., Geppert, C. M. A, & George, J. (2006). The role of twelve-step approaches in dual diagnosis treatment and recovery. *American Journal on Addictions, 15,* 50–60.

Borsari, B. (2014).Universal prevention for alcohol use disorders: 1940–2014. *Journal of Studies on Alcohol and Drugs, Supplement 17,* 89–97.

Botvin, G. J. (1990). Substance abuse prevention: Theory, practice, and effectiveness. In M. Tonry & J. Q. Wilson (Eds.), *Drugs and crime* (pp. 461–519). Chicago, IL: University of Chicago Press.

Botvin, G. J., Baker, E., Filazzola, A. D., & Botvin, E. M. (1990). A cognitive-behavioral approach to substance abuse prevention: One-year follow-up. *Addictive Behaviors, 15,* 47–63.

Botvin, G. J., & Botvin, E. M. (1994). School-based programs. In J. H. Lowinson, P. Ruiz, R. B. Millman, & J. G. Langrod (Eds.), *Substance abuse: A comprehensive textbook* (pp. 764–775). Baltimore, MD: Williams & Wilkins.

Brady, T. M., & Ashley, O. S. (Eds.). (2005). *Women in substance abuse treatment: Results from the Alcohol and Drug Services Study (ADSS)* (DHHS Publication No. SMA 04-3968). Rockville, MD: Substance Abuse and Mental Health Services Administration, Office of Applied Studies.

Brannigan, R., Schackman, B. R., Falco, M., & Millman, R. B. (2004). The quality of highly regarded adolescent substance abuse treatment programs: Results of an in-depth national survey. *Archives of Pediatric and Adolescent Medicine, 158*(9), 904–909.

Bray, J. W., & Zarkin, G. A. (2006). Economic evaluation of alcoholism treatment. *Alcohol Research & Health, 29*(1), 29–33.

Brems, C., Johnson, M. E., Neal, D., & Freemon, M. (2004). Childhood abuse history and substance use among men and women receiving detoxification services. *American Journal of Drug and Alcohol Abuse, 30*(4), 799–821.

Brody, G. H., Chen, Y. F., Kogan, S. M., Yu, T., Molgaard, V. K., DiClemente, R. J., & Wingood, G. M. (2012). Family-centered program deters substance use, conduct problems, and depressive symptoms in black adolescents. *Pediatrics, 192*(1), 108–115.

Broner, N., Mayrl, D. W., & Landsberg, G. (2005). Outcomes of mandated and nonmandated New York City jail diversion for offenders with alcohol, drug, and mental disorders. *Prison Journal, 85*(1), 18–49. doi:10.1177/0032885504274289

Broome, K. M., Flynn, P. M., & Simpson, D. D. (1999). Psychiatric comorbidity measures as predictors of retention in drug abuse treatment programs. *Health Services Research, 34*(3), 791–806.

Broome, K. M., Simpson, D. D., & Joe, G. W. (1999). Patient and program attributes related to treatment process indicators in DATOS. *Drug and Alcohol Dependence, 57*(2), 127–135.

Brown, A. E., Whitney, S. N., Schneider, M. A., & Vega, C. P. (2006). Alcohol recovery and spirituality: Strangers, friends, or partners? *Southern Medical Journal, 99*(6), 654–657.

Brown, B. S., & Flynn, P. M. (2002). The federal role in drug abuse technology transfer: A history and perspective. *Journal of Substance Abuse Treatment, 22*(4), 245–257.

Brown, C. H., Guo, J., Singer, L. T., Downes, K., & Brinales, J. M. (2007). Examining the effects of school-based drug prevention programs on drug use in rural settings: Methodology and initial findings. *Journal of Rural Health, 23*(Suppl.), 29–36. doi:10.1111/j.1748-0361.2007.00121.x

Brown, D. R., Lacey, K., Blount, J., Roman, D., & Brown, D. (2006). Black churches in substance abuse use and abuse prevention efforts. *Journal of Alcohol & Drug Education, 5*(2), 43–65.

Brown, D. R., Scott, W., Lacey, K., Blount, J., Roman, D., & Brown, D. (2006). Black churches in substance use and abuse prevention efforts. *Journal of Alcohol & Drug Education, 50*(2), 43–65.

Brown, E. S., Suppes, T., Adinoff, B., & Thomas, N. R. (2001). Drug abuse and bipolar disorder: Comorbidity or misdiagnosis? *Journal of Affective Disorders, 65*, 105–115.

Brown, J. H., & Kreft, I. G. (1998). Zero effects of drug prevention programs: Issues and solutions. *Evaluation Review, 22*, 3–14.

Brown, J. M. (2004). The effectiveness of treatment. In N. Heather & T. Stockwell (Eds.), *The essential handbook of treatment and prevention of alcohol problems* (pp. 9–20). London: John Wiley & Sons.

Brunette, M. F., Mueser, K. T., & Drake, R. E. (2004). A review of research on residential programs for people with severe mental illness and co-occurring substance use disorders. *Drug and Alcohol Review, 23*(4), 471–481.

Budde, D., Rounsaville, B., & Bryant, K. (1992). Inpatient and outpatient cocaine abusers: Clinical comparisons at intake and one-year follow-up. *Journal of Substance Abuse Treatment, 9*(4), 337–342.

Budney, A. J., & Higgins, S. T. (1998). A community reinforcement plus vouchers approach: Treating cocaine addiction. *Therapy Manual for Drug Abuse: Manual 2.* Rockville, MD: U.S. Department of Health and Human Services, National Institutes of Health.

Burdon, W. M., Dang, J., Prendergast, M. L., Messina, N. P., & Farrabee, D. (2007). Differential effectiveness of residential versus outpatient aftercare for parolees from prison-based therapeutic community treatment programs. *Substance Abuse Treatment, Prevention, and Policy, 2,* 16. doi:10.1186/1747-597X-2-16

Burdon, W. M., Roll, J. M., Prendergast, M. L., & Rawson, R. A. (2001). Drug courts and contingency management. *Journal of Drug Issues, 31*(1), 73–90.

Burgdorf, K., Dowell, K., Chen, X., Roberts, T., & Herrell, J. M. (2004). Birth outcomes for pregnant women in residential substance abuse treatment. *Evaluation and Program Planning, 27,* 199–204.

Burke, A. C., & Gregoire, T. K. (2007). Substance abuse treatment outcomes for coerced and noncoerced clients. *Health & Social Work, 32*(1), 7–15.

Burke, B. L., Arkowitz, H., & Menchola, M. (2003). The efficacy of motivational interviewing: A meta-analysis of controlled clinical trials. *Journal of Consulting and Clinical Psychology, 71*(5), 843–861.

Burleson, J. A., Kaminer, Y., & Dennis, M. L. (2006). Absence of iatrogenic or contagion effects in adolescent group therapy: Findings from the Cannabis Youth Treatment (CYT) Study. *American Journal on Addictions, 15,* 4–15.

Burnham, J. C. (1968). New perspectives on the Prohibition "experiment" of the 1920's. *Journal of Social History, 2*(1), 51–68.

Burns, L., Teesson, M., & O'Neill, K. (2005). The impact of comorbid anxiety and depression alcohol treatment outcomes. *Addiction, 100,* 787–796.

Butler Center for Research. (2010, June). *Project MATCH: A study of alcoholism treatment approaches.* Research Update. Center City, MN: Hazelden Foundation.

Butzin, C. A., Martin, S. S., & Inciardi, J. A. (2005). Treatment during transition from prison to community and subsequent illicit drug use. *Journal of Substance Abuse Treatment, 28,* 351–358.

Cadogan, D. A. (1999). Drug use harm. *American Psychologist, 54*(10), 841–842.

Caetano, R., Vaeth, A. C., & Rodriguez, L. A. (2012). The Hispanic Americans Baseline Alcohol Survey (HABLAS): Acculturation, birthplace and alcohol-related social problems across Hispanic national groups. *Hispanic Journal of Behavioral Sciences, 31*(1), 95–117.

Cagney, P., with Cossar, D. (2006, November). *A healthy drinking culture: A search and review of international and New Zealand literature.* Wellington, New Zealand: Research New Zealand.

Cain, A. H. (1964). *The cured alcoholic: New concepts in alcoholism treatment and research.* New York, NY: John Day.

Caldwell, P. E., & Cutter, H. S. G. (1998). Alcoholics Anonymous affiliation during early recovery. *Journal of Substance Abuse Treatment, 15*(3), 221–228.

Campbell, T. C., Catlin, L. A., & Melchert, T. P. (2003). Alcohol and other drug abuse counselors' attitudes and resources for integrating research and practice. *Journal of Drug Education, 33,* 307–323.

Canino, G., Vega, W. A., Sribney, W. M., Warner, L. A., & Alegria, M. (2008). Social relationships, social assimilation, and substance-use disorders among adult Latinos in the U.S. *Journal of Drug Issues, 38*(1), 69–101.

Carboni, J. (2007). *Substance abuse prevention methods for middle school students* (White Paper, Electronic Version). Retrieved October 31, 2013, from http://education.gsu.edu/schoolsafety/

Carey, K. B. (2002). Clinically useful assessments: Substance use and comorbid psychiatric disorders. *Behaviour Research and therapy, 40*, 1345–1361.

Carr, C. J. A., Xu, J., Redko, C., Lane, D. T., Rapp, R. C., Goris, J., & Carlson, R. G. (2008). Individual and system influence on waiting time for substance abuse treatment. *Journal of Substance Abuse Treatment, 34*(2), 192–201.

Carroll, K. M. (2004). Behavioral therapies for co-occurring substance use and mood disorders. *Biological Psychiatry, 56*, 778–784.

Carroll, K. M., Ball, S. A., Nich, C., Martino, S., Frankforter, T. L., Farentinos, C., Kunkel, L. E., . . . Woody, G. E., for the National Institute on Drug Abuse Clinical Trials Network. (2006). Motivational interviewing to improve treatment engagement and outcome in individuals seeking treatment for substance abuse: A multisite effectiveness study. *Drug and Alcohol Dependence, 81*(3), 301–312.

Carroll, K. M., Farentinos, C., Ball, S. A., Crits-Christoph, P., Libby, B., Morgenstern, J., Obert, J. L., Polcin, D., & Woody, G. E., for the Clinical Trials Network. (2002). MET meets the real world: Design issues and clinical strategies in the Clinical Trials Network. *Journal of Substance Abuse Treatment, 23*, 73–80.

Carroll, K. M., & Rounsaville, B. J. (2003). Bridging the gap: A hybrid model to link efficacy and effectiveness research in substance abuse treatment. *Psychiatric Services, 54*(3), 333–339.

Carson, E. A., & Sabol, W. J. (2012, December). *Prisoners in 2011.* Washington, DC: U.S. Department of Justice, Bureau of Justice Statistics.

Castro, F. G., Barrera, M., Mena, L. A., & Aguirre, K. M. (2014). Culture and alcohol use: Historical and sociocultural themes from 75 years of alcohol research. *Journal of Studies on Alcohol and Drugs, Supplement 17*, 36–49.

Castro, R. G., Stein, J. A., & Bentler, P. M. (2009). Ethnic pride, traditional family values, and acculturation in early cigarette and alcohol use among Latino adolescents. *Journal of Primary Prevention, 30*(3–4), 265–292.

Center for Effective Collaboration and Practice. (1994). *Title IV: Safe and Drug-Free Schools and Communities Act of 1994.* Retrieved November 11, 2013, from http//cecp.air.org/orphan/guide/s&dfsact.htm

Center for Substance Abuse Treatment. (1999). *Enhancing motivation for change in substance abuse treatment* (DHHS Publication No. SMA 05-4081). Rockville, MD: Substance Abuse and Mental Health Services Administration.

Center for Substance Abuse Treatment. (2004). *Substance abuse treatment and family therapy* (DHHS Publication No. SMA 08-4219). Rockville, MD: Substance Abuse and Mental Health Services Administration.

Center for Substance Abuse Treatment. (2005a). *Substance abuse relapse prevention for older adults: A group treatment approach* (DHHS Publication No. SMA 05-4053). Rockville, MD: Substance Abuse and Mental Health Services Administration.

Center for Substance Abuse Treatment. (2005b). *Substance abuse treatment for adults in the criminal justice system* (DHHS Publication No. SMA 09-4056). Rockville, MD: Substance Abuse and Mental Health Services Administration.

Center for Substance Abuse Treatment. (2005c). *Substance abuse treatment for persons with co-occurring disorders* (DHHS Publication No. SMA 05-3992). Rockville, MD: Author.

Center for Substance Abuse Treatment. (2006). *Detoxification and substance abuse treatment* (DHHS Publication No. SMA 06-4131). Rockville, MD: Substance Abuse and Mental Health Services Administration.

Center for Substance Abuse Treatment. (2009a). *Considerations for the provision of e-therapy* (DHHS Publication No. SMA 09-4450). Rockville, MD: Substance Abuse and Mental Health Services Administration.

Center for Substance Abuse Treatment. (2009b). *What are peer recovery support services?* (DHHS Publication No SMA 09-4454). Rockville, MD: Substance Abuse and Mental Health Services Administration.

Chan, K. S., Wenzel, S., Orlando, M., Montagnet, C., Mandell, W., Becker, K., & Ebener, P. (2004). How important are client characteristics to understanding the treatment process in the therapeutic community? *American Journal of Drug and Alcohol Abuse, 30*(4), 871–891.

Chan, Y.-F., Dennis, M. L., & Funk, R. R. (2008). Prevalence and comorbidity of major internalizing and externalizing problems among adolescents and adults present-ing to substance abuse treatment. *Journal of Substance Abuse Treatment, 34,* 14–24.

Chassin, L., Knight, G., Vargas-Chanes, D., Losoya, S. H., & Naranjo, D. (2009). Substance use treatment outcomes in a sample of male serious juvenile offenders. *Journal of Substance Abuse Treatment, 36*(2), 183–194. doi:10.1016/j.jsat.2008.06.001

Chi, F. W., Satre, D. D., & Weisner, C. (2006). Chemical dependency patients with cooccurring psychiatric diagnoses: Service patterns and 1-year outcomes. *Alcoholism: Clinical and Experimental Research, 30,* 851–859.

Clark, D. B. (2004). The natural history of adolescent alcohol use disorders. *Addiction, 99*(Suppl. 2), 5–22.

Clark, R. E., Samnaliev, M., & McGovern, M. P. (2009). Impact of substance disorders on medial expenditures for Medicaid beneficiaries with behavioral health disorders. *Psychiatric Services, 60*(1), 35–42.

Coalition for Evidence-Based Policy. (2012). *Social programs that work: Amity prison therapeutic community.* Retrieved October 14, 2013, from http://evidencebasedprograms.org/1366-2/amity-prison-therapeutic-community

Cochran, B. N., Peavy, K. M., & Robohm, J. S. (2007). Do specialized services exist for LGBT individuals seeking treatment for substance misuse? A study of available treatment programs. *Substance Use & Misuse, 42,* 161–176.

Colby, S. M., Lee, C. S., Lewis-Esquerre, J., Esposito-Smythers, C., & Monti, P. M. (2004). Adolescent alcohol misuse: Methodological issues for enhancing treatment research. *Addiction, 99*(Suppl. 2), 47–62.

Colliver, J. D., Compton, W. M., Gfroerer, J. C., & Condon, T. (2006). Projecting drug use among aging baby boomers in 2020. *Annals of Epidemiology, 16,* 257–265.

Colman, C., & Vander Laenen, F. (2012). "Recovery came first": Desistence versus recovery in the criminal careers of drug-using offenders. *Scientific World Journal, 2012,* 1–9. doi:10.1100/2012/657671

Colpaert, K., De Maeyer, J., Broekaert, E., & Vanderplasschen, W. (2013). Impact of addiction severity and psychiatric comorbidity on the quality of life of alcohol-, drug- and dual-dependent persons in residential treatment. *European Addiction Research, 19*(4), 173–183.

Compton, W. M., & Pringle, B. (2004). Services research on adolescent drug treatment. Commentary on "The Cannabis Youth Treatment (CYT) Study: Main findings from two randomized trials." *Journal of Substance Abuse Treatment, 27,* 195–196.

Conaboy, C. (2013, November 14). Opioid use in hospitals examined. *Boston Globe,* B1, B4.

Condelli, W. S., & De Leon, G. (1993). Fixed and dynamic predictors of client retention in therapeutic communities. *Journal of Substance Abuse Treatment, 10,* 11–16.

Condelli, W. S., & Hubbard, R. L. (1994). Relationship between time spent in treatment and client outcomes from therapeutic communities. *Journal of Substance Abuse Treatment, 11*(1), 25–33.

Condon, T. P., Miner, L. L., Balmer, C. W., & Pintello, D. (2008). Blending addiction research and practice: Strategies for technology transfer. *Journal of Substance Abuse Treatment, 35*(2), 156–160.

Conger, J. J. (1956). Alcoholism: Theory, problem and challenge. II. Reinforcement theory and the dynamics of alcoholism. *Quarterly Journal of Studies on Alcohol, 17*, 296–305.

Connors, N. A., Bradley, R. H., Whiteside-Mansell, L., & Crone, C. C. (2001). A comprehensive substance abuse treatment program for women and their children: An initial evaluation. *Journal of Substance Abuse Treatment, 21*(2), 67–75.

Copello, A. G., Templeton, L., & Velleman, R. (2006). Family interventions for drug and alcohol misuse: Is there a best practice? *Current Opinion in Psychiatry, 19*(3), 271–276.

Copenhaver, M. M., Bruce, R. D., & Altice, F. L. (2007). Behavioral counseling content for optimizing the use of buprenorphine for treatment of opioid dependence in community-based settings: A review of the empirical evidence. *American Journal of Drug and Alcohol Abuse, 33*, 643–654.

Cornelius, J. R., Douaihy, A., Buckstein, O. G., Daley, D. C., Wood, D. S., Kelly, T. M., & Salloum, I. M. (2011). Evaluation of cognitive behavioral therapy/ motivational enhancement therapy (CBT/MET) in a treatment trial of comorbid MDD/AUD adolescents. *Addictive Behaviors, 36*(8), 843–848. doi:10.1016/j.addbeh.2011.03.016

Corredoira, R. A., & Kimberly, J. R. (2006). Industry evolution through consolidation: Implications for addiction treatment. *Journal of Substance Abuse Treatment, 31*, 255–265. doi:10.1016/j.jsat.2006.06.020

Cosden, M., Basch, J. E., Campos, E., Greenwell, A., Barazani, S., & Walker, S. (2006). Effects of motivation and problem severity on court-based drug treatment. *Crime & Delinquency, 52*(4), 599–618.

Council on School Health and Committee on Substance Abuse. (2007). The role of schools in combating illicit substance abuse. *Pediatrics, 20*(6), 1379–1384. doi:10.1542/peds.2007-2905

Cox, W. M., Rosenberg, H., Hodgins, C. H. A., Macartney, J. I., & Maurer, K. A. (2004). United Kingdom and United States healthcare providers' recommendations of abstinence versus controlled drinking. *Alcohol and Alcoholism, 39*(2), 130–134.

Coyhis, D. L., & White, W. L. (2006). *Alcohol problems in Native America: The untold story of resistance and recovery—The truth about the lie.* Colorado Springs, CO: White Bison.

Crape, B. L., Latkin, C. A., Laris, A. S., & Knowlton, A. R. (2002). The effects of sponsorship in 12-step treatment of injection drug users. *Drug and Alcohol Dependence, 65*, 291–301.

CRC Health Group. (2011). *History and information about CRC Health Group.* Retrieved December 4, 2013, from http://www.crchealth.com/about-us/

Crome, I., & Crome, P. (2005). "At your age, what does it matter?" Myths and realities about older people who use substances [Editorial]. *Drugs: Education, Prevention & Policy, 12*(5), 343–347.

Cunningham, J. A. (2005). Short-term recovery from alcohol abuse or dependence: Any evidence of a relationship with treatment use in a general population sample? *Alcohol and Alcoholism, 40*(5), 419–421.

Cunningham, J. A., & Blomqvist, J. (2006). Examining treatment use among alcohol-dependent individuals from a population perspective. *Alcohol and Alcoholism, 41*(6), 632–635.

Cunningham, J. A., Koski-Jännes, A., Wild, T. C., & Cordingley, J. (2002). Treating alcohol problems with self-help materials: A population study. *Journal of Studies on Alcohol, 63*, 649–654.

Cunningham, J. A., Kypri, K., & McCambridge, J. (2011). The use of emerging technologies in alcohol treatment. *Alcohol Research & Health, 33*(4), 320–326.

Cunningham, J. A., Wild, T. C., Koski-Jännes, A., Cordingley, J., & Toneatto, T. (2002). A prospective study of quit attempts from alcohol problems in a community sample: Modeling the processes of change. *Addiction Research and Theory, 10*(2), 159–173.

Currie, E. (2003). "It's our lives they're dealing with here": Some adolescent views of residential treatment. *Journal of Drug Issues, 33*(4), 833–864.

Cutler, R. B., & Fishbain, D. (2005). Are alcoholism treatments effective? The Project MATCH data. *BMC Public Health, 5*(75). Retrieved from http://www.biomedcentral.com/1471-2458/5/75

Daley, M., Argeriou, M., McCarty, D., Callahan, J. J., Jr., Shepard, D. S., & Williams, C. N. (2000). The costs of crime and the benefits of substance abuse treatment for pregnant women. *Journal of Substance Abuse Treatment, 19*, 445–458.

Daley, M., Shepard, D. S., & Bury-Maynard, D. (2005). Changes in quality of life for pregnant women in substance user treatment: Developing a quality of life index for the Addictions. *Substance Use & Misuse, 40*, 375–393.

Darst, J. (2011). *Fiction ruined my family*. New York, NY: Riverhead Books.

Davies, D. L. (1962). Normal drinking in recovered alcohol addicts. *Quarterly Journal of Studies on Alcohol, 23*, 94–104.

Davis, M. L., Jason, L. A., Ferrari, J. R., Olson, B. D., & Alvarez, J. (2005). A collaborative action approach to researching substance abuse recovery. *American Journal of Drug and Alcohol Abuse, 31*, 537–553. doi:10.1081/ADA-200068110

Dawson, D. A., Goldstein, R. B., & Grant, B. F. (2012). Factors associated with first utilization of different types of care for alcohol problems. *Journal of Studies on Alcohol and Drugs, 73*, 647–656.

Daytop. (2012). *About Daytop*. Retrieved June 27, 2013, from http://www.daytop.org/about/html

de Bruijn, C., van den Brink, W., de Graaf, R., & Vollebergh, W. A. M. (2005). The craving withdrawal model for alcoholism: Towards the *DSM-V*. Improving the discriminant validity of alcohol use disorder diagnosis. *Alcohol and Alcoholism, 40*(4), 314–322.

De Leon, G. (1995). Residential therapeutic communities in the mainstream: Diversity and issues. *Journal of Psychoactive Drugs, 27*(1), 3–15.

De Leon, G. (2000). *The therapeutic community: Theory, model, and method*. New York, NY: Springer Publishing Company.

De Leon, G., Melnick, G., Kressel, D., & Jainchill, N. (1994). Circumstances, motivation, readiness, and suitability (the CMRS scales): Predicting retention in therapeutic community treatment. *American Journal of Drug and Alcohol Abuse, 20*(4), 495–515.

De Leon, G., Melnick, G., Thomas, G., Kressel, D., & Wexler, H. K. (2000). Motivation for treatment in a prison-based therapeutic community. *American Journal of Drug and Alcohol Abuse, 26*(1), 33–46.

De Maeyer, J., Vanderplasschen, W., & Broekaert, E. (2009). Exploratory study on drug users' perspectives on quality of life: More than health-related quality of life? *Social Indicators Research, 90*, 107–126. doi:10.007/s11205-008-9315-7

De Maeyer, J., Vanderplasschen, W., Lammertyn, J., van Nieuwenhuizen, C., Sabbe, B., & Boekaert, E. (2011). Current quality of life and its determinants among opiate-dependent individuals five years after starting methadone treatment. *Quality of Life Research, 20*(1), 139–150. doi:10.1007/s11136-010-9732-3

De Wildt, W. A. J. M., Schippers, G. M., Van Den Brink, W., Potgieter, A. S., Deckers, F., & Bets, D. (2002). Does psychosocial treatment enhance theefficacy of acamprosate in patients with alcohol problems? *Alcohol & Addiction, 37*(4), 375–382.

DeJong, W., Larimer, M. E., Wood, M. D., & Hartman, R. (2009). NIAAA's rapid response to college drinking problems initiative: Reinforcing the use of evidence-based approaches in college alcohol prevention. *Journal of Studies on Alcohol and Drugs, Supplement 16*, 5–11.

Dennis, M. L., Scott, C. K., Funk, R., & Foss, M. A. (2005). The duration and correlates of addiction and treatment careers. *Journal of Substance Abuse Treatment, 28*, S51–S62.

DiClemente, C. C., Nidecker, M., & Bellack, A. S. (2008). Motivation and the stages of change among individuals with severe mental illness and substance use disorders. *Journal of Substance Abuse Treatment, 34*(1), 25–35.

DiClemente, C. C., & Tuohy, C. M. (2010). Mixed messages: Medication and recovery from opioid dependence. *NAADAC News, 20*(3), 18–20.

Dodes, L. (2002). *The heart of addiction: A new approach to understanding and managing alcoholism and other addictive behaviors*. New York, NY: Quill.

Doran, C. M., Shanahan, M., Mattick, R. P., Ali, R., White, J., & Bell, J. (2003). Buprenorphine versus methadone maintenance: A cost-effectiveness analysis. *Drug and Alcohol Dependence, 71*, 295–302.

Doughty, M. (2012). *The book of drugs: A memoir*. Philadelphia, PA: Da Capo Press.

Downey, L., Rosengren, D. B., & Donovan, D. M. (2003). Gender, waitlists, and outcomes for public-sector drug treatment. *Journal of Substance Abuse Treatment, 25*, 19–28.

Drake, R. E., Essock, S. M., Shaner, A., Carey, K. B., Minkoff, K., Kola, L., Lynde, D., Osher, F. C., Clark, R. E., & Rickards, L. (2001). Implementing dual diagnosis services for clients with severe mental illness. *Psychiatric Services, 52*(4), 469–476.

Drake, R. E., Goldman, H. H., Leff, H. S., Lehman, A. F., Dixon, L., Mueser, K. T., & Torrey, W. C. (2001). Implementing evidence-based practices in routine mental health service settings. *Psychiatric Services, 52*(1), 45–50.

Drake, R. E., Osher, F. C., & Wallach, M. A. (1991). Homelessness and dual diagnosis. *American Psychologist, 46*, 1149–1158.

Driessen, M., Meier, S., Hill, A., Wetterling, T., Lange, W., & Junghanns, K. (2001). The course of anxiety, depression and drinking behaviours after completed detoxification in alcoholics with and without comorbid anxiety and depressive disorders. *Alcohol and Alcoholism, 36*(3), 249–255.

Drucker, E., Lurie, P., Wodak, A., & Alcabes, P. (1998). Measuring harm reduction: The effects of needle and syringe exchange programs and methadone maintenance on the ecology of HIV. *AIDS, 12*(Suppl. A), S217–S230.

Drummond, D. C. (2002). Meta-analysis in alcohol treatment research: Does it help us to know what works? *Addiction, 97*(3), 297–299.

DSM-5 to Include Controversial Changes to Criteria for Substance Use Disorders. (2012, July). *Journal of Studies on Alcohol and Drugs, 73*(4), 1–3.

Dual Recovery Anonymous. (2009). *The history of Dual Recovery Anonymous*. Retrieved September 29, 2013, from http://www.draonline.org/history.html

DuPont, R. L. (1996). Harm reduction and decriminalization in the United States: A personal perspective. *Substance Use & Misuse, 14*, 1929–1945. Discussion 1947–1972.

Durham, T. G. (2007, January–February). *First, meet ethical obligations*. Retrieved October 30, 2008 from http://www.addictionpro.com/ME2/Segmens/Publication/Print.asp

Duroy, T. H., Schmidt, S. L., & Perry, P. D. (2003). Adolescents' and young adults' perspectives on a continuum of care in a three year drug treatment program. *Journal of Drug Issues, 33*(4), 801–832.

Dusenbury, L., Brannigan, R., Falco, M., & Hansen, W. B. (2003). A review of research on fidelity of implementation: Implications for drug abuse prevention in school settings. *Health Education Research, 18*(2), 237–256.

Earley, P. (2013). ASAM textbook Chapter 4–5: Research on the ASAM criteria. Retrieved June 10, 2013, from http://paulearley.net/ASAM-PPC-Articles/asam-textbook-chapter-4-5/Research-on-the-ASAM-Criteria.html

Ebener, P., & Kilmer, B. (2003). *Barriers to treatment entry: Case studies of applicants approved for admission.* Santa Monica, CA: Rand Drug Policy Research Center.

Eckersley, R. (2006). Is modern Western culture a health hazard? *International Journal of Epidemiology, 35,* 252–258.

Edwards, A. C., & Kendler, K. S. (2012). Twin study of the relationship between adolescent attention-deficit/hyperactivity disorder and adult alcohol dependence. *Journal of Studies on Alcohol and Drugs, 73,* 185–194.

Einstein, S. (2007). Harm and risk reduction: History, theories, issues and implications. *Substance Use & Misuse, 42,* 257–265.

Eliason, M. J. (2007). *Improving substance abuse treatment: An introduction to the evidence-based practice movement.* Los Angeles, CA: Sage.

EmblemHealth. (2012). *Coverage for SBIRT expanded.* Retrieved July 5, 2012, from http://emblemhealth.com/default.aspx?Page=25735

Emrick, C. D. (1994). Alcoholics Anonymous and other 12-step groups. In M. Galanters & H. D. Kleber (Eds.), *Textbook of substance abuse treatment* (pp. 351–358). Washington, DC: American Psychiatric Press.

Emrick, C. D., Tonigan, J. S., Montgomery, & Little, L. (1993). Alcoholics Anonymous: What is currently known. In B. S. McCrady & W. R. Miller (Eds.), *Research on Alcoholics Anonymous: Opportunities and alternatives* (pp. 41–76). New Brunswick, NJ: Rutgers Center of Alcohol Studies.

Enders, K. (2009, September). *Harm reduction as a model of intervention and treatment: Theory, definition, and approaches to working with LGBT populations.* Lesbian, Gay, Bisexual, and Transgender, Treatment and Recovery Improvement, Statewide Technical Assistance Resources. New York, NY: LGBT TRISTAR.

Ennett, S. T., Ringwalt, C. L., Thorne, J., Rohrbach, L. A., Vincus, A., Simons-Rudolph, A., & Jones, S. (2003). A comparison of current practice in school-based substance use prevention programs with meta-analysis findings. *Prevention Science, 4*(1), 1–14.

Ennett, S. T., Tobler, N. S., Ringwalt, C. L., & Flewelling, R. L. (1994). How effective is Drug Abuse Resistance Education? A meta-analysis of Project DARE outcome evaluations. *American Journal of Public Health, 84*(9), 1394–1401.

Ercan, E. S., Coskunol, H., Varan, A., & Toksoz, K. (2003). Childhood attention deficit/hyperactivity disorder and alcohol dependence: A 1-year follow-up. *Alcohol and Alcoholism, 38*(4), 352–356.

Erickson, P. G. (1995). Harm reduction: What it is and is not. *Drug and Alcohol Review, 14*(3), 283–285.

Erickson, P. G. (1996). Comments on "Harm reduction and decriminalization in the United States: A personal perspective," by Robert L. DuPont. *Substance Use & Misuse, 31*(14), 1965–1970.

Espada, J. P., Griffin, K. W., Pereira, J. R., Orgiles, M., & Garcia-Fernandez, J. M. (2012). Component analysis of a school-based substance use prevention program in Spain: Contributions of problem solving and social skills content. *Prevention Science, 13*(1), 86–95.

Etheridge, R. M., Craddock, S. G., Dunteman, G. H., & Hubbard, R. L. (1995). Treatment services in two national studies of community-based drug abuse treatment programs. *Journal of Substance Abuse, 7*(1), 9–26.

European Monitoring Centre for Drugs and Drug Addiction. (2013). *Home page.* Retrieved February 7, 2013, from http://www.emcdda.europa.eu/

Fals-Stewart, W., O'Farrell, T. J., & Birchler, G. R. (2001). Behavior couples therapy for male methadone maintenance patients: Effects on drug-using behavior and relationship adjustment. *Behavior Therapy, 32*(2), 391–411. doi:10.1016/S0005-7894 (01)80010-80011

Fals-Stewart, W., O'Farrell, T. J., Birchler, G. R., Cordova, J., & Kelly, M. K. (2005). Behavioral couples therapy for alcoholism and drug abuse: Where we've been, where we are, and where we're going. *Journal of Cognitive Psychotherapy: An International Quarterly, 19*(3), 229–246.

Fals-Stewart, W., O'Farrell, T. J., Feehan, M., Birchler, G. R., Tiller, S., & McFarlin, S. K. (2000). Behavioral couples therapy versus individual-based treatment for male substance-abusing patients. An evaluation of significant individual change and comparison of improvement rates. *Journal of Substance Abuse Treatment, 18,* 249–254.

Farber, E., & Keating-O'Connor, B. (1991). Planned family intervention: Johnson Institute Method. *Journal of Chemical Dependency Treatment, 4*(1). doi:10.1300/J034vo4n01_05

Feinstein, A. R. (1970). The pre-therapeutic classification of co-morbidity in chronic disease. *Journal of Chronic Disease, 23,* 455–468.

Ferguson, C. U. (2012, October/November). President's message: Beyond self-limiting and addictive cultural scripts: The transformative power of preference in the now. *Association for Humanistic Psychology Perspective,* pp. 6–8.

Ferri, M., Amato, L., & Davoli, M. (2009). Alcoholics Anonymous and other 12-step programmes for alcohol dependence. *Cochrane Library, 3.* Retrieved August 1, 2013, from http://www.thecochranelibrary.com

Fickenscher, A., Novins, D. K., & Beals, J. (2006). A pilot study of motivation and treatment completion among American Indian adolescents in substance abuse treatment. *Addictive Behaviors, 31*(8), 1402–1414.

Fiellin, D. A., Reid, M. C., & O'Connor, P. G. (2000). Outpatient management of patients with alcohol problems. *Annals of Internal Medicine, 133*(10), 815–827.

Finlinson, H. A., Oliver-Velez, D., Deren, S., Cant, J. G. H., Colon, H. M., Robles, R. R., Kang, S.-Y., & Andia, J. F. (2006). A longitudinal study of syringe acquisition by Puerto Rican injection drug users in New York and Puerto Rico: Implication for syringe exchange and distribution programs. *Substance Use & Misuse, 41,* 1313–1336.

Finney, J. W. (2000). Limitations in using existing alcohol treatment trials to develop practice guidelines. *Addiction, 95*(10), 1491–1500.

Finney, J. W., & Monahan, S. C. (1996). The cost-effectiveness of treatment for alcoholism: A second approximation. *Journal of Studies on Alcohol, 57,* 229–243.

Finney, J. W., & Moos, R. H. (1995). Entering treatment for alcohol abuse: A stress and coping model. *Addiction, 90*(9), 1223–1240.

Fiorentine, R., & Hillhouse, M. P. (2000). Drug treatment and 12-step program participation. The additive effects of integrated recovery activities. *Journal of Substance Abuse Treatment, 18,* 65–74.

Fiorentine, R., Nakashima, J., & Anglin, M. D. (1999). Client engagement in drug treatment. *Journal of Substance Abuse Treatment, 17*(3), 199–206.

Flynn, P. M., & Brown, B. S. (2008). Co-occurring disorders in substance abuse treatment: Issues and prospects. *Journal of Substance Abuse Treatment, 34,* 36–47.

Fong, T. W., & Tsuang, J. (2007). Asian-Americans, addictions, and barriers to treatment. *Psychiatry, 4*(11), 51–59.

Ford, J. H., II, Green, C. A., Hoffman, K. A., Wisdom, J. P., Riley, K. J., Bergmann, L., & Molfenter, T. (2007). Process improvement needs in substance abuse treatment: Admissions walk-through results. *Journal of Substance Abuse Treatment, 33*(4), 379–389. doi:10.1016/j.jsat.2007.02.003

Forman, B., & Larivee, J. (2013, March). *Crime, cost and consequences: Is it time to get smart on crime?* Boston, MA: MassINC and Community Resources for Justice.

Forman, R. F., Bovasso, G., & Woody, G. (2001). Staff beliefs about addiction treatment. *Journal of Substance Abuse Treatment, 21,* 1–9.

Forys, K., McKellar, J., & Moos, R. (2007). Participation in specific treatment components predicts alcohol-specific and general coping skills. *Addictive Behaviors, 32,* 1669–1680.

French, L. A. (2004). Alcohol and other drug addictions among Native Americans: The movement toward tribal-centric treatment programs. *Alcoholism Treatment Quarterly, 22*(1), 81–91.

French, M. T. (2003). *Brief Drug Abuse Treatment Cost Analysis Program (Brief DATCAP): Program version* (1st ed.). Coral Gables, FL: University of Miami. Retrieved December 9, 2011, from http://datcap.com

French, M. T., Dunlap, L. J., Zarkin, G. A., McGeary, K. A., & McLellan, A. T. (1997). A structured instrument for estimating the economic cost of drug abuse treatment: The Drug Abuse Treatment Cost Analysis Program (DATCAP). *Journal of Substance Abuse Treatment, 14,* 445–455.

French, M. T., Salome, H. J., & McLellan, A. T. (2002). Benefit-cost analysis of addiction treatment: Methodological guidelines and empirical application using the DATCAP and ASI. *Health Services Research, 37*(2), 433–455.

Friedmann, P. D., Lemon, S. C., & D'Aunno, T. A. (2003). Accessibility of addiction treatment: Results from a national survey of outpatient substance abuse treatment organizations. *Health Services Research, 38*(3), 887–903. doi:10.1111/1475-6773.00151

Fromme, K., & Orrick, D. (2004). The Lifestyle Management Class: A harm reduction approach to college drinking. *Addiction Research and Theory, 12*(4), 335–351.

Fry, C. L., Treloar, C., & Maher, L. (2005). Ethical challenges and responses in harm reduction research: Promoting applied communitarian ethics. *Drug and Alcohol Review, 24,* 449–459.

Futterman, R., Lorente, M., & Silverman, S. (2004). Integrating harm reduction and abstinence-based substance abuse treatment in the public sector. *Substance Abuse, 25*(1), 3–7.

Galanter, M. (2007). Spirituality and recovery in a 12-step program: An empirical model. *Journal of Substance Abuse Treatment, 33,* 265–272.

Galanter, M., Egelko, S., & Edwards, H. (1993). Rational Recovery: Alternative to AA for addiction? *American Journal of Drug and Alcohol Abuse, 19*(4), 499–510.

Galanter, M., Keller, D. S., Dermatis, H., & Egelko, S. (2000). The impact of managed care on substance abuse treatment: A report of the American Society of Addiction Medicine. *Journal of Addictive Diseases, 19*(3), 13–34.

Galvan, F. H., & Caetano, R. (2003). Alcohol use and related problems among ethnic minorities in the United States. *Alcohol Research & Health, 27*(1), 87–94.

Garnick, D. W., Horgan, C. M., Lee, M. T., Panas, L., Ritter, G. A., Davis, S., Leeper, T., Moore, R., & Reynolds, M. (2007). Are Washington Circle performance measures associated with decreased criminal activity following treatment? *Journal of Substance Abuse Treatment, 33,* 341–352. doi:10.1016/j.jsat.2007.03.002

Garrett, J., Landau, J., Shea, R., Stanton, M. D., Baciewicz, G., & Brinkman-Sull, D. (1998). The ARISE intervention: Using family and network links to engage addicted persons in treatment. *Journal of Substance Abuse Treatment, 15*(4), 333–343.

Gastfriend, D. R., Garbutt, J. C., Pettinati, H. M., & Forman, R. F. (2007). A reduction in heavy drinking as a treatment outcome in alcohol dependence. *Journal of Substance Abuse Treatment, 33*(1), 71–80.

George, A. A., & Tucker, J. A. (1996). Help-seeking by problem drinkers: Social context surrounding entry into alcohol treatment or AA. *Journal of Studies on Alcohol, 57,* 449–457.

Gerard, S. (2005, June 16). *Prevention & treatment of substance abuse in Native American communities*. Phoenix, AZ: Phoenix IHS Area Health Summit.

Gerstein, D. R. (1994). Outcome research: Drug abuse. In R. K. Hester & W. R. Miller (Eds.), *Handbook of alcoholism treatment approaches: Effective alternatives* (2nd ed., pp. 45–64). Needham Heights, MA: Allyn & Bacon.

Gfroerer, J. C., Adams, E. H., & Moien, M. (1988). Drug abuse discharges from non-federal short-stay hospitals. *American Journal of Public Health, 78*(12), 1559–1562.

Gianoli, M. O., Jane, J. S., O'Brien, E., & Ralevski, E. (2012). Treatment for comorbid borderline personality disorder and alcohol use disorders: A review of the evidence and future recommendations. *Experimental and Clinical Psychopharmacology, 20*(4), 333–344. doi:10.1037/a0027999

Gil-Rivas, V., Fiorentine, R., Anglin, M. D., & Taylor, E. (1997). Sexual and physical abuse: Do they compromise drug treatment outcomes? *Journal of Substance Abuse Treatment, 14*(4), 351–358.

Gitlow, S., & Gold, M. (2007). The inadequacies of the evidence: Flaws in research methodology may result in overselling of certain treatments for addiction. *Addiction Professional, 5*(2), 17–25.

Glatt, M. M. (1995). Controlled drinking after a third of a century. Comments on Sobell & Sobell's editorial "Controlled drinking after 25 years: how important was the great debate?" *Addiction, 90*, 1157–1177.

Godin, G., Gagnon, H., Alary, M., Noel. L., & Morissette, M. R. (2001). Correctional officers' intention of accepting or refusing to make HIV preventive tools accessible to inmates. *AIDS Education and Prevention, 13*, 462–473.

Goldstein, G., Luther, J. F., Haas, G. L., Gordon, A. J., & Appelt, C. (2009). Comorbidity between psychiatric and general medical disorders in homeless veterans. *Psychiatric Quarterly, 80*(4), 199–212. doi:10.1007/s11126-009-9106-6

Gossop, M., Harris, J., Best, D., Man, L.-H., Manning, V., Marshall, J., & Strang, J. (2003). Is attendance at Alcoholics Anonymous meetings after inpatient treatment related to improved outcomes? A 6-month follow-up study. *Alcohol and Alcoholism, 38*(5), 421–426.

Gossop, M., Stewart, D., & Marsden, J. (2008). Attendance at Narcotics Anonymous and Alcoholics Anonymous meetings, frequency of attendance and substance use outcomes after residential treatment for drug dependence: A 5-year follow-up study. *Addiction, 103*(1), 119–125.

Gottfredson, D. C., & Wilson, D. B. (2003). Characteristics of effective school-based substance abuse prevention. *Prevention Science, 4*(1), 27–38.

Governors Highway Safety Commission. (2013, October). *Drunk driving laws*. Retrieved October 22, 2013, from http://www.ghsa.org/html/stateinfo/laws/impaired_laws.html

Grady, K., Gersick, K. E., & Boratynski, M. (1985). Preparing parents for teenagers: A step in the prevention of adolescent substance abuse. *Family Relations, 34*, 541–549.

Granfield, R., & Cloud, W. (1996). The elephant that no one sees: Natural recovery among middle-class addicts. *Journal of Drug Issues, 26*(1), 45–61.

Granfield, R., & Cloud, W. (1999). *Coming clean: Overcoming addiction without treatment*. New York, NY: New York University Press.

Grant, L. P., Haughton, B., & Sachan, D. S. (2004). Nutrition education is positively associated with substance abuse treatment program outcomes. *Journal of the American Dietetic Association, 104*(4), 604–610.

Green, B. L., Rockhill, A., & Furrer, C. (2006). Understanding patterns of substance abuse treatment for women involved with child welfare: The influence of the Adoption and Safe Families Act (ASFA). *American Journal of Drug and Alcohol Abuse, 32*, 149–176.

Green, C. A. (2006). Gender and use of substance abuse treatment services. *Alcohol Research & Health, 29*(1), 55–62.

Green, L. L., Fullilove, M. T., & Fullilove, R. E. (1998). Stories of spiritual awakening: The nature of spirituality in recovery. *Journal of Substance Abuse Treatment, 15*(4), 325–331.

Green, L. W., Ottoson, J. M., Garcia, C., & Hiatt, R. A. (2009). Diffusion theory and knowledge dissemination, utilization, and integration in public health. *Annual Review of Public Health, 30*(1), 151–174.

Greenberg, G. (2013). *The book of woe: The* DSM *and the unmaking of psychiatry.* New York, NY: Blue Rider Press.

Greenfield, S. F., Brooks, A. J., Gordon, S. M., Green, C. A., Kropp, F., McHugh, R. K., . . . Miele, G. M. (2007). Substance abuse treatment entry, retention, and outcome in women: A review of the literature. *Drug and Alcohol Dependence, 86*, 1–21.

Greer, P. M., & Kuehn, D. (2009, May 4). National education standards vital for addiction professionals. *Alcoholism and Drug Abuse Weekly, 21*(18), 5.

Gregoire, T. K. (2000). Factors associated with level of care assignment in substance abuse treatment. *Journal of Substance Abuse Treatment, 18*, 241–248.

Gregory, R. J., Chlebowski, S., Kang, D., Remen, A. L., Soderberg, M. G., Stepkovitch, J., & Virk, S. (2008). A controlled trial of psychodynamic psychotherapy for co-occurring borderline personal disorder and alcohol use disorder. *Psychotherapy, 45*(1), 28–41. doi:10.1037/0033-3204.45.1.28

Gregory, R. J., DeLucia-Deranja, E., & Mogle, J. A. (2010). Dynamic deconstructive psychotherapy versus optimized community care for borderline personality disorder co-occurring with alcohol use disorders: A 30-month follow-up. *Journal of Nervous and Mental Disease, 198*(4), 292–298. doi:10.1097/NMD.0b013e3181d6172d

Grella, C. E., Greenwell, L., Prendergast, M., Farabee, D., Hall, E., Cartier, J., & Burdon, W. (2007). Organizational characteristics of drug abuse treatment programs for offenders. *Journal of Substance Abuse Treatment, 32*, 291–300. doi:10.1016/j.jsat.2007.01.001

Griswold, K. S., Aronoff, H., Kernan, J. B., & Kahn, L. S. (2008). Adolescent substance use and abuse: recognition and management. *American Family Physician, 77*(3), 331–336.

Gumbley, S. J. (2012). *ATTC of New England 2012 regional workforce report.* Providence, RI: New England Addiction Technology Transfer Center Network.

Gustafson, D. (2012). Essential ingredients for successful design of addiction treatment. *The Bridge, 2*(2). Retrieved November 25, 2013, from http://www.attcnetwork.org/find/news/attcnews/epubs/v212_article01b.asp

Hahn, E., & Papazian, K. (1987). Substance abuse prevention with preschool children. *Journal of Community Health Nursing, 4*(3), 165–170.

Hall, E. A., Prendergast, M. L., Wellisch, J., Patten, M., & Cao, Y. (2004). Treating drug-abusing women prisoners: An outcomes evaluation of the Forever Free program. *Prison Journal, 84*(1), 81–105. doi:10.1177/0032885503262456

Hall, W. (2010). What are the policy lessons of national alcohol prohibition in the United States, 1920–1933? *Addiction, 105*(7), 1164–1173.

Halloway, K. R., Bennett, T. H., & Farrington, D. P. (2006). The effectiveness of drug treatment programs in reducing criminal behavior: a meta-analysis. *Psicothema, 18*(3), 620–629.

Hamill, P. (1994). *A drinking life: A memoir.* New York, NY: Little, Brown.

Hanson, M., & Gutheil, I. A. (2004). Motivational strategies with alcohol-involved older adults: Implications for social work practice. *Social Work, 49*(3), 364–372.

Hardy-Fanta, C., & Mignon, S. I. (2000, October). *Alternatives to incarceration for substance abusing female defendants/offenders in Massachusetts, 1996–1998.* Boston, MA: University of Massachusetts Boston, Center for Women in Politics and Public Policy.

Harris, A. H. S., McKellar, J. D., Moos, R. H., Schaefer, J. A., & Conkite, R. C. (2006). Predictors of engagement in continuing care following residential substance use disorder treatment. *Drug and Alcohol Dependence, 84*, 93–101.

Hart, C. (2013). *High price: A neuroscientist's journey of self-discovery that challenges everything you know about drugs and society.* New York, NY: HarperCollins.

Hartmann, D. J., Wolk, J. L., & Sullivan, W. P. (1995). State-wide self-report of treatment effectiveness: Promise, pitfalls, and potential. *Alcoholism Treatment Quarterly, 13*(1), 45–56.

Hathaway, A. D. (2005). Ushering in another harm reduction era? Discursive authenticity, drug policy and research. *Drug and Alcohol Review, 24*, 549–550.

Hawkins, J. D., Catalano, R. F., & Miller, J. Y. (1992). Risk and protective factors for alcohol and other drug problems in adolescence and early adulthood: Implications for substance abuse prevention. *Psychological Bulletin, 112*(1), 64–105.

Hawkins, R. L., & Abrams, C. (2007). Disappearing acts: The social networks of formerly homeless individuals with co-occurring disorders. *Social Science & Medicine, 65*, 2031–2042.

Hazelden Foundation. (2013). *Double Trouble in Recovery.* Retrieved September 15, 2013, from http://www.bhevolution.org/public/doubletroubleinrecovery.page

Hazelden Foundation. (n.d.). *Hazelden Foundation history.* Retrieved June 24, 2013, from http://www.fundinguniverse.com/company-histories/hazelden-foundation-history/

Heath, D. B. (2001). Cultures and substance abuse. *Psychiatric Clinics of North America, 24*, 479–496.

Heather, N. (2007). How should the effectiveness of treatment for alcohol problems be evaluated? *Drugs and Alcohol Today, 7*(4), 22–32.

Heather, N., Adamson, S. J., Raistrick, D., & Slegg, G. P. (2010). Initial preference for drinking goal in the treatment of alcohol problems: I. Baseline differences between abstinence and non-abstinence groups. *Alcohol and Alcoholism, 45*(2), 128–135.

Heather, N., & Dawe, S. (2005). Level of impaired control predicts outcome of moderation-oriented treatment for alcohol problems. *Addiction, 100*, 945–952.

Heinz, A. J., Disney, E. R., Epstein, D. H., Glezen, L. A., Clark, P. I., & Preston, K. L. (2010). A focus-group study on spirituality and substance-abuse treatment. *Substance Use & Misuse, 45*(1–2), 134–153.

Henderson, C. E., Taxman, F. S., & Young, D. W. (2008). A Rasch model analysis of evidence-based treatment practices used in the criminal justice system. *Drug and Alcohol Dependence, 93*(1–2), 163–175. doi:10.1016/j.drugalcdep.2007.09.010

Henderson, C. E., Young, D. W., Jainchill, N., Hawke, J., Farkas, S., & Davis, R. M. (2007). Program use of effective drug abuse treatment practices for juvenile offenders. *Journal of Substance Abuse Treatment, 32*(3), 279–290.

Herbeck, D. M., Fitek, D. J., Svikis, D. S., Montoya, I. D., Marcus, S. C., & West, J. C. (2005). Treatment compliance in patients with comorbid psychiatric and substance use disorders. *American Journal on Addictions, 14*(3), 195–207.

Herman, M., Galanter, M., & Lifshutz, H. (1991). Combined substance abuse and psychiatric disorders in homeless and domiciled patients. *American Journal of Drug and Alcohol Abuse, 17*(4), 415–422.

Hersey, B. (2001, April). *The controlled drinking debates: A review of four decades of acrimony.* Retrieved January 26, 2013, from http://www.doctordeluca.com/

Herzig, S. J., Rothberg, M. B., Cheung, M., Ngo, L. H., Marcantonio, E. R. (2013). Opioid utilization and opioid-related adverse events in nonsurgical patients in US hospitals. *Journal of Hospital Medicine.* doi:10.1002/jhm.2102

Hester, R. K. (1994). Outcome research: Alcoholism. In M. Galanter & H. Kleber (Eds.), *Textbook of substance abuse treatment* (pp. 35–44). Washington, DC: American Psychiatric Press.

Higgins, S. T., & Petry, N. M. (1999). Contingency management incentives for sobriety. *Alcohol Research & Health, 23*(2), 122–127.

Higgins, S. T., Wong, C. J., Badger, G. J., Ogden, D. E., & Dantona, R. L. (2000). Contingent reinforcement increases cocaine abstinence during outpatient treatment and 1 year of follow-up. *Journal of Consulting and Clinical Psychology, 68*(1)), 64–72.

Hiller, M. L., Narevic, E., Webster, J. M., Rosen, P., Staton, M., Leukefeld, C., . . . Kayo, R. (2009). Problem severity and motivation for treatment in incarcerated substance abusers. *Substance Use & Misuse, 44*, 28–41.

Hitchcock, H. C., Stainback, R. D., & Roque, G. M. (1995). Effects of halfway house placement on retention of patients in substance abuse aftercare. *American Journal of Drug and Alcohol Abuse, 21*(3), 379–390.

Hodgins, D. C., Leigh, G., Milne, R., & Gerrish, R. (1997). Drinking goal selection in behavioral self-management treatment of chronic alcoholics. *Addictive Behaviors, 22*(2), 247–255.

Hoffman, K. A., Green, C. A., Ford, J. H., II, Wisdom, J. P., Gustafson, D. H., & McCarty, D. (2012). Improving quality of care in substance abuse treatment using five key process improvement variables. *Journal of Behavioral Health Services & Research, 39*(3), 234–244. doi:10.1007/s11414-011-9270-y

Holder, H., Longabaugh, R., Miller, W. M., & Rubonis, A. V. (1991). The cost-effectiveness of treatment for alcoholism: A first approximation. *Journal of Studies on Alcohol, 52*, 517–540.

Hong, Y., Mitchell, S. G., Peterson, J. A., Latkin, C. A., Tobin, K., & Gann, D. (2005). Ethnographic process evaluation: Piloting an HIV prevention intervention program among injection drug users. *International Journal of Qualitative Methods, 4*(1), Article 1. Retrieved October 23, 2013, from http://www.ualberta.ca~iiqm/backissues/4_1/pdf/hong.pdf

Human Rights Watch. (2009). *Decades of disparity: Drug arrests and race in the United States.* New York, NY: Author.

Humphreys, K. (2003). A research-based analysis of the Moderation Management controversy. *Psychiatric Services, 54*(5), 621–622.

Humphreys, K. (2006a). Closing remarks: Swimming to the horizon-reflections on a special series. *Addiction, 101*, 1238–1240.

Humphreys, K. (2006b).The trials of Alcoholics Anonymous [Editorial]. *Addiction, 101*, 617–618. doi:10.1111/j.1360-0443.2006.01447.x

Humphreys, K., Huebsch, P. D., Finney, J. W., & Moos, R. H. (1999). A comparative evaluation of substance abuse treatment: V. Substance abuse treatment can enhance the effectiveness of self-help groups. *Alcoholism: Clinical and Experimental Research, 23*(3), 558–563.

Humphreys, K., Kaskutas, L. A., & Weisner, C. (1998). The relationship of pre-treatment Alcoholics Anonymous affiliation with problem severity, social resources and treatment history. *Drug and Alcohol Dependence, 49*, 123–131.

Humphreys, K., & Moos, R. (2001). Can encouraging substance abuse patients to participate in self-help groups reduce demand for health care? A quasi-experimental study. *Alcoholism: Clinical and Experimental Research, 25*(5), 711–716.

Humphreys, K., & Noke, J. M. (1997). The influence of posttreatment mutual help group participation on the friendship networks of substance abuse patients. *American Journal of Community Psychology, 25*(1), 1–16.

Hunt, J. (2012, March 9). *Why the gay and transgender population experiences high rates of substance abuse.* Retrieved September 18, 2013, from http://www.americanprogress.org/wp-content/uploads/issues/2012/03/pdf/lgbt_substance_abuse.pdf

Hunter, S. B., Watkins, K. E., Wenzel, S., Gilmore, J., Sheehe, J., & Griffin, B. (2005). Training substance abuse treatment staff to care for co-occurring disorders. *Journal of Substance Abuse Treatment, 28,* 239–245.

Hyde, P. S. (2013). Youth behavioral health: Strengthening families, schools, communities. *SAMHSA News, 21*(2). Retrieved November 11, 2013, from http://samhsa.gov/samhsanewsletter/Volune_21_Number_2/administrator.aspx

Ichiyama, M. A., Fairlie, A. M., Wood, M. D., Turrisi, R., Francis, D. P., Ray, A. E., & Stanger, L. A. (2009). A randomized trial of a parent-based intervention of drinking behavior among incoming college freshman. *Journal of Studies on Alcohol and Drugs, Supplement 16,* 67–76.

Ilgen, M. A., McKellar, J., Moos, R., & Finney, J. W. (2006). Therapeutic alliance and the relationship between motivation and treatment outcomes in patients with alcohol use disorder. *Journal of Substance Abuse Treatment, 31*(2), 157–162.

Imel, Z. E., Wampold, B. E., Miller, S. D., & Fleming, R. R. (2008). Distinctions without a difference: Direct comparisons of psychotherapies for alcohol use disorders. *Psychology of Addictive Behaviors, 22*(4), 533–543.

Institute of Medicine. (1990). *Broadening the base of treatment for alcohol problems.* Report of a study by a committee of the Institute of Medicine, Division of Mental Health and Behavioral Medicine. Washington, DC: National Academies Press.

International Certification and Reciprocity Consortium. (2013). *Setting global standards for addiction professionals.* Retrieved December 8, 2013, from http://internationalcredentialing.org/

International Coalition of Addiction Studies Education. (2013). *Welcome to INCASE.* Retrieved December 10, 2013, from http://www.incase.org/

Irwin, J. E., Bowers, C. A., Dunn, M. E., & Wang, M. C. (1999). Efficacy of relapse prevention: A meta-analytic review. *Journal of Consulting and Clinical Psychology, 67*(4), 563–570. Look for in Neff and MacMaster.

Janowsky, D. S., Boone, A., Morter, S., & Howe, L. (1999). Personality and alcohol/substance-use disorder patient relapse and attendance at self-help group meetings. *Alcohol and Alcoholism, 34*(3), 359–369.

Jarvis, T. J., & Copeland, J. (1997). Child sexual abuse as a predictor of psychiatric co-morbidity and its implications for drug and alcohol treatment. *Drug and Alcohol Dependence, 49,* 61–69.

Jason, L. A., Olson, B. D., Ferrari, J. R., & Lo Sasso, A. T. (2006). Communal housing settings enhance substance abuse recovery. *American Journal of Public Health, 96*(10), 1727–1729.

Javier, S. J., Belgrave, F. Z., Hill, E. V., & Richardson, J. T. (2013). Ethnic and gender differences in normative perceptions of substance use and actual use among college students. *Journal of Ethnicity in Substance Abuse, 12,* 228–241. doi:15332640.2013.798847

Jay, J., Jay, D., & McGovern, G. (2008). *Love first: A family's guide to intervention.* Center City, MN: Hazelden.

Jerrell, J. M., & Wilson, J. L. (1997). Ethnic differences in the treatment of dual mental and substance disorders: A preliminary analysis. *Journal of Substance Abuse Treatment, 14,* 122–140.

Joe, G. W., Simpson, D. D., & Broome, K. M. (1998). Effects of readiness for drug abuse treatment on client retention and assessment of process. *Addiction, 93,* 1177–1190.

Johnsen, E., & Herringer, L. G. (1993). A note on the utilization of common support activities and relapse following substance abuse treatment. *Journal of Psychology, 127*(1), 73–77.

Johnson, G., & Chamberlain, C. (2008). Homelessness and substance abuse: Which comes first? *Australian Social Work, 61*(4), 342–356. doi:10.1080/03124070802428191

Johnson, K. A., Ford, J. H., II, & McCluskey, M. (2012). Promoting new practices to increase access to and retention in addiction treatment: An analysis of five communication channels. *Addictive Behaviors, 37*, 1193–1197.

Johnson, V. (1973). *I'll quit tomorrow.* New York, NY: Harper & Row.

Johnson, V. (1986). *Intervention, how to help some who doesn't want help: A step-by-step guide for families and friends of chemically dependent persons.* Minneapolis, MN: Johnson Institute Books.

Jonas, S. (1997). Public health approaches. In J. J. Lowinson, P. Ruiz, R. B. Millman, & J. G. Langrod (Eds.), *Substance abuse: A comprehensive textbook* (3rd ed., pp. 775–785). Baltimore, MD: Williams & Wilkins.

Jones, H. E., Martin, P. R., Heil, S. H., Kaltenbach, K., Selby, P., Coyle, M. G., Stine, S. M., O'Grady, K. E., Arria, A. M., & Fischer, G. (2008). Treatment of opioid-dependent pregnant women: Clinical and research issues. *Journal of Substance Abuse Treatment, 35*(3), 245–259. doi:10.1016/j.jsat.2007.10.007

Jurgens, R. (1996). *HIV/AIDS in prison.* Final Report. Montreal, Quebec, Canada: Canadian HIV/AIDS Legal Network.

Kahler, C. W., Read, J. P., Ramsey, S. E., Stuart, G. L., McCrady, B. S., & Brown, R. A. (2004). Motivational enhancement for 12-step involvement among patients undergoing alcohol detoxification. *Journal of Consulting and Clinical Psychology, 74*(4), 736–741.

Karno, M. P., & Longabaugh, R. (2003). Patient depressive symptoms and therapist focus on emotional material: A new look at Project MATCH. *Journal of Studies on Alcohol, 64*(5), 607–615.

Karno, M. P., & Longabaugh, R. (2005a). An examination of how therapist directiveness interacts with patient anger and reactance to predict alcohol use. *Journal of Studies on Alcohol, 66*, 825–832.

Karno, M. P., & Longabaugh, R. (2005b). Less directiveness by therapists improves drinking outcomes of reactant clients in alcoholism treatment. *Journal of Consulting and Clinical Psychology, 73*(2), 262–267.

Karriker-Jaffe, K. J., & Zemore, S. E. (2009). Associations between acculturation and alcohol consumption of Latino men in the United States. *Journal of Studies on Alcohol and Drugs, 70*(1), 27–31.

Kaskutas, L. A. (2009). Alcoholics Anonymous effectiveness: Faith meets science. *Journal of Addictive Diseases, 28*(2), 145–157. doi:10.1080/10550880902772464

Kaskutas, L. A., & Subbaraman, M. (2011). Integrating addiction treatment and mutual aid recovery resources. In J. F Kelly & W. L. White (Eds.), *Addiction recovery management: Theory, research and practice* (pp. 31–43). New York, NY: Humana Press.

Kates, E., Mignon, S., & Ransford, P. (2008, June). *Parenting from prison: Family relationships of incarcerated women in Massachusetts.* Boston, MA: University of Massachusetts Boston, Center for Women in Politics and Public Policy.

Keane, H. (2005a). Critiques of harm reduction: Toward a morally invested drug reform strategy. *International Journal of Drug Policy, 14*, 222–232.

Keane, H. (2005b). Moral frameworks, ethical engagement and harm reduction: Commentary on "Ethical challenges and responses in harm reduction research: Promoting applied communitarian ethics" by C. L. Fry, C. Treloar & L. Maher. *Drug and Alcohol Review, 24*(6), 551–552.

Kelly, J. F. (2003). Self-help for substance-use disorders: History, effectiveness, knowledge gaps, and research opportunities. *Clinical Psychology Review, 23*(5), 639–663.

Kelly, J. F., Magill, M., & Stout, R. L. (2009). How do people recover from alcohol dependence? A systematic review of the research on mechanisms of behavior change in Alcoholics Anonymous. *Addiction Research and Theory, 17*(3), 236–259.

Kelly, J. F., & McCrady, B. S. (2009). Twelve-step facilitation in non-specialty settings. In M. Galanter & L. A. Kaskutas (Eds.), *Recent developments in alcoholism* (Vol. 18, pp. 321–346). New York, NY: Springer.

Kelly, J. F., & Moos, R. (2003). Dropout from 12-step self-help groups: Prevalence, predictors, and counteracting treatment influences. *Journal of Substance Abuse Treatment, 24*(3), 241–250.

Kelly, J. F., Stout, R. L., Magill, M., Tonigan, J. S., & Pagano, M. E. (2010). Mechanisms of behavior change in Alcoholics Anonymous: Does AA lead to better alcohol use outcomes by reducing depression symptoms? *Addiction, 105*(4), 626–636.

Kelly, J. F., & Yeterian, J. D. (2010, July). Using mutual-help groups to address alcohol problems: Research is beginning to show that attendance at Alcoholics Anonymous meeting increases the odds of recovery and improves mood and well-being. *Journal of Employee Assistance.* Retrieved May 9, 2014, from http://www.thefreelibrary.com/Using+mutual-help+groups+to+address+alcohol+problems%3A+research+is...-a0234062750

Kelly, J. F., & Yeterian, J. D. (2011). The role of mutual-help groups in extending the framework of treatment. *Alcohol Research & Health, 33*(4), 350–355.

Kerr, T., Wood, E., Betteridge, G., Lines, R., & Jurgens, R. (2004). Harm reduction in prison: A "rights based analysis." *Critical Public Health, 14*(4), 345–360.

Kertesz, S. G., Horton, N. J., Friedmann, P. D., Saitz, R., & Samet, J. H. (2003). Slowing the revolving door: Stabilization programs reduce homeless persons' substance use after detoxification. *Journal of Substance Abuse Treatment, 24*(3), 197–207.

Kerwin, M. L. E., Walker-Smith, K., & Kirby, K. C. (2006). Comparative analysis of state requirements for the training of substance abuse and mental health counselors. *Journal of Substance Abuse Treatment, 30,* 173–181.

Kidorf, M., King, V. L., Pierce, J., Kolodner, K., & Brooner. R. K. (2011). Benefits of concurrent syringe exchange and substance abuse treatment participation. *Journal of Substance Abuse Treatment, 40*(3), 265–271.

Kimberly, J. R., & McLellan, A. T. (2006). The business of addiction treatment: A research agenda. *Journal of Substance Abuse Treatment, 31,* 213–219.

Kishline, A. (1994). *Moderate drinking: The Moderation Management guide for people who want to reduce their drinking.* New York, NY: Crown.

Kleinig, J. (2008). The ethics of harm reduction. *Substance Use & Misuse, 43,* 1–16.

Klingemann, H., & Bergmark, A. (2006). The legitimacy of addiction treatment in a world of smart people. *Addiction, 100*(9), 1230–1237.

Knapp. C. (1996). *Drinking: A love story.* New York, NY: Dell.

Knight, K. L., Hiller, M. L., Broome, K. M., & Simpson, D. D. (2000). Legal pressure, treatment readiness, and engagement in long-term residential programs. *Journal of Offender Rehabilitation, 31*(1/2), 101–115.

Knott, A. M., Corredoira, R., & Kimberly, J. (2008). Improving consistency and quality of service delivery: Implications for the addiction treatment field. *Journal of Substance Abuse Treatment, 35,* 99–108. doi:10.1016/j.jsat.2007.09.005

Knudsen, H. K., Ducharme, L. J., & Roman, P. M. (2006). Early adoption of buprenorphine in substance abuse treatment centers: Data from the private and public sectors. *Journal of Substance Abuse Treatment, 30,* 363–373.

Knudsen, H. K., Ducharme, L. J., & Roman, P. M. (2007). The adoption of medication in substance abuse treatment: Associations with organizational characteristics and technology clusters. *Drug and Alcohol Dependence, 87,* 164–174.

Knudsen, H. K., Ducharme, L. J., Roman, P. M., & Link, T. (2005). Buprenorphine diffusion: The attitudes of substance abuse treatment counselors. *Journal of Substance Abuse Treatment, 29,* 95–106.

Kogan, S. M., Brody, G. H., Molgaard, V. K., Grange, C. M., Oliver, D. A., Anderson, T. N., . . . Sperr, M. C. (2012). The Strong African American Families–Teen trial: Rationale, design, engagement processes, and family-specific effects. *Prevention Science, 13*(2), 206–217. doi:10.1007/s11121-011-0257-y

Kosok, A. (2006). The Moderation Management programme in 2004: What type of drinker seeks controlled drinking? *International Journal of Drug Policy, 17,* 295–303.

Kownacki, R. J., & Shadish, W. R. (1999). Does Alcoholics Anonymous work? The results from a meta-analysis of controlled experiments. *Substance Use & Misuse, 34*(13), 1897–1916.

Kraemer, H. C., Gardner, C., Brooks, J. O., III, & Yesavage, J. A. (1998). Advantages of excluding underpowered studies in meta-analysis: Inclusionist vs. exclusionist viewpoints. *Psychological Methods, 3,* 23–31.

Kurtz, E. (2002). Alcoholics Anonymous and the disease concept of alcoholism. *Alcoholism Treatment Quarterly, 20*(3/4), 5–39.

Kurtz, L. F., & Fisher, M. (2003). Twelve-step recovery and community service. *Health & Social Work, 28*(2), 137–145.

Kushner, M. G. (2014). Seventy-five years of comorbidity research. *Journal of Studies on Alcohol and Drugs, Supplement 17,* 50–58.

LaBrie, J. W., Huchting, K. K., Lac, A., Tawalbeh, S., Thompson, A. D., & Larimer, M. E. (2009). Preventing risky drinking in first-year college women: Further validation of a female specific motivational-enhancement group intervention. *Journal of Studies on Alcohol and Drugs, Supplement 16,* 77–85.

Lackner, N., Unterrainer, H. F., & Neubauer, A. C. (2013). Differences in Big Five personality traits between alcohol and polydrug abusers: Implications for treatment in the therapeutic community. *International Journal of Mental Health and Addiction, 101*(11). doi:10.1007/s11469-013-9445-2

Lamb, S., Greenlick, M. R., & McCarty, D. (Eds.). (1998). *Bridging the gap between practice and research: Forging partnerships with community-based drug and alcohol treatment.* Washington, DC: Institute of Medicine, National Academies Press.

Lambert, M. J., & Bergin, A. E. (1994). The effectiveness of psychotherapy. In A. E. Bergin & S. L. Garfield (Eds.), *Handbook of psychotherapy and behavior change* (pp. 143–179). New York, NY: John Wiley & Sons.

L., K. (2011). *The intervention book: Stories and solutions from addicts, professionals, and families.* San Francisco, CA: Conari Press.

Larimer, M. E., Palmer, R. S., & Marlatt, G. A. (1999). Relapse prevention: An overview of Marlatt's cognitive-behavioral model. *Alcohol Research & Health, 23*(2), 151–160.

Larney, S., Corcoran, K., Wodak, A. D., & Dolan, K. (2006). *The integration of harm reduction into abstinence-based therapeutic communities: A case study of We Help Ourselves* (Technical Report No. 263). Sydney, Australia: National Drug and Alcohol Research Centre.

Laudet, A. B. (2003). Attitudes and beliefs about 12-step groups among addiction treatment clients and clinicians: Toward identifying obstacles to participation.

Substance Use & Misuse, 38(14), 2017–2047. Retrieved August 7, 2013, from http://www.ncbi.nlm.nih.gov/pmc/articles/PMC1855195/

Laudet, A. B. (2011). The case for considering quality of life in addiction research and clinical practice. *Addiction Science & Clinical Practice, 6*(1), 44–55.

Laudet, A. B., Magura, S., Cleland, C. M., Vogel, H. S., & Knight, E. L. (2003). Predictors of retention in dual-focus self-help groups. *Community Mental Health Journal, 39*(4), 281–297.

Laudet, A. B., Magura, S., Cleland, C. M., Vogel, H. S., & Knight, E. L. (2004). The effect of 12-step based fellowship participation on abstinence among dually diagnosed persons: A two-year longitudinal study. *Journal of Psychoactive Drugs, 36*(2), 207–216.

Laudet, A. B., Magura, S., Vogel, H. S., & Knight, E. L. (2000). Recovery challenges among dually diagnosed individuals. *Journal of Substance Abuse Treatment, 18*, 321–329.

Laudet, A. B., Magura, S., Vogel, H. S., & Knight, E. L. (2004). Perceived reasons for substance misuse among persons with a psychiatric disorder. *American Journal of Orthopsychiatry, 74*, 365–375.

Lee, T. R., & Goddard, H. W. (1989). Developing family relationship skills to prevent substance abuse among high-risk youth. *Family Relations, 38*, 301–305.

Lemieux, C. M. (2002). Social support among offenders with substance abuse problems: Overlooked and underused? *Journal of Addictions & Offender Counseling, 23*(1), 41–57.

Lemke, S., & Moos, R. H. (2003). Outcomes at 1 and 5 years for older patients with alcohol use disorders. *Journal of Substance Abuse Treatment, 24*, 43–50.

Lennings, C. J., Kenny, D. T., & Nelson, P. (2006). Substance use and treatment seeking in young offenders on community orders. *Journal of Substance Abuse Treatment, 31*(4), 425–432.

Lenton, S., & Single, E. (1998). The definition of harm reduction. *Drug and Alcohol Review, 17*, 213–220.

Leshner, A. I. (2008). By now harm reduction harms both science and the public health. *Clinical Pharmacology & Therapeutics, 83*(4), 513–514.

Levin, F. R., & Hennessey, G. (2004). Bipolar disorder and substance abuse. *Biological Psychiatry, 56*, 738–748.

Levine, S. (2002). *Turning toward the mystery: A seeker's journey.* New York, NY: HarperSanFrancisco.

Lewis, M. W., & Petry, N. M. (2005). Contingency management treatments that reinforce completion of goal-related activities: Participation in family activities and its association with outcomes. *Drug and Alcohol Dependence, 79*, 267–271.

Libby, A. M., Orton, H. D., Stover, S. K., & Riggs, P. D. (2005). What came first, major depression or substance use disorder? Clinical characteristics and substance use comparing teens in a treatment cohort. *Addictive Behaviors, 30*, 1649–1662.

Liepman, M. R., Nirenberg, T. D., & Begin, A. M. (1989). Evaluation of a program designed to help family and significant others to motivate resistant alcoholics into recovery. *American Journal of Drug and Alcohol Abuse, 15*, 209–221.

LifeRing. (2012). *LifeRing: Empower your sober self.* Retrieved July 28, 2013, from http://lifering.org/

Lloyd, R. W., & Salzberg, H. C. (1975). Controlled social drinking: An alternative to abstinence as a treatment goal for some alcohol abusers. *Psychological Bulletin, 82*(6), 815–842.

Loff, B. (2006). Ethical challenges and responses in harm reduction research: A critique of applied communitarian ethics. *Drug and Alcohol Review, 25*, 371–372.

Longabaugh, R., Donovan, D. D., Karno, M. P., McCrady, B. S., Morgenstern, J., & Tonigan, J. S. (2005). Active ingredients: How and why evidence-based alcohol behavioral treatment interventions work. *Alcoholism: Clinical and Experimental Research, 29*(2), 235–247.

Longabaugh, R., Wirtz, P. W., Zweben, A., & Stout, R. L. (1998). Network support for drinking, Alcoholics. Anonymous and long-term matching effects. *Addiction, 93*(9), 1313–1333.

Lucas, W. L. (2008). Parents' perceptions of the Drug Abuse Resistance Education Program (DARE). *Journal of Child & Adolescent Substance Abuse, 17*(4), 99–114.

Lundgren, L., & Delgado, M. (2008). HIV outreach and substance abuse treatment for Latino drug users: Implication for program planning. *Evaluation and Program Planning, 31*(1), 61–63.

Lurie, P., & Drucker, E. (1997). An opportunity lost: HIV infections associated with lack of a national needle-exchange programme in the USA. *Lancet, 349*(9052), 604–608.

Lussier, J. P., Heil, S. H., Mongeon, J. A., Badger, G. J., & Higgins, S. T. (2006). A meta-analysis of voucher-based reinforcement therapy for substance use disorders. *Addiction, 101*(2), 192–203.

MacCoun, R. J. (2009). Harm reduction is a good label for a criterion all drug programs should meet. *Addiction, 104,* 341–342.

MacCoun, R. J. (2013). Moral outrage and opposition to harm reduction. *Criminal Law and Philosophy, 7*(1), 83–98.

MacMaster, S. A. (2004). Harm reduction: A new perspective on substance abuse service. *Social Work, 49*(3), 356–363.

Mader, T. J., Smithline, H., Nyquist, S., Letourneau, P. (2001). Social services referral of adolescent trauma patients admitted following alcohol-related injury. *Journal of Substance Abuse Treatment, 21,* 167–172.

Madras, B. K., Compton, W. M., & Clark, H. W. (2009). Screening, brief interventions, referral to treatment (SBIRT) for illicit drug and alcohol use at multiple healthcare sites: Comparison at intake and six months. *Drug and Alcohol Dependence, 99*(1–3), 280–295.

Magill, M., & Ray, L. A. (2009). Cognitive-behavioral treatment with adult alcohol and illicit drug users: A meta-analysis of randomized controlled trials. *Journal of Studies on Alcohol and Drugs, 70*(4), 516–527.

Magura, S. (2007). The relationship between substance user treatment and 12-step fellowships: Current knowledge and research questions. *Substance Use & Misuse, 42,* 343–360.

Maisto, S. A., Conigliaro, J., McNeil, M., Kraemer, K., Conigliaro, R. L., & Kelley, M. E. (2001). Effects of two types of brief intervention and readiness to change on alcohol use in hazardous drinkers. *Journal of Studies on Alcohol and Drugs, 62,* 605–614.

Marinelli-Casey, P., Domier, C. P., & Rawson, R. A. (2002). The gap between research and practice in substance abuse treatment. *Psychiatric Services, 53*(8), 984–987. Retrieved November 21, 2011, from http://psychservices.psychiatryonline.org

Marion, I. J. (2005). Methadone maintenance at forty. *Science & Practice Perspectives, 3*(1), 25–33.

Mark, T. L., Coffey. R. M., McKusick, D. R., Harwood, H. H., King, E. C., Bouchery, E., . . . Dilonardo, J. D. (2005). *National expenditures for mental health services and substance abuse treatment, 1991–2001* (DHHS Publication No. SMA 05-3999). Rockville, MD: Substance Abuse and Mental Health Services Administration.

Mark, T. L., Dilonardo, J. D., Chalk, M., & Coffey, R. M. (2003). Factors associated with the receipt of treatment following detoxification. *Journal of Substance Abuse Treatment, 24*(4), 299–304.

Mark, T. L., Levit, K. R., Coffey, R. M., McKusick, D. R., Harwood, H. H., King, E. C., . . . Ryan, K. (2007). *National expenditures for mental health services and substance abuse treatment, 1993–2003* (DHHS Publication No. SMA 07-4227). Rockville, MD: Substance Abuse and Mental Health Services Administration.

Mark, T. L., Song, X., Vandivort, R., Duffy, S., Butler, J., Coffey, R., & Schabert, V. F. (2006). Characterizing substance abuse programs that treat adolescents. *Journal of Substance Abuse Treatment, 31*, 59–65.

Marlatt, G. A., Larimer, M. E., Baer, J. S., & Quigley, L. A. (1993). Harm reduction for alcohol problems: Moving beyond the controlled drinking controversy. *Behavior Therapy, 24*, 461–504.

Marlatt, G. A., & Witkiewitz, K. (2002). Harm reduction approaches to alcohol use: Health promotion, prevention, and treatment. *Addictive Behaviors, 27*, 867–886.

Marlatt, G. A., & Witkiewitz, K. (2010). Update on harm-reduction policy and intervention research. *Annual Review of Clinical Psychology, 6*, 591–606.

Marmorstein, N. R. (2012). Anxiety disorders and substance use disorders: different associations by anxiety disorder. *Journal of Anxiety Disorders, 26*(1), 88–94. doi:10.1016/j.janxdis.2011.09.005

Marsiglia, F. F., Ayers, S., Gance-Cleveland, B., Mettler, K., & Booth, J. (2012). Beyond primary prevention of alcohol use: A culturally specific secondary prevention program for Mexican heritage adolescents. *Prevention Science, 13*(3), 241–251.

Marsiglia, F. F., Kulis, S., Yabiku, S. T., Nieri, T. A., & Coleman, E. (2011). When to intervene: Elementary school, middle school or both? Effects of Keepin' It REAL on substance use trajectories of Mexican heritage youth. *Prevention Science, 12*(1), 48–62. doi:10.1007/s11121-010-0189-y

Martin, S. E., Maxwell, C. D., White, H. R., & Zhang, Y. (2004, Spring). Trends in alcohol use, cocaine use, and crime: 1989–1998. *Journal of Drug Issues, 34*(34), 333–359.

Massachusetts Bar Association Drug Policy Task Force. (2009a, April 29). *Drug crimes and incarceration rates in the Commonwealth: Trends and proposed reforms.* Boston, MA: Massachusetts Bar Association.

Massachusetts Bar Association Drug Policy Task Force. (2009b). *The failure of the war on drugs: Charting a new course for the Commonwealth.* Boston, MA: Massachusetts Bar Association.

Massachusetts Department of Public Health, Bureau of Substance Abuse Services. (2013). *Section 35.* Retrieved October 22, 2013, from http://www.mass.gov/eohhs/gov/departments/dph/programs/substance-abuse/addictions/drugs-and-alcohol/section-35-faq

Massachusetts Sentencing Commission. (2010, June). *Survey of sentencing practices FY2009.* Boston, MA: Author.

Matzger, H., Kaskutas, L. A., & Weisner, C. (2005). Reasons for drinking less and their relationship to sustained remission from problem drinking. *Addiction, 100*(11), 1637–1646.

Mauer, B. J. (2006, February). *Behavioral health/primary care integration: The four quadrant model and evidence-based practices.* Rockville, MD: National Council for Community Behavioral Healthcare.

McAndrew, C., & Edgerton, R. (1969). *Drunken comportment: A social explanation.* Chicago, IL: Aldine.

McBride, J. L. (1991). Abstinence among members of Alcoholics Anonymous. *Alcoholism Treatment Quarterly, 8*, 113–121.

McCarty, D., Caspi, Y., Panas, L., Krakow, M., & Mulligan, D. H. (2000). Detoxification centers: Who's in the revolving door? *Journal of Behavioral Health Services & Research, 27*(3), 245–257.

McCarty, D., Gustafson, D. H., Wisdom, J. P., Ford, J., Choi, D., Molfenter, T., Capoccia, V., & Cotter, F. (2007). The Network for the Improvement of Addiction Treatment (NIATx): Enhancing access and retention. *Drug and Alcohol Dependence, 88*(2–3), 138–145. doi:10.1016/j.drugalcdep.2006.10.009

McCrady, B. S., Epstein, E. E., & Kahler, C. W. (2004). Alcoholics Anonymous and relapse prevention as maintenance strategies after conjoint behavioral alcohol treatment for men: 18-month outcomes. *Journal of Consulting and Clinical Psychology, 72*(5), 870–878.

McCrady, B. S., & Miller, W. R. (Eds.). (1993). *Research on Alcoholics Anonymous: Opportunities and alternatives.* New Brunswick, NJ: Rutgers Center of Alcohol Studies.

McCrady, B. S., Owens, M. D., Bordens, A. Z., & Brovko, J. M. (2014). Psychosocial approaches to alcohol use disorders since 1940: A review. *Journal of Studies on Alcohol and Drugs, Supplement 17,* 68-78.

McGovern, M. P., Fox, T. S., Xie, H., & Drake, R. E. (2004). A survey of clinical practices and readiness to adopt evidence-based practices: Dissemination research in an addiction treatment system. *Journal of Substance Abuse Treatment, 26,* 305–312.

McGovern, M. P., Xie, H., Segal, S. R., Siembab, L., & Drake, R. E. (2006). Addiction treatment services and co-occurring disorders: Prevalence estimates, treatment practices, and barriers. *Journal of Substance Abuse Treatment, 31,* 267–275.

McHugh, R. K., Murray, H. W., Hearon, B. A., Pratt, E. M., Pollack, M. H., Safren, S. A., & Otto, M. W. (2013). Predictors of dropout from psychosocial treatment in opioid-dependent outpatients. *American Journal on Addictions, 22,* 18–22.

McKay, J. R. (2005). Is there a case for extended interventions for alcohol and drug use disorders? *Addiction, 100*(11), 1594–1610.

McKay, J. R., & Hiller-Sturmhofel, S. (2011). Treating alcoholism as a chronic disease: Approaches to long-term continuing care. *Alcohol Research & Health, 33*(4), 356–370.

McKay, J. R., Lynch, K. G., Shepard, D. S., & Pettinati, H. M. (2005). The effectiveness of telephone-based continuing care for alcohol and cocaine dependence. 24-month outcomes. *Archives of General Psychiatry, 62,* 199–207.

McKeganey, N. (2005). Abstinence and harm reduction: Two roads to one destination? *Drugs: Education, Prevention & Policy, 12*(4), 251–253.

McKeganey, N., Bloor, M., Robertson, M., Neale, J., & MacDougall, J. (2006). Abstinence and drug abuse treatment: Results from the Drug Outcome Research in Scotland study. *Drugs: Education, Prevention & Policy, 13*(6), 537–550.

McKeganey, N., Morris, Z., Neale, J., & Robertson, M. (2004). What are users looking for when they contact drug services: Abstinence or harm reduction? *Drugs: Education, Prevention & Policy, 11*(5), 423–435.

McKellar, J., Stewart, E., & Humphreys, K. (2003). Alcoholics Anonymous involvement and positive alcohol-related outcomes: Cause, consequence, or just a correlate? A prospective 2-year study of 2,319 alcohol-dependent men. *Journal of Consulting and Clinical Psychology, 71*(2), 302–308.

McLellan, A. T. (2002). Have we evaluated addiction treatment correctly? Implications from a chronic care perspective [Editorial]. *Addiction, 97,* 249–252.

McLellan, A. T., Carise, D., & Kleber, H. D. (2003). Can the national addiction treatment infrastructure support the public's demand for quality care? *Journal of Substance Abuse Treatment, 25,* 117–121.

McLellan, A. T., Grissom, G. R., Brill, P., Durell, J., Metzger, D. S., & O'Brien, C. P. (1993). Private substance abuse treatment: Are some programs more effective than others? *Journal of Substance Abuse Treatment, 10,* 243–254.

McLellan, A. T., McKay, J. R., Forman, R., Cacciola, J., & Kemp, J. (2005). Reconsidering the evaluation of addiction treatment: From retrospective follow-up to concurrent recovery monitoring. *Addiction, 100*(4), 447–458.

McLellan, A. T., & Meyers, K. (2004), Contemporary addiction treatment: A review of systems problems for adults and adolescents. *Biological Psychiatry, 56*(10), 764–770.

McMurran, M. (2007). What works in substance misuse treatments for offenders? *Criminal Behaviour and Mental Health, 17*(4), 225–233.

McNulty, T. L., Oser, C. B., Johnson, J. A., Knudsen, H. K., & Roman, P. M. (2007). Counselor turnover in substance abuse treatment centers: An organizational-level analysis. *Sociological Inquiry, 77*(2), 166–193.

Meara, E., & Frank, R. G. (2005). Spending on substance abuse treatment: How much is enough? *Addiction, 100*(9), 1240–1248. doi:10.1111?j.1360-0443.2005.01227.x

Mee-Lee, D. (2013). *The ASAM criteria: Treatment criteria for substance-related, addictive, and co-occurring conditions* (3rd ed.). Annapolis Junction, MD: ASAM.

Meier, P. S., Barrowclough, C., & Donmall, M. C. (2005). The role of the therapeutic alliance in the treatment of substance misuse: A critical review of the literature. *Addiction, 100*(3), 304–316.

Meier, P. S., Donmall, M. C., McElduff, P., Barrowclough, C., & Heller, R. F. (2006). The role of the early therapeutic alliance in predicting drug treatment dropout. *Drug and Alcohol Dependence, 83,* 57–64.

Melnick, G., De Leon, G., Hawke, J., Jainchill, N., & Kressel, D. (1997). Motivation and readiness for therapeutic community treatment among adolescents and adult substance abusers. *American Journal of Drug and Alcohol Abuse, 23*(4), 485–507.

Merikangas, K. R., Dierker, L., & Fenton, B. (1998). Familial factors and substance abuse: Implications for prevention. *NIDA Research Monograph, 177,* 12–41.

Merikangas, K. R., & Swanson, S. A. (2010). Comorbidity in anxiety disorders. *Current Topics in Behavioral Neurosciences, 2,* 37–59.

Messina, N., Wish, E., & Nemes, S. (2000). Predictor of treatment outcomes in men and women admitted to a therapeutic community. *American Journal of Drug and Alcohol Abuse, 26*(2), 207–227.

Meyers, R. J., & Squires, D. D. (2001). *The community reinforcement approach: A guideline developed for the Behavioral Health Recovery Management project.* Albuquerque, NM: University of New Mexico Center on Alcoholism, Substance Abuse, and Addiction.

Mignon, S. I. (1995). The discovery of patients' alcoholism by physicians. *Research in the Sociology of Health Care, 21,* 175–187.

Mignon, S. I. (1996). Physicians' perceptions of alcoholics: The disease concept reconsidered. *Alcoholism Treatment Quarterly, 41*(4), 33–45.

Mignon, S. I., Faiia, M. M., Myers, P., & Rubington, E. (2009). *Substance use and abuse: Exploring alcohol and drug issues.* Boulder, CO: Lynne Rienner.

Mignon, S. I., & Holmes, W. M. (2013). Substance abuse and mental health issues within Native American grandparenting families. *Journal of Ethnicity in Substance Abuse, 12,* 210–227.

Mignon, S. I., & Ransford, P. (2012). Mothers in prison: Maintaining connections with children. *Social Work in Public Health, 27*(1), 1–20.

Miles, J. N. V., Mandell, W., & Wenzel, S. (2008). The relationship between the Dimensions of Change instrument and retention in therapeutic community treatment: The moderating influence of time in treatment. *American Journal of Drug and Alcohol Abuse, 34*(6), 667–672. doi:10.1080/0095990802308130

Miller, F. (1963). *What the alcoholic owes to Marty Mann: Out of her suffering has been born a network of hope and help for thousands.* Retrieved June 24, 2013, from http://www.silkworth.net. (Original work published in *Reader's Digest,* January 1963)

Miller, M. (2006). Commentary: The seductiveness of evidence. *Journal of Substance Abuse Treatment, 30*(2), 91–92.

Miller, P. (2005). Harm reduction ethics: A promising basis for drug policy. *Drug and Alcohol Review, 24,* 553–554.

Miller, W. R. (1992). The effectiveness of treatment for substance abuse. Reasons for optimism. *Journal of Substance Abuse Treatment, 9*(2), 93–102.

Miller, W. R., Brown, J. M., Simpson, T. L., Handmaker, N. S., Bien, T. H., Luckie, L. F., . . . Tonigan, J. S. (1995).What works? A methodological analysis of the alcohol treatment outcome literature. In R. K. Hester & W. R. Miller (Eds.), *Handbook of alcoholism treatment approaches: Effective alternatives* (2nd ed., pp. 12–44). Needham Heights, MA: Allyn & Bacon.

Miller, W. R., & Hester, R. K. (1986). Inpatient alcoholism treatment: Who benefits? *American Psychologist, 41,* 794–805.

Miller, W. R., & Joyce, M. A. (1979). Prediction of abstinence, controlled drinking, and heavy drinking outcomes following behavioral self-control training. *Journal of Consulting and Clinical Psychology, 47*(4), 773–775.

Miller, W. R., & Kurtz, E. (1994). Models of alcoholism used in treatment: Contrasting AA and other perspectives with which it is often confused. *Journal of Studies on Alcohol, 55,* 159–166.

Miller, W. R., Leckman, A. L., Delaney, H. D., & Tinkcom, M. (1992). Long-term follow-up of behavioral self-control training. *Journal of Studies on Alcohol and Drugs, 53*(3), 249–261.

Miller, W. R., Meyers, R. J., & Hiller-Sturmhofel, S. (1999). The community-reinforcement approach. *Alcohol Research & Health, 23*(2), 116–121.

Miller, W. R., Meyers, R. J., & Tonigan, J. S. (1999). Engaging the unmotivated in treatment for alcohol problems: A comparison of three strategies for intervention through family members. *Journal of Consulting and Clinical Psychology, 67*(5), 688–697.

Miller, W. R., & Rollnick, S. (1991). *Motivational interviewing: Preparing people to change addictive behavior.* New York, NY: Guilford Press.

Miller, W. R., & Rollnick, S. (2002). *Motivational interviewing: Preparing people for change* (2nd ed.). New York, NY: Guilford Press.

Miller, W. R., & Rose, G. S. (2010). Motivational interviewing in relational context. *American Psychologist, 65*(4), 298–299.

Miller, W. R., Sorensen, J. L., Selzer, J. A., & Brigham, G. S. (2006). Disseminating evidence-based practices in substance abuse treatment: A review with suggestions. *Journal of Substance Abuse Treatment, 31*(1), 25–39.

Miller, W. R., & Tonigan, J. S. (1996). Assessing drinkers' motivation for change: The Stages of Change Readiness and Treatment Eagerness Scale (SOCRATES). *Psychology of Addictive Behaviors, 10,* 81–89.

Miller, W. R., Walters, S. T., & Bennett, M. E. (2001). How effective is alcoholism treatment in the United States? *Journal of Studies on Alcohol, 62*(2), 211–220.

Miller, W. R., & Wilbourne, P. L. (2002). Mesa Grande: A methodological analysis of clinical trials of treatments for alcohol use disorders. *Addiction, 97*(3), 265–277.

Mojtabai, R. (2005). Use of specialty substance abuse and mental health services in adults with substance use disorders in the community. *Drug and Alcohol Dependence, 78,* 345–354.

Mojtabai, R., & Zivin, J. G. (2003). Effectiveness and cost-effectiveness of four treatment modalities for substance disorders: A propensity score analysis. *Health Services Research, 38*(1), 233–259.

Molfenter, T., Capoccia, V. A., Boyle, M. G., & Sherbeck, C. K. (2012). The readiness of addiction treatment agencies for health care reform. *Substance Abuse Treatment, Prevention, and Policy, 7,* 16. doi:10.1186/1747-597X-7-16

Montgomery, H. A., Miller, W. R., & Tonigan, J. S. (1995). Does Alcoholics Anonymous involvement predict treatment outcome? *Journal of Substance Abuse Treatment, 12*(4), 241–246.

Moos, R. H., & Finney, J. W. (1983). The expanding scope of alcoholism treatment evaluation. *American Psychologist, 38*(10), 1036–1044.

Moos, R. H., Finney, J. W., Ouimette, P. C., & Suchinsky, R. T. (1999). A comparative evaluation of substance abuse treatment: I. Treatment orientation, amount of care, and 1-year outcomes. *Alcoholism: Clinical and Experimental Research, 23*(3), 529–536.

Moos, R. H., & Moos, B. S. (2004a). Help-seeking careers: Connections between participation in professional treatment and Alcoholics Anonymous. *Journal of Substance Abuse Treatment, 26*(3), 167–173.

Moos, R. H., & Moos, B. S. (2004b). The interplay between help-seeking and alcohol-related outcomes: Divergent processes for professional treatment and self-help groups. *Drug and Alcohol Dependence, 75*(2), 155–164. doi:10.1016/j.drugalcdep.2004.01.016

Moos, R. H., & Moos, B. S. (2006). Participation in treatment and Alcoholics Anonymous: A 16-year follow-up of initially untreated individuals. *Journal of Clinical Psychology, 62*(6), 735–750. doi:10.1002/jclp.20259

Moos, R. H., & Moos, B. S. (2007). Treatment and untreated alcohol-use disorders: Course and predictors of remission and relapse. *Evaluation Review, 31*(6), 564–584. doi:10.1177/0193841X07306749

Moos, R. H., & Timko, C. (2008). Outcome research on twelve-step and other self-help program. In M. Galanter & H. D. Kleber (Eds.), *Textbook of substance abuse treatment* (4th ed., pp. 511–521). Washington, DC: American Psychiatric Press.

Morell, C. (1996). Radicalizing recovery: Addiction, spirituality, and politics. *Social Work, 41*(3), 306–312.

Morgan, O. J., & Lizke, C. H. (Eds.). (2007). *Family interventions in substance abuse: Current best practices.* New York, NY: Routledge.

Morgan, T. B., & Crane, D. R. (2010). Cost-effectiveness of family-based substance abuse treatment. *Journal of Marital and Family Therapy, 36*(4), 486–498. doi:10.1111/j.1752-0606.2010.00195.x

Morgenstern, J., & Longabaugh, R. (2000). Cognitive-behavioral treatment for alcohol dependence: A review of evidence for its hypothesized mechanism of action. *Addiction, 95*(10), 1475–1490.

Morgenstern, J., & McKay, J. R. (2007). Rethinking the paradigms that inform behavioral treatment research for substance use disorders. *Addiction, 102*(9), 1377–1389.

Morley, J. A., Finney, J. W., Monahan, S. C., & Floyd, A. S. (1996). Alcoholism treatment outcome studies, 1980–1992: Methodological characteristics and quality. *Addictive Behaviors, 21,* 429–433.

Moyer, A., Finney, J. W., & Swearingen, C. E. (2002). Methodological characteristics and quality of alcohol treatment outcome studies, 1970–98: An expanded evaluation. *Addiction, 97*(3), 253–263.

Moyer, A., Finney, J. W., Swearingen, C. E., & Vergun, P. (2002). Brief interventions for alcohol problems: A meta-analytic review of controlled investigations in treatment-seeking and non–treatment-seeking populations. *Addiction, 97*(3), 279–292.

Mueller, S. E., Petitjean, S., Boening, J., & Weisbeck, G. A. (2007). The impact of self-help group attendance on relapse rates after alcohol detoxification in a controlled study. *Alcohol and Alcoholism, 41*(4), 108–112.

Mueser, K. T., Gottlieb, J. D., Cather, C., Glynn, S. M., Zarate, R., Smith, L. F., . . . Wolfe, R. (2012). Antisocial personality disorder in people with co-occurring severe mental illness and substance use disorders: Clinical, functional, and family relationship correlates. *Psychosis, 4*(1), 52–62.

Mullen, E. J. (2004). Facilitating practitioner use of evidence-based practice. In R. Roberts & K. Yeager (Eds.), *Desk reference for evidence-based practice in healthcare and human services*. New York, NY: Oxford University Press.

Mulvey, K. P., Hayashi, S. W., Hubbard, S. M., Kopstien, A., & Huang, J. Y. (2003). The TIPS evaluation project: A theory-driven approach to dissemination research. *Evaluation and Program Planning, 26,* 45–47.

Mulvey, K. P., Hubbard, S., & Hayashi, S. (2003). A national study of the substance abuse treatment workforce. *Journal of Substance Abuse Treatment, 24*(1), 51–57.

Nace, E. P., & Tinsley, J. A. (2007). *Patients with substance abuse problems: Effective identification, diagnosis and treatment*. New York, NY: W. W. Norton.

Naegle, M. A., Ng, A., Barron, C., & Lai, T.-F. M. (2002). Alcohol and substance abuse. *Western Journal of Medicine, 176*(4), 259–263.

Narcotics Anonymous World Services. (2012). *Narcotics Anonymous 2011 membership survey*. Retrieved May 12, 2014, from http://www.na.org

National Addiction Studies Accreditation Commission. (2012). *Who we are*. Retrieved from http://nasacaccreditation.org/who-we-are/

National Association of Alcoholism and Drug Abuse Counselors. (2009, December 3). *Report of the NAADA National Addiction Studies and Standards Collaborative Committee*. Alexandria, VA: Author.

National Association of Alcoholism and Drug Abuse Counselors. (2013). *About NAADAC*. Retrieved December 7, 2013, from http://naadac.org/about

National Association of Drug Court Professionals. (2013). *Adult drug court best practice standards* (Vol. 1). Alexandria, VA: Author.

National Center on Addiction and Substance Abuse at Columbia University. (2007, March) *Wasting the best and the brightest: Substance abuse at America's colleges and universities*. New York, NY: Author.

National Institute of Corrections. (n.d.). *Thinking for a Change*. Retrieved October 27, 2013, from http://nicic.gov/T4C

National Institute on Drug Abuse. (1997). *Drug abuse prevention: What works* (NIH Publication No. 97-4110). Rockville, MD: Office of Science Policy and Communications, Public Information Branch.

National Institute on Drug Abuse. (2002, August). *Therapeutic community*. Research Report Series. Bethesda, MD: U.S. Department of Health and Human Services, National Institutes of Health. Retrieved June 26, 2013, from http://www.drugabuse.gov

National Institute on Drug Abuse. (2003). *Group therapy research*. Retrieved July 16, 2013, from http://archives.drugabuse.gov/meetings/grouptherapy.html

National Institute on Drug Abuse. (2009, September). *Drug facts: Treatment approaches for drug addiction*. Retrieved July 5, 2012, from http://www.drugabuse.gov/publications/drugfacts/treatment-approaches-drug-addiction

National Institute on Drug Abuse. (2011, August). *NIDA info facts: Lessons from prevention research*. Rockville, MD: Author. Retrieved November 3, 2013, from http://www.drugabuse.gov

National Institute on Drug Abuse. (2012a, May). *HIV/AIDS and drug abuse: Intertwined epidemics*. Retrieved August 29, 3013, from http://www.drugabuse.gov

National Institute on Drug Abuse. (2012b, December). *Principles of drug addiction treatment: A research-based guide*. (3rd ed.). Bethesda, MD: Author.

National Institute on Drug Abuse. (2012c, March) *Resource guide: Screening for drug use in general medical settings*. Retrieved July 11, 2013, from http://www.drugabuse.gov/publication/resource-guide/nida-quick-screen

National Institutes of Health. (2013, August 6). *The NIH almanac*. Retrieved November 17, 2013, from http://www.nih.gov/about/almanac/organization/NIDA.htm

Needle, R. H., Su, S. S., & Doherty, W. J. (1990). Divorce, remarriage, and adolescent substance use: A prospective longitudinal study. *Journal of Marriage and the Family, 52*, 157–169.

Neff, J. A., & MacMaster, S. A. (2005). Applying behavior change models to understand spiritual mechanisms underlying change in substance abuse treatment. *American Journal of Drug and Alcohol Abuse, 31*, 1–16.

Network for the Improvement of Addiction Treatment. (2013). *Simple process improvement for behavioral health*. Retrieved December 1, 2013, from http://www.niatx.net/Home/Home.aspx?CategorySelected_Home

Newman, R. (2005). Comment on "What are drug users looking for when they contact drug services: Abstinence or harm reduction?" by Neil McKeganey, Zoe Morris, Joanne Neal, & Michele Robertson. *Drugs: Education, Prevention & Policy, 12*(4), 265–266.

Newton, A. S., Dong, K., Mabood, N., Ata, N., Ali, S., Gokiert, R., . . . Wild, T. C. (2013). Brief emergency departmentinterventions for youth who use alcohol and other drugs: A systematic review. *Pediatric Emergency Care, 29*(5), 673–684.

Nirenberg, R., Longabaugh, R., Baird, J., & Mello, M. J. (2013). Treatment may influence self-report and jeopardize our understanding of outcome. *Journal of Studies on Alcohol and Drugs, 74*, 770–776.

Nissen, L. B. (2007). Reclaiming futures: Communities helping teens overcome drugs, alcohol and crime—A new practice framework for juvenile justice. *Journal of Psychoactive Drugs, 39*(1), 51–58.

Nunes, E. V., & Levin, F. R. (2008). Treatment of co-occurring depression and substance dependence. *Psychiatric Annals, 38*(11). Retrieved September 29, 2013, from http://www.ncbi.nim.nih.gov/pmc/articles/PM2722074

Nunes, E. V., Sullivan, M. A., & Levin, F. R. (2004). Treatment of depression in patients with opiate dependence. *Biological Psychiatry, 56*(10), 793–802.

Ohlin, L., Hesse, M., Fridell, M., & Tatting, P. (2011). Poly-substance use and antisocial personality traits at admission predict cumulative retention in a buprenorphine programme with mandatory work and high compliance profile. *BMC Psychiatry, 11*, 81. Retrieved October 11, 2013, from http://www.biomedcentral.com/1471-244X/11/81

Ohlmeier, M. D., Peters, K., Kordon, A., Seifert, J., Te Wildt, B., Wiese, B., . . . Schneider, U. (2007). Nicotine and alcohol dependence in patients with comorbid attention-deficit/hyperactivity disorder (ADHD). *Alcohol and Alcoholism, 42*(6), 539–543.

Olmstead, T., White, W. D., & Sindelar, J. (2004). The impact of managed care on substance abuse treatment services. *Health Services Research, 39*(2), 319–344. doi:10.1111/j.1475-6773.2004.00230.x

Orford, J., & Keddie, A. (1986). Abstinence or controlled drinking in clinical practice: Indications at initial assessment. *Addictive Behaviors, 11*(2), 71–86.

Orford, J., & Keddie, A. (2006). Abstinence or controlled drinking in clinical practice: A test of the dependence and persuasion hypotheses. *British Journal of Addiction, 81*(4), 495–504.

Osborn, K. (2003, December/January) Finding new paths: Using complementary therapies to combat addiction. *Massage & Bodywork*. Retrieved July 16, 2013, from http://www.massagetherapy.com/articles/index.php/article_id/50/Finding-New-Paths

Osher, F. D'Amora, D. A., Plotkin, M., Jarrett, N., & Eggleston, A. (2012). *Adults with behavioral health needs under correctional supervision: A shared framework for reducing recidivism and promoting recovery.* New York, NY: Council of State Governments Justice Center.

Oslin, D. W., Slaymaker, V. J., Blow, F. C., Owen, P. L., & Colleran, C. (2005). Treatment outcomes for alcohol dependence among middle-aged and older adults. *Addictive Behaviors, 30*, 1431–1436.

Ouimette, P. C., Finney, J. W., & Moos, R. H. (1997). Twelve-step and cognitive behavioral treatment for substance abuse: A comparison of treatment effectiveness. *Journal of Consulting and Clinical Psychology, 65*(2), 230–240.

Ouimette, P., Jemelka, R., Hall, J., Brimner, K., Kruspski, A., & Stark, K. (2007). Services to patients with dual diagnoses: Finding from Washington's mental health service system. *Substance Use & Misuse, 42*, 113–127.

Oxford House. (2013). *The purpose and structure of Oxford House.* Retrieved May 11, 2014, from http://www.oxfordhouse.org/userfiles/file/purpose_and_structure.php

Palepu, A., Horton, N. J., Tibbetts, N., Dukes, K., Meli, S., & Samet, J. H. (2003). Substance abuse treatment and emergency department utilization among a cohort of HIV-infected persons with alcohol problems. *Journal of Substance Abuse Treatment, 25*, 37–42.

Palepu, A., Horton, N. J., Tibbetts, N., Meli, S., & Samet, J. H. (2004). Uptake and adherence to highly active antiretroviral therapy among HIV-infected people with alcohol and other substance use problems: The impact of substance abuse treatment. *Addiction, 99*, 361–368.

Palepu, A., Raj, A., Horton, N. J., Tibbetts, N., Meli, S., & Samet, J. H. (2005). Substance abuse treatment and risk behaviors among HIV-infected persons with alcohol problems. *Journal of Substance Abuse Treatment, 28*, 3–9.

Panas, L., Caspi, Y., Fournier, E., & McCarty, D. (2003). Performance measures for outpatient substance abuse services: Group versus individual counseling. *Journal of Substance Abuse Treatment, 25*(4), 271–278. doi:10.1016/SO740-5472(03)00142-9

Parhar, K. K., Wormith, J. S., Derkzen, D. M., & Beauregard, A. M. (2008). Offender coercion in treatment: A meta-analysis of effectiveness. *Criminal Justice and Behavior, 35*(9), 1109–1135.

Pearson, F. S., & Lipton, D. S. (1999). A meta-analytic review of the effectiveness of corrections-based treatments for drug abuse. *Prison Journal, 79*, 384–410. FIND.

Pearson, J. (2012, June 8). Drug treatment saves N.Y. money. *Boston Globe*, pp. A10.

Peele, S. (1987). Why do controlled-drinking outcomes vary by investigator, by country and by era? *Drug and Alcohol Dependence, 20*(3), 173–201.

Peele, S. (2000, November). *After the crash.* Retrieved July 23, 2012, from http://reason.com/archives/2000/11/01/after-the-crash

Pelc, I., Hanak, C., Baert, I., Houtain, C., Lehert, P., Landron, F., & Verbanck, P. (2005). Effect of community nurse follow-up when treating alcohol dependence with acamprosate. *Alcohol & Addiction, 40*(4), 302–307.

Pelissier, B., Jones, N., & Cadigan, T. (2007). Drug treatment aftercare in the criminal justice system: A systematic review. *Journal of Substance Abuse Treatment, 32*(3), 311–320.

Pendery, M. L., Maltzman, I. M., & West, L. J. (1982). Controlled drinking by alcoholics? New findings and a reevaluation of a major affirmative study. *Science, 217*, 169–175.

Pennay, A., Cameron, J., Reichert, T., Strickland, H., Lee, N. K., Hall, K., & Lubman, D. I. (2011). A systematic review of interventions for co-occurring substance use disorder and borderline personality disorder. *Journal of Substance Abuse Treatment, 41*(4), 363–373.

Perron, B. E., & Bright, C. L. (2008). The influence of legal coercion on dropout from substance abuse treatment: Results from a national survey. *Drug and Alcohol Dependence, 92*(1–3), 123–131. doi:10.1016/j.drugalcdep.2007.07.011

Petry, N. M. (2000). A comprehensive guide to the application of contingency management procedures in clinical settings. *Drug and Alcohol Dependence, 58*, 9–25.

Petry, N. M., Cooney, J. L., & Kranzler, H. R. (2000). Give them prizes, and they will come: Contingency management for treatment of alcohol dependence. *Journal of Consulting and Clinical Psychology, 68*(2), 250–257.

Petry, N. M., DePhilippis, D., Rash, C. J., Drapkin, M., & McKay, J. R. (2013). Nationwide dissemination of contingency management: The Veterans Administration initiative. *American Journal on Addictions.* doi:10.1111/j.1521-0391.2013.12092.x

Petry, N. M., Martin, B., & Simcic, F. (2005). Prize reinforcement contingency management for cocaine dependence: integration with group therapy in a methadone clinic. *Journal of Consulting and Clinical Psychology, 73*(2), 354–359.

Phillips, J. A., Nixon, S. J., Phillips, M., Pfefferbaum, B., & Briody, R. (2000). A comparison of substance use between female inmates and female substance misusers in treatment. *Alcohol and Alcoholism, 35*(1), 60–65.

Pine Street Inn. (n.d.). *Stabilization.* Retrieved July 2, 2013, from http://www.pinstreet inn.org/our_program/recovery_services

Polcin, D. L. (2001). Sober living houses: Potential roles in substance abuse services and suggestions for research. *Substance Use & Misuse, 36*(3), 301–311.

Polcin, D. L., & Henderson, D. (2008). A clean and sober place to live: Philosophy, structure, and purported therapeutic factors in sober living houses. *Journal of Psychoactive Drugs, 40*(2), 153–159.

Polcin, D. L., Korcha, R., & Galloway, G. (2010). What did we learn from our study on sober living houses and where do we go from here? *Journal of Psychoactive Drugs, 42*(4), 425–433.

Powell, D. J. (2005). Trends in counseling challenge profession, but there are positives. *Addiction Professional, 3*(2), 33–36.

Prendergast, M. L., Hall, E. A., Wexler, H. K., Melnick, G., & Cao, Y., 2004). Amity prison-based therapeutic community: 5-year outcomes. *Prison Journal, 84*(1), 36–60.

Pride Institute. *About Pride Institute.* Retrieved May 9, 2014, from http://pride-institute.com/about/

Pringle, J. L., Emptage, N. P., & Hubbard, R. L. (2006). Unmet needs for comprehensive services in outpatient addiction treatment. *Journal of Substance Abuse Treatment, 30*(3), 183–189.

Prochaska, J. O., & DiClemente, C. C. (1984). *The transtheoretical approach: Crossing traditional boundaries of therapy.* Homewood, IL: Dow Jones-Irwin.

Prochaska, J. O., & DiClemente, C. C. (1992). Stages of change in the modification of problem behaviors. In Y. Klar, J. D. Fisher, J. M. Chinsky, & A. Nadler (Eds.), *Self-change: Social, psychological, and clinical perspectives* (pp. 87–114). New York, NY: Springer-Verlag.

ProCon.org. (2013, November 6). *Is the D.A.R.E. program good for America's kids (K–12)?* Retrieved November 10, 2013, from http://dare.procon.org/

Project MATCH Research Group. (1997). Matching alcoholism treatments to client heterogeneity: Project MATCH posttreatment drinking outcomes. *Journal of Studies on Alcohol, 58*, 435–440.

Project MATCH Research Group. (1998). Matching alcoholism treatment to client heterogeneity: Project MATCH three-year drinking outcomes. *Alcoholism: Clinical and Experimental Research, 22*(6), 1300–1311.

Quanbeck, A., Wheelock, A., Ford, J. H., II, Pulvermacher, A., Capoccia, V., & Gustafson, D. (2013). Examining access to addiction treatment: Scheduling processes and barriers. *Journal of Substance Abuse Treatment, 44,* 343–348. doi:10.1016/j.jsat.2012.08.017

Ravndal, E., Vaglum, P., & Lauritzen, G. (2005). Completion of long-term inpatient treatment of drug abusers: A prospective study from 13 different units. *European Addiction Research, 11,* 180–185. doi:10.1159/000086399

Rawson, R. A., & Obert, J. L. (2002). The substance abuse treatment system in the U.S. What is it? What does it do? Myths and misconceptions. *Occupational Medicine, 17*(1), 27–39.

Read, J. P., Kahler, C. W., & Stevenson, J. F. (2001). Bridging the gap between alcoholism treatment research and practice: Identifying what works and why. *Professional Psychology: Research and Practice, 32*(3), 227–238.

Redko, C., Rapp, R. C., & Carlson, R. G. (2006). Waiting time as a barrier to treatment entry: Perceptions of substance users. *Journal of Drug Issues, 36*(4), 831–852.

Reigle, N., & Dowd, E. T. (2004). Predicting Alcoholics Anonymous affiliation. *Health Education Journal, 63*(1), 81–88.

Reinert, R. E., & Bowen, W. T. (1968). Social drinking following treatment for alcoholism. *Bulletin of the Menninger Clinic, 32*(5), 280–290.

Reis, A. D., & Laranjeira, R. (2008). Halfway houses for alcohol dependents: From theoretical bases to implications for the organization of facilities. *Clinics, 63*(6), 827–832.

Reisinger, H. S., Bush, T., Colom, M. A., Agar, M., & Battjes, R. (2003). Navigation and engagement: How does one measure success? *Journal of Drug Issues, 33*(4), 777–800.

Resnicow, K., Soler, R., & Braithwaite, R. L. (2000). Cultural sensitivity in substance abuse prevention. *Journal of Community Psychology, 28*(3), 271–290.

Reuter, P. H., & Pollack, H. (2006). How much can treatment reduce national drug problems? *Addiction, 101*(3), 341–347.

Reznicek, M. J. (2012). *Blowing smoke: Rethinking the war on drugs without Prohibition and rehab.* Lanham, MD: Roman & Littlefield.

Rhodes, T., & Hedrich, D. (2010). Harm reduction and the mainstream. In *Harm reduction: Evidence, impacts and challenges* (pp. 19–33). Lisbon, Portugal: European Monitoring Centre for Drugs and Drug Addiction.

Ricchuito, A. D. (2012). Yoga as adjunct therapy for substance use. *Social Work Today, 12*(5), 8.

Robbins, M. S., Kumar, S., Walker-Barnes, C., Feaster, D., Briones, E., & Szapocznik, J. (2002). Ethnic differences in comorbidity among substance-abusing adolescents referred to outpatient therapy. *Journal of the American Academy of Child and Adolescent Psychiatry, 41*(4), 394–401.

Roberts, M. (2005). Comment on "What are drug users looking for when they contact drug services: Abstinence or harm reduction?" by Neil McKeganey, Zoe Morris, Joanne Neal, & Michele Robertson. *Drugs: Education, Prevention & Policy, 12*(4), 261–263.

Roman, P. M., Ducharme, L. J., & Knudsen, H. K. (2006). Patterns of organization and management in private and public substance abuse treatment programs. *Journal of Substance Abuse Treatment, 31,* 235–243.

Roman, P. M., Johnson, J. A., & Blum, T. C. (2000). The transformation of private alcohol problem treatment: Results of a national study. *Advances in Medical Sociology, 7,* 321–342.

Rosen, P. J., Hiller, M. L., Webster, J. M., Staton, M., & Leukefeld, C. (2004). Treatment motivation and therapeutic engagement in prison-based substance use treatment. *Journal of Psychoactive Drugs, 36*(4), 387–396.

Rosenberg, H. (1993). Prediction of controlled drinking by alcoholics and problem drinkers. *Psychological Bulletin, 113*(1), 129–139.

Rosenberg, H., & Davis, L.-A. (1994). Acceptance of moderate drinking by alcohol treatment services in the United States. *Journal of Studies on Alcohol and Drugs, 55*(2), 167–172.

Rosenberg, H., Devine, E. G., & Rothrock, N. (1996). Acceptance of moderate drinking by alcoholism treatment services in Canada. *Journal of Studies on Alcohol and Drugs, 57*(5), 559–562.

Rossegger, A., Keller, A., Odenwald, M., & Endrass, J. (2009). The appropriateness of the treatment setting for the inpatient post-acute treatment of alcohol dependence disorders in Switzerland. *International Journal of Mental Health Systems, 3*, 16. doi:10.1186/1752-4458-3-16

Roueche, B. (1960). *The neutral spirit: A portrait of alcohol*. Boston, MA: Little, Brown.

Rubio, G., Ponce, G., Rodriguez-Jimenez, R., Jimenez-Arriero, M. A., Hoenicka, J., & Palomo, T. (2005). Clinical predictors of response to naltrexone in alcoholic patients: Who benefits most from treatment with naltrexone? *Alcohol and Alcoholism, 40*(3), 227–233.

Ruiz, M. A., Pincus, A. L., & Schinka, J. A. (2008). Externalizing pathology and the five-factor model: A meta-analysis of personality traits associated with antisocial personality disorder, substance use disorder, and their co-occurrence. *Journal of Personality Disorders, 22*(4), 365–388. doi:10.1521/pedi.2008.22.4.365

Russell, C., Davies, J. B., & Hunter, S. C. (2011). Predictors of addiction treatment providers' beliefs in the disease and choice models of addiction. *Journal of Substance Abuse Treatment, 40*(2), 150–164.

Sacks, J. Y., McKendrick, K., & Banks, S. (2008). The impact of early trauma and abuse on residential substance abuse treatment outcomes for women. *Journal of Substance Abuse Treatment, 34*, 90–100. doi:10.1016/j.jsat.2007.01.010

Sacks, S., McKendrick, K., Sacks, J. Y., Banks, S., & Harle, M. (2008). Enhanced outpatient treatment for co-occurring disorders: Main outcomes. *Journal of Substance Abuse Treatment, 34*(1), 48–60.

Sadler, M. J. (2003). The convergence of group psychotherapy and the twelve steps of AA. *Journal of Addictive Disorders*. Retrieved June 13, 2013, from http://www.breining.edu

Saleh, S. S., & Szebenyi, S. E. (2005). Resources use of elderly emergency department patients with alcohol-related diagnoses. *Journal of Substance Abuse Treatment, 29*(4), 313–319. doi:10.1016/j,jsat.2005.08.007

Saloner, B., & Le Cook, B. (2013). Blacks and Hispanics are less likely than Whites to complete addiction treatment, largely due to socioeconomic factors. *Health Affairs, 32*(1), 135–145. doi:10.1377/hihaff.2011.0983

Saltz, R. F., Welker, L. R., Paschall, M. J., Feeney, M. A., & Fabiano, P. M. (2009). Evaluating a comprehensive campus–community intervention to reduce alcohol-related problems in a college population. *Journal of Studies on Alcohol and Drugs, Supplement 16*, 21–27.

Saum, C. A., Hiller, M. L., Leigey, M. E., Inciardi, J. A., & Surratt, H. L. (2007). Predictors of substance abuse treatment entry for crime-involved, cocaine-dependent women. *Drug and Alcohol Dependence, 91*(2–3), 253–259.

Saxe, L. D., Dougherty, D., Estey, K., & Fine, F. M. (1983). *The effectiveness and costs of alcoholism treatment* (Health Technology Case Study No. 22). Washington, DC: Office of Technology Assessment, U.S. Congress.

Sayegh, G. (2010, February). After the Rockefeller drug laws: A new direction in New York and the nation. *Drug Policy Alliance.* Retrieved October 27, 2013, from http://www.drugpolicy.org/docUploads/AftertheRockefellerDrugLawsFeb_2010.pdf

Schmidt, G. J., Villarivera, & Aguiar, C. (2005). Addiction counselors today and the clients they encounter: Comprehensive findings from latest NAADAC survey. *Addiction Professional, 3*(3), 28–31.

Schoeneberger, M. L., Leukefeld, C. G., Hiller, M. L., & Godlaski, T. (2006). Substance abuse among rural and very rural drug users at treatment entry. *American Journal of Drug and Alcohol Abuse, 32,* 87–110.

Schuckit, M. (1994). *Textbook of substance abuse treatment.* Washington, DC: American Psychiatric Press.

Schuckit, M. (2013). Editor's corner: *DSM-5*—Ready or not, here it comes. *Journal of Studies on Alcohol and Drugs, 74*(5), 661–663.

Schuckit, M. A., Smith, T. L., & Kalmijn, J. (2013). Relationships among independent major depressions, alcohol use, and other substance use and related problems over 30 years in 397 families. *Journal of Studies on Alcohol and Drugs, 74,* 271–279.

Schutt, R. K., & Goldfinger, S. M. (2009). Fundamental causes of housing loss among persons diagnosed with serious and persistent mental illness: A theoretically guided test. *Asian Journal of Psychiatry, 2*(4), 132–138.

Scott, C. K., Dennis, M. L., & White, W. L. (2004, September). Recovery management checkups: A future function of addiction professionals? *Addiction Professional,* pp. 33–38.

Selzer, M. L., & Holloway, W. H. (1957). A follow-up of alcoholics committed to a state hospital. *Quarterly Journal of Studies on Alcohol, 18,* 98–120.

Shane, P. A., Jasiukaitis, P., & Green, R. S. (2003). Treatment outcomes among adolescents with substance abuse problems: The relationship between comorbidities and post-treatment substance involvement. *Evaluation and Program Planning, 26,* 393–402.

Sharma, M., & Branscum. P. (2010). Is Alcoholics Anonymous effective? *Journal of Alcohol & Drug Education, 54*(3), 3–6.

Shea, J. E. (1954). Psychoanalytic therapy and alcoholism. *Quarterly Journal of Studies on Alcohol, 15,* 595–605.

Sheed, W. (1995). *In love with daylight: A memoir of recovery.* New York, NY: Simon & Schuster.

Shin, H. C., Marsh, J. C., Cao, D. C., & Andrews, C. M. (2011). Client–provider relationship in comprehensive substance abuse treatment: Differences in residential and nonresidential settings. *Journal of Substance Abuse Treatment, 41*(4), 335–346.

Simoni-Wastila, L., & Yang, H. K. (2006). Psychoactive drug abuse in older adults. *American Journal of Geriatric Pharmacotherapy, 4*(6), 380–394.

Simpson, D. D. (2002). A conceptual framework for transferring research to practice. *Journal of Substance Abuse Treatment, 22*(4), 171–182.

Simpson, D. D., Joe, G. W., Rowan-Szal, G. A., & Greener, J. M. (1997). Drug abuse treatment process components that improve retention. *Journal of Substance Abuse Treatment, 14*(6), 565–572.

Sinclair, U. (1956). *The cup of fury.* Great Neck, NY: Channel Press.

Skiba, D., Monroe, J., & Wodarski, J. S. (2004). Adolescent substance use: Reviewing the effectiveness of prevention strategies. *Social Work, 49*(3), 343–353.

Smiley-McDonald, H. M., & Leukefeld, C. G. (2005). Incarcerated clients' perceptions of therapeutic change in substance abuse treatment: A 4-year case study. *International Journal of Offender Therapy and Comparative Criminology, 49*(5), 574–589. doi:10.1177/0306624X05274624

Smith, D. C., Hall, J. A., Williams, J. K., An, H., & Gotman, N. (2006). Comparative efficacy of family and group treatment for adolescent substance abuse. *American Journal on Addictions, 15*(Suppl. 1), 131–136.

Smith, J. E., & Meyers, R. J. (2004). *Motivating substance abusers to enter treatment: Working with family members.* New York, NY: Guilford Press.

Smith, J. W., & Frawley, P. J. (1993). Treatment outcome of 600 chemically dependent patients treated in a multimodel inpatient program including aversion therapy and pentothal interviews. *Journal of Substance Abuse Treatment, 10*(4), 359–369.

Smith, P. C., Schmidt, S. M., & Saitz, R. (2009). Primary care validation of a single-question alcohol screening test. *Journal of General Internal Medicine, 24*(7), 783–788. doi:10.1007/s11606-009-0928-6

Smith, S., Thomas, S., & Jackson, A. (2004). An exploration of the therapeutic relationship and counseling outcomes in a problem gambling counseling service. *Journal of Social Work Practice, 18*(1), 99–112.

Snow, D., & Delaney, K. R. (2006). Substance use and recovery: Charting a course toward optimism. *Archives of Psychiatric Nursing, 20*(6), 288–290.

Sobell, M. B., & Sobell, L. C. (1973). Alcoholics treated by individualized behavior therapy: One year treatment outcomes. *Behavior Research and Therapy, 11,* 599–618.

Sobell, M. B., & Sobell, L. C. (1978). *Behavioral treatment of alcohol problems: Individualized therapy and controlled drinking.* New York, NY: Plenum Press.

Sobell, M. B., & Sobell, L. C. (1995). Controlled drinking after 25 years: How important was the great debate? [Editorial]. *Addiction, 90,* 1149–1153.

Sorensen, J. L., & Midkiff, E. E. (2000). Bridging the gap between research and drug abuse treatment. *Journal of Psychoactive Drugs, 32*(4), 379–382.

Soyka, M., & Horak, M. (2004). Outpatient alcohol detoxification: Implementation efficacy and outcome effectiveness of a model project. *European Addiction Research, 10,* 180–187. doi:10.1159/000079840

Spanagel, R. (2009). Alcoholism: A systems approach from molecular physiology to addictive behavior. *Physiological Reviews, 89,* 640–705.

Sparks, S. N., Tisch, R., & Gardner, M. (2013). Family-centered interventions for substance abuse in Hispanic communities. *Journal of Ethnicity in Substance Abuse, 12*(1), 68–81. doi:10.1080/15332640.2013.759785

Spillane, N. S., & Smith, G. T. (2007). A theory of reservation-dwelling American Indian alcohol use risk. *Psychological Bulletin, 133,* 395–418.

Springer, J. F., Sale, E., Hermann, J., Sambrano, S., Kasim, R., & Nistler, M. (2004). Characteristics of effective substance abuse prevention programs for high-risk youth. *Journal of Primary Prevention, 25*(2), 171–194.

Squeglia, l. M., Jacobus, J., & Tapert, S. F. (2009). The influence of substance use on adolescent brain development. *Clinical EEG and Neuroscience, 40*(1), 31–38.

St. Regis Mohawk Tribe. (2013). *Tribe Indian Health Service: Partridge House.* Retrieved August 29, 2013, from http://www.srmt-nsn.gov/divisions/indian_health_service/

Sterne, M. W., & Pittman, D. J. (1965). The concept of motivation: A source of institutional and professional blockage in the treatment of alcoholics. *Quarterly Journal of Studies on Alcohol, 26,* 41–57.

Stevens, P., & Smith, R. L. (2005). *Substance abuse counseling: Theory and practice.* (3rd ed.). Upper Saddle River, NJ: Pearson Education.

Stigler, M. H., Neusel, E., & Perry, C. L. (2011). School-based programs to prevent and reduce alcohol use among youth. *Alcohol Research & Health, 34*(2), 157–162.

Stinchfield, R., & Owen, P. (1998). Hazelden's model of treatment and its outcome. *Addictive Behaviors, 5,* 669–683.

Strang, J., & McCambridge, J. (2004). Can the practitioner correctly predict outcome in motivational interviewing? *Journal of Substance Abuse Treatment, 27,* 83–88.

Strathdee, S. A., & Patterson, T. L. (2009). Supply reduction's hidden casualties: A view from the trenches. *Addiction, 104,* 340–341.

Strathdee, S. A., & Pollini, R. A. (2007). A 21st-century Lazarus: The role of safer injection sites in harm reduction and recovery. [Editorial]. *Addiction, 102,* 848–849.

Stupak, D., Hook, M. K., & Hall, D. M. (2007). Participation in counseling: does family matter? An analysis of a community population. *Journal of Mental Health Counseling, 29*(3), 259–268.

Sturm, R., & Sherbourne, C. D. (2001). Are barriers to mental health and substance abuse care still rising? *Journal of Behavioral Health Services & Research, 28*(1), 81–88.

Subbaraman, M. S., Kaskutas, L. A., & Zemore, S. (2011). Sponsorship and service as mediators of the effects of making Alcoholics Anonymous Easier (MAA), a 12-step facilitation intervention. *Drug and Alcohol Dependence, 116,* 117–124.

Substance Abuse and Mental Health Services Administration. (1999). *Cultural issues in substance abuse treatment.* Rockville, MD: Author.

Substance Abuse and Mental Health Services Administration. (2001a, August). *Drug Abuse Services Information System.* Rockville, MD: Author.

Substance Abuse and Mental Health Services Administration. (2001b). *A provider's introduction to substance abuse treatment for lesbian, gay, bisexual, and transgender individuals* (DHHS Publication No. SMA 01-3498). Rockville, MD: Center for Substance Abuse Treatment.

Substance Abuse and Mental Health Services Administration. (2006, June 19). *The OAS report: The Office of Applied Studies.* Retrieved December 30, 2012, from http://www.oas.samhsa.gov/2k5/oas/oas.cfm

Substance Abuse and Mental Health Services Administration. (2008). *About us.* Retrieved June 25, 2013, from http://www.samhsa.gov/about/background.aspx

Substance Abuse and Mental Health Services Administration. (2010, May 20). *The NSDUH Report: Substance use among Asian adults.* Rockville, MD: Office of Applied Studies.

Substance Abuse and Mental Health Services Administration. (2011a). *National Survey of Substance Abuse Treatment Services (N-SSATS): 2010. Data on substance abuse treatment facilities* (DHHS Publication No. SMA 11-4665). Rockville, MD: Author.

Substance Abuse and Mental Health Services Administration. (2011b, April 28). *The NSDUH Report: Major depressive episode and treatment among adolescents: 2009.* Rockville, MD: Office of Applied Studies.

Substance Abuse and Mental Health Services Administration. (2011c, July 12). *SAMHSA's strategic initiatives.* Rockville, MD: Author.

Substance Abuse and Mental Health Services Administration. (2012a). *2010 town hall meetings: Mobilizing communities to prevent and reduce underage alcohol use* (DHHS Publication No. SMA 12-4448). Rockville, MD: Author.

Substance Abuse and Mental Health Services Administration. (2012b). An introduction to extended-release injectable naltrexone for the treatment of people with opioid dependence. *SAMHSA Advisory, 11*(1). Retrieved November 19, 2013, from http://store.samhsa.gov/shin/content/SMA12-4682/SMA12-4682.pdf

Substance Abuse and Mental Health Services Administration. (2012c). *Results from the 2011 National Survey on Drug Use and Health: Summary of national findings* (DHHS Publication No. SMA 12-4713). Rockville, MD: Author.

Substance Abuse and Mental Health Services Administration. (2013a). *Mental Health Parity and Addiction Equity Act.* Retrieved June 24, 2013, from http://www.samhsa.gov/healthreform/parity

Substance Abuse and Mental Health Services Administration. (2013b, September). *Results from the 2012 National Survey on Drug Use and Health: Summary of national findings* (DHHS Publication No. SMA 13-4795). Rockville, MD: Author.

Substance Abuse and Mental Health Services Administration. (2013c). *SAMHSA's Center for Substance Abuse Prevention 2013 Native American Services to Science Initiative announcement.* Retrieved December 5, 2013, from http://www.tribalyouthprogram.org/sites/tribalyouthprogram.org/files/2013%20NA%20STS%20ANNOUNCEMENT.pdf

Substance Abuse and Mental Health Services Administration. (2013d, October 24). *SAMHSA's National Registry of Evidence-Based Programs and Practices.* Retrieved October 30, 2013, from http://nrepp.samhsa.gov/

Substance Abuse and Mental Health Services Administration. (2013e). Need for and receipt of substance treatment among Asian Americans and Pacific Islanders. The NSDUH Report, Retrieved on May 12, 2014, from http://www.samhsa.gov/data/2k13/NSDUH125/sr125-aapi-tx.pdf

Substance Abuse and Mental Health Services Administration. (n.d.-a). *Behavioral health and Black/African Americans: From the National Survey on Drug Use and Health, 2010.* Retrieved September 16, 2013, from http://www.samhsa.gov/obhe/African-American.aspx

Substance Abuse and Mental Health Services Administration. (n.d.-b). *Behavioral health and Hispanics/Latinos: From the National Survey on Drug Use and Health, 2010.* Retrieved September 16, 2013, from http://www.samhsa.gov/obhe/hispanic-latino.aspx

Substance Abuse and Mental Health Services Administration. (n.d.-c). *SBIRT: Screening, Brief Intervention and Referral to Treatment: Opportunities of implementation and points for consideration.* Retrieved July 3, 2013, from http://www.integration.samhsa.gov

Sullivan, C. J., Veysey, B. M., Hamilton, Z. K., & Grillo, M. (2007). Reducing out-of-community placement and recidivism: Diversion of delinquent youth with mental health and substance use problems from the justice system. *International Journal of Offender Therapy and Comparative Criminology, 51*(5), 555–577.

Sun, A.-P. (2007). Relapse among substance abusing women: Components and processes. *Substance Use & Misuse, 42*, 1–21.

Sung, H.-E., Belenko, S., Feng, L., & Tabachnick, C. (2004). Predicting treatment noncompliance among criminal justice–mandated clients: A theoretical and empirical exploration. *Journal of Substance Abuse Treatment, 26*, 13–26. doi: 10.1016/S0740-5472(03)00144-2

Tanner-Smith, E. E., Wilson, S. J., & Lipsey, M. W. (2012). The comparative effectiveness of outpatient treatment for adolescent substance abuse: A meta-analysis. *Journal of Substance Abuse Treatment, 44*(2), 145–158.

Texas Department of State Health Services. (2010, April 2). *Universal, selective and indicated prevention.* Retrieved November 8, 2013, from http://www.dshs.state.tx.us/sa/Prevention/classification.shtm

Thyrian, J. R., Freyer-Adam, J., Hannover, W., Roske, K., Mentzel, F., Kufeld, C., Bischof, G., Rumpf, H.-J., John, U., & Hapke, U. (2007). Adherence to the principles of motivational interviewing, clients' characteristics and behavior outcome in a smoking cessation and relapse prevention trial in women postpartum. *Addictive Behaviors, 32*(10), 2297–2303.

Timko, C., Cronkite, R., Kaskutas, L. A., Laudet, A., Roth, J., & Moos, R. H. (2013). Al-Anon family groups: Newcomers and members. *Journal of Studies on Alcohol and Drugs, 74*(6), 965–976.

Timko, C., & DeBenedetti, A. (2007). A randomized controlled trial of intensive referral to 12-step self-help groups: One-year outcomes. *Drug and Alcohol Dependence, 90*(2–3), 270–279.

Timko, C., Moos, R. H., Finney, J. W., & Lesar, M. D. (2000). Long-term outcomes of alcohol use disorders: Comparing untreated individuals with those in Alcoholics Anonymous and formal treatment. *Journal of Studies on Alcohol, 61,* 529–540.

Timko, C., Young, B., & Moos, R. H. (2012). Al-Anon family groups: Origins, conceptual basis, outcomes, and research opportunities. *Journal of Groups in Addiction & Recovery, 7,* 279–296. doi:10.1080/1556035X.2012.705713

Tobler, A. L., Livingston, M. D., & Komro, K. A. (2011). Racial/ethnic differences in the etiology of alcohol use among urban adolescents. *Journal of Studies on Alcohol and Drugs, 72,* 799–810.

Tobler, N. S., Roona, M. R., Ochshorn, P., Marshall, D. G., Streke, A. V., & Stackpole, K. M. (2000). School-based adolescent drug prevention programs: 1998 meta-analysis. *Journal of Primary Prevention, 20*(4), 275–336.

Tobler, N. S., & Stratton, H. H. (1997). Effectiveness of school-based drug prevention program: A meta-analysis of the research. *Journal of Primary Prevention, 18*(1), 71–128.

Tomolillo, C. M., Crothers, L. J., & Aberson, C. L. (2007). The damage done: A study of injection drug use, injection related abscesses and needle exchange regulation. *Substance Use & Misuse, 42,* 1603–1611.

Tonigan, J. S., & Beatty, G. K. (2011). Twelve-step program attendance and polysubstance use: Interplay of alcohol and illicit drug use. *Journal of Studies on Alcohol and Drugs, 72*(5), 864–871).

Tonigan, J. S., Connors, G. J., & Miller, W. R. (1996). Alcoholics Anonymous Scale (AAI) Scale. *Psychology of Addictive Behaviors, 10*(2), 75–80.

Tonigan, J. S., Miller, W., & Connors, G. (2000). Project MATCH client impressions about Alcoholics Anonymous: Measurement issues and relationship to treatment outcome. *Alcoholism Treatment Quarterly, 18*(1), 25–41.

Tonigan, J. S., Toscova, R., & Miller, W. R. (1996b). Meta-analysis of the literature on Alcoholics Anonymous: Sample and study characteristics moderate findings. *Journal of Studies on Alcohol and Drugs, 57*(1), 65–72.

Toumbourou, J. W., Hamilton, M., U'Ren, A., Steven-Jones, P., & Storey, G. (2002). Narcotics Anonymous participation and changes in substance use and social support. *Journal of Substance Abuse Treatment, 23,* 61–66.

Townsend, A. L., Biegel, D. E., Ishler, K. J., Wieder, B., & Rini, A. (2006). Families of persons with substance use and mental disorders: A literature review and conceptual framework. *Family Relations, 55*(4), 473–486.

Trace, M. (2005). Comment on "What are drug users looking for when they contact drug services: Abstinence or harm reduction?" by Neil McKeganey, Zoe Morris, Joanne Neal, & Michele Robertson. *Drugs: Education, Prevention & Policy, 12*(4), 267–268.

Trepper, T. S., Nelson, T. S., McCollum, E. E., & McAvoy, P. (1997). Improving substance abuse service delivery to Hispanic women through increased cultural competencies: A qualitative study. *Journal of Substance Abuse Treatment, 14*(2), 225–234.

Trice, H. M. (1957). A study of the process of affiliation with Alcoholics Anonymous. *Quarterly Journal of Studies on Alcohol, 18,* 39–54.

Tripodi, S. J., Bledsoe, S. E., Kim, J. S., & Bender, K. (2011). Effects of correctional-based programs for female inmates: A systematic review. *Research on Social Work Practice, 21*(1), 15–31.

Tucker, J. A., & Roth, D. L. (2006). Extending the evidence hierarchy to enhance evidence-based practice for substance use disorders. *Addiction, 101*(7), 918–932.

Tucker, J. A., & Simpson, C. A. (2011). The recovery spectrum: From self-change to seeking treatment. *Alcohol Research & Health, 33*(4), 371–379.

Tucker, J. A., Vuchinich, R. E., & Rippens, P. D. (2004). A factor analytic study of influences on patterns of help-seeking among treated and untreated alcohol dependent persons. *Journal of Substance Abuse Treatment, 26*, 237–242.

Turner, R. J., Lloyd, D. A., & Taylor, J. (2006). Stress burden, drug dependence and the nativity paradox among U.S. Hispanics. *Drug and Alcohol Dependence, 83*(1), 79–89.

Tuten, M., Jones, H. E., Lertch, E. W., & Stitzer, M. L. (2007). Aftercare plans of inpatients undergoing detoxification. *American Journal of Drug and Alcohol Abuse, 33*(4), 547–555.

United Nations Office on Drugs and Crime. (2004). *Substance abuse treatment and care for women: Case studies and lessons learned.* Vienna: Author.

United Nations Office on Drugs and Crime. (2013). *Preventing drug use among youth works.* Retrieved October 31, 2013, from http://www.unodc.org/unodc/en/prevention/

Valente, R. W., Chou, C. P., & Pentz, M. A. (2007). Community coalitions as a system: Effects of Network change on adoption of evidence-based substance abuse prevention. *American Journal of Public Health, 97*(5), 880–886.

Van Den Berg, C., Smit, C., Van Brussel, G., Coutinho, R., & Prins, M. (2007). Full participation in harm reduction programmes is associated with decreased risk for human immunodeficiency virus and hepatitis C virus: Evidence from the Amsterdam Cohort Studies among drug users. *Addiction, 102*, 1454–1462.

van den Bosch, L. M. C., Verheul, R., Schippers, G. M., & van den Brink, W. (2002). Dialectical behavior therapy of borderline patients with and without substance use problems. Implementation and long-term effects. *Addictive Behaviors, 27*, 911–923.

Vanderplasschen, W., Colpaert, K., Autrique, M., Rapp, R. C., Pearce, S., Broekaert, E., & Vandevelde, S. (2013). Therapeutic communities for addictions: A review of their effectiveness from a recovery-oriented perspective. *Scientific World Journal, 2013*, 1–22. doi:.0rg/10.1155/2013/427817

Vanderplasschen, W., Wolf, J., Rapp, R. C., & Broekaert, E. (2007). Effectiveness of Different Models of Case Management for Substance-Abusing Populations. *Journal of Psychoactive Drugs, 39*(1), 81–95.

Vandevelde, S., Broekaert, E., Schuyten, G., & Van Hove, G. (2005). Intellectual abilities and motivation toward substance abuse treatment in drug-involved offenders: A pilot study in the Belgian criminal justice system. *International Journal of Offender Therapy and Comparative Criminology, 49*(3), 277–297.

Vasilaki, E. I., Hosier, S. G., & Cox, W. M. (2006). The efficacy of motivational interviewing as a brief intervention for excessive drinking: A meta-analytic review. *Alcohol and Alcoholism, 41*(3), 328–335.

Vogel, H. S., Knight, E., Laudet, A. B., & Magura, S. (1998). Double Trouble in Recovery: Self-help for people with dual diagnoses. *Psychiatric Rehabilitation Journal, 21*(4), 356–364.

Volkow, N. D., & Montaner, J. (2011). The urgency of providing comprehensive and integrated treatment for substance abusers with HIV. *Health Affairs, 30*(8), 1411–1419.

Wallace, J., McNeill, D., Gilfillan, D., MacLean, K., & Fanella, F. (1988). Six-month treatment outcomes in socially stable alcoholics: Abstinence rates. *Journal of Substance Abuse Treatment, 5*(4), 247–252.

Walter, H., Gutierrez, K., Ramskogler, K., Hertling, I., Dvorak, A., & Lesch, O. M. (2003). Gender-specific differences in alcoholism: Implications for treatment. *Archives of Women's Mental Health, 6*, 253–258.

Walters, G. D. (2000). Behavioral self-control training for problem drinkers: A meta-analysis of randomized control studies. *Behavior Therapy, 31*, 135–149.

Walton, M. A., Blow, F. C., & Booth, B. M. (2001). Diversity in relapse prevention needs: Gender and race comparisons among substance abuse treatment patients. *American Journal of Drug and Alcohol Abuse, 27*(2), 225–240.

Warren, J. L., Stein, J. A., & Grella, C. E. (2007). Role of social support and self-efficacy in treatment outcomes among clients with co-occurring disorders. *Drug and Alcohol Dependence, 89*, 267–274.

Warren, K., Hiance, D., Doogan, N., De Leon, G., & Phillips, G. (2013). Verbal feedback in therapeutic communities: Pull-ups and reciprocated pull-ups as predictors of graduation. *Journal of Substance Abuse Treatment, 44*(4), 361–368.

Watkins, K. E., Hunter, S. B., Burnam, M. A., Pincus, H. A., & Nicholson, G. (2005). Review of treatment recommendations for persons with a co-occurring affective or anxiety and substance use disorder. *Psychiatric Services, 56*(8), 913–926.

Watson, D. W. (2004). Juvenile offender comprehensive reentry substance abuse treatment. *Journal of Correctional Education, 55*(3), 211–224.

Weatherburn, D. J. (2009). Dilemmas in harm minimization: A response to my critics. *Addiction, 104*, 345–346.

Wechsberg, W. M., Zule, W. A., Riehman, K. S., Luseno, W. K., & Lam, W. K. K. (2007). African-American crack abusers and drug treatment initiation: Barriers and effects of a pretreatment intervention. *Substance Abuse Treatment, Prevention, and Policy, 2*, 10. doi:10.1186/1747-597x-2-10

Weisner, C., Delucchi, K., Matzger, H., & Schmidt, L. (2003). The role of community services and informal support on five-year drinking trajectories of alcohol dependent and problem drinkers. *Journal of Studies on Alcohol, 64*, 862–873.

Weisner, C., Greenfield, T., & Room, R. (1995). Trends in the treatment of alcohol problems in the US general population, 1979 through 1990. *American Journal of Public Health, 85*(1), 55–60.

Weisner, C., Mertens, J., Parthasarathy, S., Moore, C., & Lu, Y. (2001, October 10). Integrating primary medical care with addiction treatment: A randomized controlled trial. *Journal of the American Medical Association, 286*(14), 1715–1723.

Weiss, R. D. (1994). Inpatient treatment. In M. Galanter & H. D. Kleber (Eds.), *Textbook of substance abuse treatment* (pp. 359–368). Washington, DC: American Psychiatric Press.

Weiss, R. D., Griffin, M. L., Kolodziej, M. E., Greenfield, S. F., Najavits, L. M., Daley, D. C., . . . Hennen, J. A. (2007). A randomized trial of integrated group therapy versus group drug counseling for patients with bipolar disorder and substance dependence. *American Journal of Psychiatry, 164*(1), 100–107. doi:10.1176/appi.ajp.164.1.100

Wells, K., Klap, R., Koike, A., & Sherbourne, C. (2001). Ethnic disparities in unmet need for alcoholism, drug abuse and mental health care. *American Journal of Psychiatry, 158*, 2027–2032.

Wells, R., Lemak, C. H., & D'Aunno, T. A. (2006). Insights from a national survey into why substance abuse treatment units add prevention and outreach services. *Substance Abuse Treatment, Prevention, and Policy, 1*, 21. doi:10.1186/1747-597X-1-21

Welsh, W. N., & McGrain, P. N. (2008). Predictors of therapeutic engagement in prison-based drug treatment. *Drug and Alcohol Dependence, 96*(1), 271–280. doi:10.1016j/drugalcdep.2008.03.019

WestBridge Community Services. (2012a, Fall). *The Bridge Newsletter: Family perspective*, p. 3. Retrieved September 30, 2013, from http://www.westbridge.org/news-resources/publications/the-bridge-newsletter/

WestBridge Community Services. (2012b). *Home page.* Retrieved September 29, 2013, from http://www.westbridge.org/default.aspx

Westermeyer, J. (1987). Cultural patterns of drug and alcohol use: An analysis of host and agent in the cultural environment. *Bulletin on Narcotics, 39*(2), 11–27.

Westermeyer, J. (1999). The role of cultural and social factors in the cause of addictive disorders. *Psychiatric Clinics of North America, 22*(2), 253–273.

Wexler, H. K. (1995). The success of therapeutic communities for substance abusers in American prisons. *American Journal of Psychoactive Drugs, 27*(1), 57–66.

Wexler, H. K. (2003). The promise of prison-based treatment for dually diagnosed inmates. *Journal of Substance Abuse Treatment, 25*, 223–231.

White Bison, Inc. (2002). *The Red Road to wellbriety in the Native American way.* Colorado Springs, CO: Author.

White, W. L. (1998). *Slaying the dragon: The history of addiction treatment and recovery in America.* Bloomington, IL: Chestnut Health Systems/Lighthouse Institute.

White, W. L. (2005). Treatment Works! Is it time for a new slogan? *Addiction Professional, 3*(1), 22–27.

White, W. L., & Albright, L. (2006, January–February). *Calling a new generation of leaders: Frontline professionals don't need to feel ready in every capacity to get involved.* Retrieved October 30, 2008 from http://addictionpro.com/ME2/dirmod.asp

White, W. L., Budnick, C., & Pickard, B. (2011). *Narcotics Anonymous: A chronology of the scientific and professional literature.* Retrieved July 31, 2013, from http://www.williamwhitepapers.com

White, W. L., & Kurtz, E. (2006). *Linking addiction treatment and communities of recovery: A primer for addiction counselors and recovery coaches.* Providence, RI: Northeast Addiction Technology Transfer Center Network. Retrieved December 8, 2013, from http://www.dldocs.stir.ac.uk/documents/recovery.pdf

White, W. L., & Kurtz, E. (2008). Twelve defining moments in the history of Alcoholics Anonymous. In M. Galanter & L. Kaskutas (Eds.), *Recent developments in alcoholism* (Vol. 18, pp. 37–57). New York, NY: Plenum.

Wiener, C. L. (1981). *The politics of alcoholism: Building an arena around a social problem.* New Brunswick, NJ: Transaction.

Wilson, D. B., Gottfredson, D. C., & Najaka, S. S. (2001). School-based prevention of problems behaviors: A meta-analysis. *Journal of Quantitative Criminology, 17*(3), 247–272.

Wilson, W. (1957). *Alcoholics Anonymous comes of age: A brief history of AA.* New York, NY: Alcoholics Anonymous World Services.

Winters, K. C., Fahnhorst, T., Botzet, A., Lee, S., & Lalone, B. (2012). Brief intervention for drug-abusing adolescents in a school setting: Outcomes and mediating factors. *Journal of Substance Abuse Treatment, 42*(3), 279–288. doi:10.1016/j.jsat2001.08.005

Wiseman, E. J., Henderson, K. L., & Briggs, M. J. (1998). Individualized treatment for outpatient withdrawing from alcohol. *Journal of Clinical Psychiatry, 59*(6), 289–293.

Witkiewitz, K., & Marlatt, G. A. (2006). Overview of harm reduction treatments for alcohol problems. *International Journal of Drug Policy, 17*, 285–294.

Wittouck, C., Dekkers, A., De Ruyver, B., Vanderplasschen, W. M., & Vander Laenen, F. (2013). The impact of drug treatment courts on recovery: A systematic review. *Scientific World Journal, 2013*, 1–12. doi:10.1155/2013/493679

Wodak, A. (2009). Harm reduction is now the mainstream global drug policy. *Addiction, 104*, 343–344.

Wodak, A., & Cooney, A. (2006). Do needle syringe programs reduce HIV infection among injecting drug users: A comprehensive review of the international evidence. *Substance Use & Misuse, 41*, 777–813.

Wodarski, J., & MacMaster, S. (2012). HIV AIDS and substance abuse primary prevention in minority adolescents. *Retrovirology, 9*(Suppl. 1), 128. doi:10.1186/1742-4690-9-S1-P128

Wolfe, B. L., & Meyers, R. J. (1999). Cost-effective alcohol treatment: The community reinforcement approach. *Cognitive and Behavioral Practice, 6*(2), 105–109.

Wolfer, L. (2006). Graduates speak: A qualitative exploration of drug court graduates' views of the strengths and weaknesses of the program. *Contemporary Drug Problems, 33*, 303–320.

World Health Organization. (2004). *Policy brief: Reduction of HIV transmission through drug-dependence treatment*. Geneva, Switzerland: Author.

World Health Organization. (2011). *A new health sector agenda for HIV/AIDS: Global health sector strategy on HIV/AIDS, 2011–2015*. Geneva, Switzerland: Author. Retrieved November 24, 2013, from http://whqlibdoc.who.int/hq/2011/WHO_HIV_11.03_eng.pdf

World Health Organization. (n.d.). *UNODC/WHO global initiative on primary prevention of substance abuse*. Retrieved October 30, 2013, from http://www.who.int/substance_abuse/activities/global_initiative/en/

Yalisove, D. (1998). The origins and evolution of the disease concept of treatment. *Journal of Studies on Alcohol, 59*(4), 469–476.

Yellow Horse Brave Heart, M. (2003). The historical trauma response among Natives and its relationship with substance abuse: A Lakota illustration. *Journal of Psychoactive Drugs, 35*, 7–13.

Young, C. A. (2013, June 28). Man charged with killing South Boston woman. *Boston Globe*, pp. B1, B13.

Young, D. W., Dembo, R., & Henderson, C. E. (2007). A national survey of substance abuse treatment for juvenile offenders. *Journal of Substance Abuse Treatment, 32*, 255–266.

Zailckas, K. (2005). *Smashed: Story of a drunken girlhood*. Boston, MA: Viking.

Zavala, S. K., French, M. T., Henderson, C. E., Alberga, L., Rowe, C., & Liddle, H. A. (2005). Guidelines and challenges for estimating the economic costs and benefits of adolescent substance abuse treatment. *Journal of Substance Abuse Treatment, 29*, 191–205.

Zeese, K. B., & Lewin, P. M. (1998). *The effective drug control strategy*. Washington, DC: Network of Reform Groups and the National Coalition for Effective Drug Policies. Retrieved November 10, 2013, from http://www.csdp.org/edcs/edcs.htm

Zimmerman, P., Wittchen, H. U., Hofler, M., Pfister, H., Kessler, R. C., & Lieb, R. (2003). Primary anxiety disorders and the development of substance alcohol use disorders: A 4-year community study of adolescents and young adults. *Psychological Medicine, 33*, 1211–1222.

Zindel, L. R. & Kranzler, H. R. (2014). Pharmacotherapy of alcohol use disorders: Seventy-five years of progress. *Journal of Studies on Alcohol and Drugs, Supplement 17*, 79–88.

Zuroff, D. C., Blatt, S. J., Sotsky, S. M., Krupnick, J. L., Martin. D. J., Sanislow, C. A., & Simmens, S. (2000). Relation of therapeutic alliance and perfectionism to outcome in brief outpatient treatment of depression. *Journal of Consulting and Clinical Psychology, 68*(1), 114–124.

INDEX

CPSIA information can be obtained
at www.ICGtesting.com
Printed in the USA
BVHW012337061020
590426BV00007BA/82